This is the first of a four-volume series consisting of:

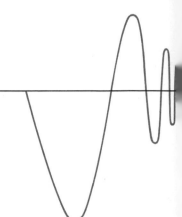

Houghton Mifflin Company
Boston

New York
Atlanta
Geneva, Illinois
Dallas
Palo Alto

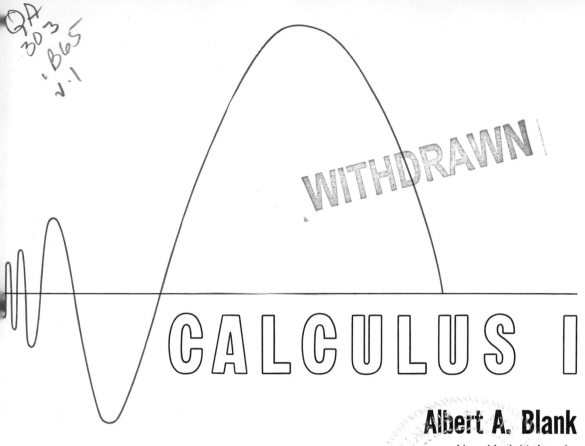

CALCULUS I

Albert A. Blank
New York University

With the assistance of

Florence L. Elder
West Hempstead High School,
West Hempstead, New York

Clarence W. Leeds III
School Mathematics Study Group,
Stanford University, Palo Alto, California

To Richard Courant,
the spiritual godfather of this work.

Foreword

This calculus is offered to you as a whole fabric. We shall not present the subject as a loosely strung together sequence of topics designed to help you recite the "right" answers to traditional examination questions. We have tried to present our attitude toward the subject as it is conceived maturely; a development based upon few major themes, with many lesser ones all tightly interwoven with them. This sense of total structure is worth your effort to comprehend. When the calculus is seen in this perspective, the multitudinous details no longer confuse, but take their proper place in relation to the grand structure.

Calculus is an old part of the body of human thought, yet it remains alive and useful. Even though the subject is old and well-explored, we, the authors, have had to think hard about what we wished to say concerning the calculus. Each of us has gained new insights in re-creating the calculus for himself. It has been a high intellectual adventure. We envy you, to whom the subject is entirely new; you will have the pleasure of re-creating it in its entirety. We hope that you will find the task of re-creation as we did, always absorbing, sometimes amusing, and often exciting.

A.A.B., F.L.E., C.W.L.

Contents

Appendix 𝔸𝟛 **Analytic Geometry** *283*

Appendix 𝔸𝟜 **Mathematical Induction** *403*

Preface

The four books of this text are meant to satisfy the broad requirement in elementary calculus and differential equations offered in most colleges. The first two books, covering the basic differential and integral calculus, were planned also for use in high school to meet the need for an advanced placement course at a level which would receive unquestioning acceptance in our universities.

This work will stand or fall on its own merits. Yet, with so many calculus texts available today, the authors of a new text should have some clearly defined objectives which are not met by existent texts, if only to justify their effort to themselves. We set forth our self-justification in the form of standards which we have tried to meet, standards which are not met entirely by any other introductory text we know of. We expect to be held accountable if we have failed to meet those standards.

Although this calculus is intended for the niche occupied by traditional courses, its fundamental purpose is not to cover the traditional subject matter, but to help the reader organize his knowledge in an orderly rational system. Our aim is to convert the reader into a mature user of the calculus in mathematics and mathematical sciences. To this end we have contemplated the subject in retrospect and considered what we ourselves as users of the calculus have found useful and illuminating. Those traditional topics which lack contemporary interest have been pruned away. At the same time, although we have added unconventional topics and used unconventional approaches, we have not done so for the sake of novelty alone but for the sake of present clarity and future utility. It is not enough to promise the reader that the subject will someday prove to have meaning and value; for too many that great by-and-by never comes. Nor should the reader be content with vague promises of future good; he should demand and be given as much of an understanding of the purpose of his studies as his present state of knowledge allows. We have tried to communicate such an understanding in ample measure. Our faith is that a student armed with a mature sense of purpose will be motivated to explore more widely and probe more deeply than is common.

Depth of understanding rather than superficial coverage is the goal. For this, the fundamental ideas must be mulled over continually and be revealed in different settings. If a concept appears once, never to be used again, we take it as a pedagogical tenet that the concept is seldom well learned. When we have decided that some traditional textbook topic is not worth learning well, we have usually advanced to the conclusion that it is not worth learning at all and have omitted it altogether. At the other extreme, we have woven fundamental ideas deeply into the fabric of the text so that they are reinforced by anticipation, extensive development, and frequent employment. We take issue, for example, with the common practice which introduces the idea of limit, only to abandon it completely at the threshold of the formal calculus. If the concept of limit were useful only as a crutch to support the ideas of derivative and integral, to be discarded when these ideas become familiar, there would be little justification for a careful development of the limit concept for any but prospective mathematicians. The ideas of approximation and error estimation which underlie the concept of limit are too important for mathematics and the sciences to be slighted. On the contrary, they deserve careful development and emphasis. We have taken approximation and error estimation as one of the major strands of our exposition, and it is seldom out of sight for long.

The task we have set ourselves, to reverse Gresham's Law in calculus texts, may seem a quixotic ideal. It is certainly not enough to set high ideals for ourselves and for the student; the ideals must also prove to be practical. To make them practical we have devoted our greatest efforts to make the book completely serviceable for teaching and learning. The text has already been tested in our classes and others, and we have little doubt that it is usable and generates the kind of excitement in the student that we hope for. Yet, we are under no illusion that we have met the ideal of teachability, or any of our other ideals, to the fullest practicable degree. We shall be most grateful for any corrections, criticisms, and suggestions for the improvement of the text which you may communicate to us.

Outline for Instruction and Self-instruction

The text presumes a background equivalent to a three-year college preparatory program. Little of the Analytic Geometry of Appendix Chapter A3 is needed for the first two books, where only the ideas of coordinates in the plane and in space, the distance formula, and the point-slope formula are indispensable. Chapter A3 serves principally as a foundation for Chapter 11 (Vectors and Curves) Chapter 12 (Mechanics) and Chapter 15 (Linear Algebra) in the third book, and for all of the fourth book on Multivariate Calculus.

The first book, Chapters 1 to 5, covers the differential calculus, the second book, Chapters 6 to 10, the integral calculus. The topic of elementary differential equations is subsumed under integration. The remainder of the text will contain enough material for a full second year devoted to further development of the univariate calculus and its applications as well as the basic multivariate calculus.

The arrangement of the text simplifies the secondary school problem of preparing students for different levels of advanced standing in a sound college program. The school may have the choice of a one semester course in differential calculus or a full year course in the basic differential and integral calculus of functions of one real variable. In either case, this kind of text makes it possible for the secondary school to provide a course at the same depth as is sought in a thorough college course.

If you are using the book for self-instruction, you may test your proficiency in the prerequisites by reading Sections 1.1 and 1.2. If you have difficulty with the concepts of inequality, absolute value, function, graph, interval, and slope of a straight line, it is essential to familiarize yourself with such prerequisite material in the appendix, Chapters A1 to A3 before proceeding in main body of the text. Even if you are familiar with these concepts it may still be desirable to review the ideas of Sections A 1.2 (Ordering of the Real Numbers), A 1.3 (Absolute Value and Inequality), and A 1.4 (Intervals, Neighborhoods), in order to acquaint yourself with the terminology of this book. In general, you will be likely to find the prerequisite material in the appendices developed in a way that has something new to offer you, even if you already have the basic facts at your fingertips. Appendix Chapter A4, "Mathematical Induction," is desirable for some problems and supplies a more precise language in which you may prefer to restate some of the arguments of the text.

It is not expected that you will fully understand the limit concepts introduced in Sections 1.1 and 1.2; you are only expected to see in a general way how the concept of limit enables us to come to grips with the geometrical ideas of slope of a curve and area bounded by a curve. Do not spend too much time on these sections; a substantial part of the remainder of the text is devoted to making the limit concepts clear and precise.

The first ten chapters are planned for consecutive reading. After Chapter 10, if you wish to go on as quickly as possible into multivariate calculus, you may leap over the chapters "Mechanics," "Numerical Analysis," and

"Sequences and Series." If you wish to learn as early as possible about sequences and series, you may bypass "Vectors and Curves" and "Mechanics."

In a first reading, you may omit some of the more complex proofs. This is not necessarily an unsatisfactory procedure. If your tastes are directed toward the applications of mathematics rather than mathematics itself, you may never need to know in detail how some theorems are proved. You may be content to leave that to the experts. But you should always know what you are talking about, which means that you should be precise about definitions, you should know the exact content of a theorem to know the limitations on its application, and if possible, you should learn enough about the theorem to have some personal faith in its truth—after all, mathematicians make mistakes, too.

The extension sections, marked **E**, carry out deeper explorations than are essential for a first reading. For a richer appreciation of the calculus, we commend these to your attention. Later extension sections sometimes depend on earlier ones, and peaked problems, marked   , are often so designated only because their solutions involve mathematical induction or other ideas developed in extension sections.

Acknowledgements

The text is a revision and amplification of the calculus text of the School Mathematics Study Group (SMSG). We are grateful to the Board of Trustees of Leland Stanford University for permission to use the copyright SMSG materials. This permission in no way implies an endorsement of the uses to which the SMSG materials have been put in this revision.

We have had two primary reasons for revising the SMSG text. The SMSG texts are not intended as completely finished products, but as samples presenting ideas for the betterment of the curriculum, and these samples are meant to stimulate improvements in texts produced through normal channels. The time for the preparation of an SMSG text is limited. There is only one trial of a preliminary edition before the final revised edition is issued. While associated with SMSG, the authors and their colleagues did their utmost to attain the maximum degree of polish and serviceability that time allowed. We wish now to incorporate our further reflections and classroom experience. We have made a number of textual changes and reordered some of the SMSG material. The most significant internal modification is the inclusion of Appendix Chapter A3, analytic geometry based on vector concepts. The principal extensions of the SMSG material, the chapters on linear algebra and multivariate calculus, round out the text for general college use.

The authors formed the editorial group of the SMSG Calculus Writers' Committee from 1964 to 1966. The editorial group also included Imanuel

Marx of Purdue University until his untimely death, and, thereafter, from the fall of 1965, Richard Pollack of New York University. In the summers of 1964 and 1965 the editorial group was part of the Calculus Writers' Committee. Apart from the editorial group, the summer writers were, with period of service:

Alexander Beck ('65), Olney High School, Philadelphia, Pa.

C. E. Kerr ('64), Dickinson College, Carlisle, Pa.

M. S. Klamkin ('65), Ford Scientific Laboratory, Dearborn, Mich.

I. I. Kolodner ('65), Carnegie Institute of Technology, Pittsburgh, Pa.

M. D. Kruskal ('64), Princeton University, Princeton, N.J.

M. A. Linton ('64–5), William Penn Charter School, Philadelphia, Pa.

Helen Marston ('64), Rutgers, The State University, New Brunswick, N.J.

T. L. Reynolds ('64), College of William and Mary, Williamsburg, Va.

Victor Twersky ('64–5), University of Illinois, Chicago, Ill.

Harold Weitzner ('65), New York University, New York, N.Y.

All summer members of the Calculus Writers' Committee contributed to every section of the SMSG text through writing, editorial work, and criticism, but some parts were primarily the conception of a single writer. To rescue such writers from undeserved anonymity we list their contributions here:

Linton (Chapter A2)

Klamkin (Exercises)

Kolodner (Chapter 10)

Kruskal (4.8, 8.1 to 8.4)

Marx (Chapter 2)

Pollack (The chapter "Sequences and Series")

Twersky (Chapter 9, the chapter "Optics and Waves")

Weitzner (The chapters "Vectors and Curves," "Mechanics")

The introductory sections 1.1, 1.2, and sections 6.1 to 6.3 were largely forged in the white heat of argument with Warren Stenberg. The late Bernard Friedman gave us encouragement to be ambitious in our initial plans for the text. Imanuel Marx was a prodigious editor and stout defender of the English language; if any dangling participles appear in this text they were inserted after his death.

We are extremely grateful to E. G. Begle who permitted the SMSG Calculus Writers the greatest latitude in going beyond the conventions set by earlier SMSG writing committees.

Not least, much credit belongs to our tolerant families who have watched over us with uncomprehending understanding.

Usage

Sections and subsections are referred to by code; for example, 5.4a means Subsection a of Section 4 in Chapter 5.

Theorems, examples, formulas, exercises, and figures are numbered within their subsections. Thus, a reference to 5.4a (2) means Formula 2 of 5.4a. Within its subsection, the designation of a reference is usually omitted; thus a reference to Theorem 1 of Subsection 5.4b would usually be given simply as "Theorem 1" within that subsection, but as "5.4b Theorem 1" elsewhere. A corollary is given the same code as its theorem followed by a letter; for example, 5.4b Corollary 1c is the third corollary to Theorem 1 in 5.4b. Sometimes exercise sets from consecutive subsections are combined; the reference 5.4b,c Exercise 3 or 5.4b,c Ex. 3 is to the third exercise following the latter subsection, 5.4c.

Digressions and commentary are indicated by an indented margin and small print.

Some of the symbols used in the text usually have a restricted denotation; for example, the early letters of the alphabet are generally reserved for constants, n for integers. Those sections and exercises marked with the symbol

(for a Himalayan peak) are expected to present an extra challenge. You will want to work this material through for the reason Sir Edmund Hillary gave for climbing Mt. Everest, "because it is there." The conclusion of each proof is marked (after Halmos) by a bar in the right margin, as shown.   ☐

We shall use the Greek alphabet as well as the English.

A	α	alpha		N	ν	nu
B	β	beta		Ξ	ξ	xi
Γ	γ	gamma		O	o	omicron
Δ	δ	delta		Π	π	pi
E	ϵ	epsilon		P	ρ	rho
Z	ζ	zeta		Σ	δ	sigma
H	η	eta		T	τ	tau
Θ	θ	theta		Υ	υ	upsilon
I	ι	iota		Φ	ϕ	phi
K	κ	kappa		X	χ	chi
Λ	λ	lambda		Ψ	ψ	psi
M	μ	mu		Ω	ω	omega

1

Introduction

The calculus is a collection of powerful and flexible techniques for obtaining useful solutions to an astonishing variety of problems in science, technology, and industry. It is also a mathematical discipline with precisely stated definitions and theorems logically deduced from carefully stated postulates. These are complementary aspects of the subject. To make the most efficient use of the calculus, it is important to understand the reasoning upon which its techniques are based. To understand why the concepts and theory of the calculus are significant, even to care about developing the theory in the first place, it is important to be able to interpret concepts and theory in terms of models, whether geometrical, physical, or other, to which they apply. In this text, we shall find the origins of the ideas of the calculus in practical problems; we shall attempt to express these ideas precisely so that we may reason about them logically; finally, we shall return to problems and apply the theorems resulting from our reasoning.

The two basic ideas of the elementary calculus are "derivative" and "integral." It is easy to appreciate these ideas intuitively and know why they are useful before they are defined precisely. We shall now see how these ideas arise in the attempt to solve specific problems.

1.1 OPTIMIZATION, THE DERIVATIVE

It is in the nature of human enterprise to seek improvement and to try to push the process of improvement to an optimum, the highest degree attainable: a manufacturer seeks the smallest unit cost for his product or the highest possible price; a student tries to complete his homework assignment in the shortest possible time; a demagogue expounds the political philosophy which he believes will catch the greatest number of votes. It is seldom clear what must be done to achieve an optimum. We may even fail to see that we have a problem of optimization. Immediately below the surface of daily life lie countless optimization problems which are often overlooked because they reach our consciousness cloaked in a wealth of detail which must be stripped away for the central problem to be perceived. Not all of these problems can be solved by the calculus alone, but many of them can, and it is just such a problem which we now consider.

This text in its first incarnation was produced by a committee of writers (see Acknowledgements, p. xii). Every writer had to make himself familiar with the work of each of the others in order to fit his own effort into the general framework. In addition, each writer had the duty to review all manuscripts and to communicate criticisms and suggestions to their authors. For these reasons, the larger such a committee becomes, the more the time required for discussion among the members of the committee, and the less the time each member has for writing. It is not surprising, then, that there may be a size at which the committee becomes totally ineffective, with all the available time spent in interaction among members of the group, so that no useful writing gets done. According to the great sage, C. Northcote Parkinson,† a committee reaches the point of ineffectiveness at twenty-one members. Somewhere between zero and twenty-one there must be a number of members that is optimally effective and, ideally, our writers' committee should have been fixed at that size.

As the measure of effectiveness of the writing committee, we shall take the number of hours per week available for writing after accounting for the time spent in mutual distraction. Our hypothesis is that the time devoted by an individual to interaction with others is proportional to the product of the number of people who may interfere with his work by the number of people with whose work he may interfere, and this formula holds until the number reaches the point where he becomes totally ineffective.‡   For a

---

†C. Northcote Parkinson, *Parkinson's Law*, Houghton Mifflin, Boston, 1957.

‡Some committologists, experts in the study of committees, use other formulas, but a different formula would not change the nature of the following analysis.

committee of x members, with no outside distraction, the time spent in social interaction is proportional to $(x - 1)^2$. Accepting Parkinson's figure of twenty-one members as the point of total ineffectiveness, and assuming a forty-hour work week, we get as the total number of hours remaining to an individual for writing, $40\left[1 - \left(\dfrac{x - 1}{20}\right)^2\right]$. Thus, the time T available to the total committee for writing is

(1) $$T = 40x\left[1 - \left(\frac{x - 1}{20}\right)^2\right].$$

In consideration of the requirement that the committee was to complete its work in a definite and all too brief assigned time, we should have chosen the size of the committee so as to maximize the available writing time T.

Our problem is not so much to determine the largest value of T obtained from (1) for some positive integral x, although that information may also be useful, but to determine the number x for which the maximum is achieved; the maximum output of the committee is less relevant for our purpose than the determination of the size of the committee which produces that output.

The problem has now been expressed in purely mathematical terms: we have defined a function $f : x \rightarrow T$ by

(2) $$f(x) = T = \begin{cases} 40x\left[1 - \left(\dfrac{x - 1}{20}\right)^2\right], & \text{for } 0 \le x \le 21, \\ 0, & \text{for } x \ge 21, \end{cases}$$

where x is integral; we must find the value of x for which T is a maximum. In solving this problem, we shall go far beyond the particulars from which it arose. The solution introduces some of the deeper ideas in the history of human thought and, in presenting this solution, we hope to convey an intuitive appreciation of those ideas. Furthermore, the systematic approach by which the problem is solved will be valuable not only for the solution of this problem, but also as a general method of solution for an extensive and important class of optimization problems. In Chapter 5, this systematic attack will be refined to give an extremely simple and direct method for finding optimal values.

The formula (2) defines a function $x \rightarrow T$ for all nonnegative numbers x, not just the integers. It will be convenient to take the function f as defined on this extended domain. First, on the set of all nonnegative real numbers we shall determine the value a for which $f(a)$ is maximal, $f(a) = T_{\max}$; then, we shall use this result to help us locate the maximum of f on the restricted domain of whole numbers.

In order to estimate the location a of the maximum value, we sketch a graph of the function. Taking a few well-distributed numbers x, we obtain the easily calculated coordinates of a few points of the graph.

x	0	1	5	10	15	20	21
T	0	40	192	319	306	78	0

We plot the corresponding points of the graph and sketch a smooth curve joining them, the darker curve in Figure 1. The curve does suggest the ap-

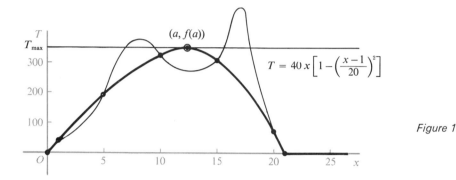

$$T = 40\,x\left[1 - \left(\frac{x-1}{20}\right)^2\right]$$

Figure 1

proximate location of a peak of the graph, and the table does give some definite information about the size of the maximum, such as

$$T_{\max} \geq f(10) = 319.$$

We may get a great deal of information by plotting points, yet the method must always leave us somewhat dissatisfied. In the first place, we have exact information about the function only at a few calculated points so that even if we stumbled upon the maximum we might not be aware of it. In the second place, the idea of drawing a smooth curve through the calculated points has its limitations. For example, without further calculation, we could not be sure that the darker curve in Figure 1 is a more reasonable representation of the graph of the function than the lighter one, and, furthermore, we cannot completely eliminate this kind of ambiguity by calculating more points. One of our objectives is to devise systematic methods for resolving these difficulties.

Thinking of the problem in geometrical terms, we see that the condition for a maximum, $f(a) = T_{\max}$, means that the graph of f cannot cross over the horizontal line through $(a, f(a))$ to a higher point. The direction of the graph at $(a, f(a))$ must, therefore, also be horizontal, for, if the graph met the line at a nonzero angle, the graph would have to cross.† We conclude that to locate a peak of the graph, we may seek among the points where the direction of the graph is horizontal.

In order to make use of this geometrical idea, we express it quantitatively so that it may serve as a basis for computation. The direction of the graph at $(a, f(a))$ is determined by the angle the graph makes with the horizontal line $y = f(a)$ through the point. For our purposes, the direction is most conveniently measured by the tangent of this angle, the slope of the graph. We represent the direction of the graph numerically in terms of slope and reformulate our idea: at a peak of the graph the slope is zero.

We introduce the function f' where $f'(x)$ is the slope of the graph of f at the point $(x, f(x))$. The function f' is called the derivative of f (meaning derived from f), and the slope $f'(x)$ of the graph of f at $(x, f(x))$ is called the derivative of f at x. When there is a peak of the graph of f at $(a, f(a))$, we have $f'(a) = 0$; to locate a peak, then, we look among the zeros of f'.

Turning back to our original problem, we find that thus far we have only replaced it by new problems. In particular, we have not clearly defined the slope of the graph of f at a given point, the derivative at the point. Furthermore, even if this derivative is defined, there remains the problem of describing the function f' in such a way that we can find its zeros in order to locate a peak of the graph of f.

By now, you may feel that we are very far from the point of beginning and that you would like to know what we have accomplished. What we have done is this: we have replaced a problem about which we know very little with a problem about which we know a great deal: to locate a peak of one function, we look among the zeros of another function (the derivative). It may seem to you that the line of approach is indirect and it is still not clear that it will be fruitful; we promise that it will. You should not think that the discovery of such an avenue of investigation requires superhuman powers. Whenever you become unduly impressed by the ingenuity and power of mathematical methods, reflect that an investigator will try not one but many approaches. To his admiring audience, he will present the one idea that worked and never mention the failures which filled his waste basket with reams of paper. In fact, we briefly considered and rejected one idea already, that of finding the maximum value of f by examining a number of its values.

†In this, we make an outright assumption, that the graph has a definite direction at each point in the vicinity of the peak. In particular, the graph may not have a sharp corner at $(a, f(a))$.

Before we go on to solve our optimization problem, let it be said openly that the method of solution we rejected is an effective one. Since we are ultimately interested only in integers x, we could have calculated $f(x)$ for all the integers $x = 0, 1, 2, \ldots, 21$ and chosen the maximizing x from this finite set. Even if the ultimate application required the maximation of $f(x)$ on the set of all real nonnegative x, we might proceed by calculating values of $f(x)$ and come as close to the optimal solution as we may need for some practical purpose.† The issue is that problems of this kind arise often, and if we have a great many similar problems, it pays to devote some attention to more refined methods of solution. Similarly, if you wished to make just one pin, you would be content to do it by hand, but if you wished to produce pins by the million, you would put a great deal of effort into designing suitable machinery for the purpose. You will soon learn methods that will make the solution of our present problem appear no more consequential than the production of a single pin in the operation of a pin factory.

To attack the problem of defining the derivative, we resort to a standard method of the calculus. We seek a number, in this case, the slope of the graph of f at the point $(a, f(a))$. This number will be described by approximations. The set of approximations must be adequate; that is, there must always be an approximation which is closer to the number than any error we may tolerate, no matter how small the specified error tolerance. In the language of the calculus, we say the number is the limit of the approximations.

To approximate the slope of the graph of f at a point $(a, f(a))$, we consider the arc of the graph between the point $(a, f(a))$ and another point $(x, f(x))$. The statement that the graph of f at $(a, f(a))$ has a certain slope $f'(a)$ will mean, now, that it is possible to approximate $f'(a)$ closely by the slope of the chord between $(x, f(x))$ and $(a, f(a))$. More precisely, the error in approximating $f'(a)$ by the slope of the chord can be reduced below any given tolerance by taking x close enough to a; see Figure 2.

Now, we are ready for a direct attack on the problem. Since the maximum of the function f defined by (2) must be located between $x = 0$ and $x = 21$, we need to investigate only that part of the graph over the

†Since the graph is nearly horizontal in the neighborhood of a peak, the penalty for missing the exact location of the peak can be expected to be quite small. We shall return to this point later in the text.

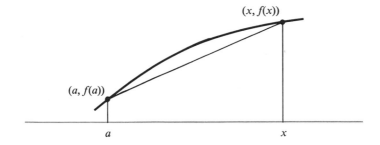

Figure 2

open interval $(0, 21)$. The slope of the chord to the graph joining $(x, f(x))$ to $(a, f(a))$ is the ratio

$$\frac{f(x) - f(a)}{x - a} = \frac{1}{x - a}\left\{40x\left[1 - \left(\frac{x - 1}{20}\right)^2\right] - 40a\left[1 - \left(\frac{a - 1}{20}\right)^2\right]\right\}$$

$$= \frac{40(x - a) - \frac{1}{10}[x(x - 1)^2 - a(a - 1)^2]}{x - a}$$

$$= \frac{x - a}{x - a}\{40 - \tfrac{1}{10}[x^2 + ax + a^2 - 2x - 2a + 1]\} \ .$$

When $x = a$, the ratio $\dfrac{x - a}{x - a}$ is undefined. This is to be expected since the geometrical interpretation of the ratio as the slope of the chord joining two points loses its meaning if $(a, f(a))$ and $(x, f(x))$ represent the same point. For any value of x other than a, we have $\dfrac{x - a}{x - a} = 1$, and the remaining factor $40 - \tfrac{1}{10}[x^2 + ax + a^2 - 2x - 2a + 1]$ is a polynomial which at $x = a$ has the value $\tfrac{1}{10}[399 + 4a - 3a^2]$. We shall prove later for a polynomial function p that $p(x)$ approximates $p(a)$ within any fixed margin of error when x is sufficiently close to a. It follows that the slope of the graph at $(a, f(a))$ is

(3) $$f'(a) = \tfrac{1}{10}[399 + 4a - 3a^2] \ .$$

We are now able to make use of the criterion that the slope of the graph at a peak is zero. The two zeros of f' are $\dfrac{2 \pm \sqrt{1201}}{3}$. The negative zero of f' lies outside the domain of f. Having eliminated every other possibility, we see that the desired maximum must be located at

(4) $$a = \frac{2 + \sqrt{1201}}{3} \approx 12.22 \ .$$

You will have noticed that the actual computation leading to the solution is quite short. Most of the effort and time was spent in explaining the considerations underlying this method of solution. Later, we shall see that we may write out $f'(a)$ at sight and the labor of solution will then be almost negligible. We shall have also to solve yet another problem: if we want to find the maximum of f, and we know the zeros of f', then which of these zeros, if any, yields the best value we are seeking? This question, too, we shall leave to be answered later in the text.

Our work is not yet complete. The maximum has to be located on the set of nonnegative integers, not on the set of all nonnegative real numbers. We may surmise that the maximum on the set of integers occurs at $x = 12$. For the two integers nearest to a, we have $f(12) = 334.8$ and $f(13) = 332.8$, which supports our belief, but how can we be sure? For this, we observe the sign of $f'(x)$ on either side of the critical value (4) defined by $f'(a) = 0$. From (3), we find that $f'(x) > 0$ for $0 \leq x < a$ and $f'(x) < 0$ for $a < x \leq 21$. We expect, as for a straight line (see the appendix, Chapter A3) that f is an increasing function where the slope of its graph is positive, decreasing, if the slope is negative. This is so, and will be proved in Chapter 5. It follows that $f(12)$ is the largest value of the function for integers less than a, $f(13)$ for integers greater than a. Given (2), then, for the committee to produce maximal output its size should be restricted to twelve members.

1.2 AREA, THE INTEGRAL

From the idea of slope of a curve, we have extracted one of the two basic limit concepts of the calculus, the derivative. The second basic concept, the integral, is directly related to another geometrical idea, that of plane area.

Like the idea of the direction of a curve at a point, the idea of planar area remains elusive unless it is explained in terms of limits. From Greek geometry, we have obtained clear ideas about the areas of certain kinds of regions. We know how to calculate the areas of triangles. Hence, we can calculate the areas of all figures built up of triangles, that is, of all polygons. It is a problem of another kind to determine the area of a region with curved boundaries like the shaded region in Figure 1.

You may know the ancient Greek approach to the problem of determining the area of a circle: the area is described as the limit approximated by the areas of inscribed polygons. This is a special application of the "method of exhaustion" attributed to Eudoxus. Archimedes used this method to calculate the areas of ellipses and the areas of sections of a parab-

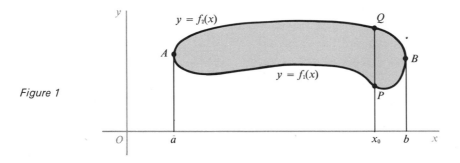

Figure 1

ola, such a section being the region bounded by a line segment and a parabolic arc. This work of Archimedes marked the end of the Greek contribution to the theory of area.

The calculus successfully applies the basic idea of the method of exhaustion in broad generality. By means of the calculus, we shall be able to determine the areas of planar regions without placing excessively restrictive conditions on the nature of their boundaries. You may wonder, then, why the Greeks did not generalize the method of exhaustion themselves. If the Greeks did not go farther, it was probably because they did not have adequate general schemes for describing their problems numerically. Not until the invention of analytic geometry by Descartes was it possible to give a completely numerical description of a curve without a geometrical method for its construction. Nowadays, we have a broad base for thinking both geometrically and numerically, and we take whichever point of view is the more convenient for the problem at hand. The enormous flexibility of this dual approach will enable you to solve handily problems which were beyond the greatest Greek mathematicians.

In order to express the problem of determining the area of a given region numerically, we introduce a coordinate system in the plane. For simplicity, we place the axes so that the region in question is contained in the upper half-plane, $y \geq 0$, as in Figure 1. Next, we attack the problem of describing the region numerically. We know that some curves are the graphs of functions, and we may be led to think of describing the boundary curve in terms of functions. The only difficulty is that the boundary curve is closed, so that a vertical line will generally meet the curve more than once. In Figure 1, the vertical line $x = x_0$ meets the curve in two points P and Q. For this region, the boundary curve can be divided into a lower arc APB and an upper arc AQB so that a vertical line intersects each arc at no more than one point. Each arc can then be considered as the graph of a nonnegative function defined on the interval $[a, b]$, that is, defined for all values of x satisfying $a \leq x \leq b$, where a is the abscissa of

A and b the abscissa of B. The numerical description of the boundary curve may now be given in terms of two functions, a function $f_1 : x \rightarrow f_1(x)$ corresponding to the lower arc APB, and function $f_2 : x \rightarrow f_2(x)$ corresponding to the upper arc AQB. Since we have two functions to deal with, we are led to separate the calculation of the area into two parts. The area we seek is simply the difference between the areas of two regions of the same type. These are regions cut out of the strip between the vertical lines through A and B: the smaller region is bounded above by the graph of f_1 and below by the x-axis; see Figure 2a; the larger region is bounded above by the graph f_2 and below by the x-axis; see Figure 2b.

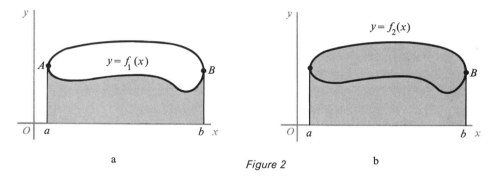

a

Figure 2

b

We have reduced the problem of determining the area of the given region to the problem of determining the area of regions of a certain standard type, regions describable in terms of a single function. Of course, the region we began with was especially simple. In more complicated cases, a vertical line may meet the boundary curve in more than two points and we shall then need more than two functions to describe the curve; see Figure 3. We can

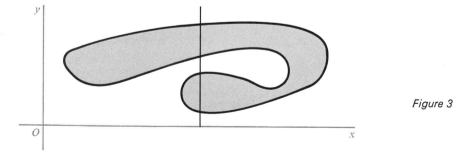

Figure 3

still approach the problem by introducing standard regions, one for each function; the method for doing so in general is left for you to think about since the details are not needed at the moment. For the time being, we shall be concerned only with the problem of calculating the area of a standard region, for example, the shaded region in Figure 4.

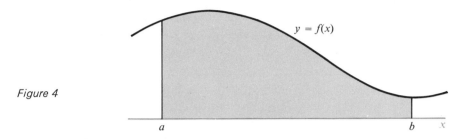

Figure 4

In general, given a nonnegative function f on an interval $[a,b]$, we define the corresponding standard region under the graph of f on $[a,b]$ as the set of points (x, y) for which $a \leq x \leq b$ and $0 \leq y \leq f(x)$. Again, we are faced with the problem of determining a number, the area A of the standard region based on the interval $[a,b]$, and the problem is apparently insoluble by elementary geometrical methods unless the graph of f is composed of line segments. Again, we approach the problem by treating the area as a limit. We approximate the area by areas of polygonal regions as the Greeks did, but we are looking for a systematic scheme of approximation, one that does not depend on the particular function involved.

A first crude estimate of the area A of the standard region on the interval $[a,b]$ can be given in terms of the minimum value m and the maximum value M of f; see Figure 5. Clearly, the rectangle of

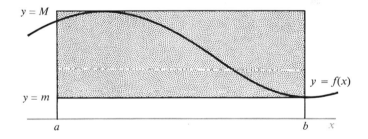

Figure 5

height m based on the interval $[a,b]$ is contained in the given standard region; the given region, in turn, is contained in the rectangle of height M with the same base. For the area A of the standard region, we then have estimates from below and above:

$$m(b - a) \leq A \leq M(b - a) .$$

If we approximate A by either of these estimates, or by some value between, we cannot be in error by more than $(M - m)(b - a)$; that is, by the area of the stippled region indicated in Figure 5.

This simple method of estimation can easily be refined. For this we only have to observe that the minimum m^* of $f(x)$ on any subinterval $[x_1, x_2]$ cannot be less than the over-all minimum m; see Figure 6.

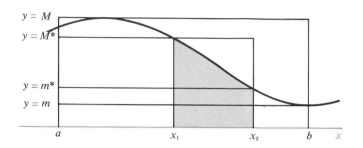

Figure 6

Similarly, the maximum M^* of $f(x)$ on the same subinterval cannot be greater than the over-all maximum M; that is,

$$m \leq m^* \quad \text{and} \quad M^* \leq M.$$

It follows for the area A^* of the standard subregion based on the interval $[x_1, x_2]$ that

$$m(x_2 - x_1) \leq m^*(x_2 - x_1) \leq A^* \leq M^*(x_2 - x_1) \leq M(x_2 - x_1).$$

From this we see that the largest possible error in estimating the area of the subregion on $[x_1, x_2]$ has been reduced from the former value of $(M - m)(x_2 - x_1)$ to $(M^* - m^*)(x_2 - x_1)$. Employing this idea, we can reduce the maximum error in estimating the entire area A by subdividing the interval $[a, b]$ into smaller intervals and making the same sort of estimate of area separately for each subregion. The sum of these estimates will be a better approximation to the area A than the first crude estimate. For example, the subdivision of Figure 7 reduces the margin of

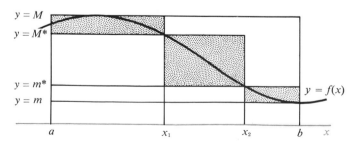

Figure 7

error from the area of the stippled region in Figure 5 to the area of the stippled region in Figure 7.

The process of subdivision can be repeated indefinitely, and this suggests that we now try to reduce the maximum error below any given tolerance by making the subdivision sufficiently fine. If we do so, the area will be given as the limit of both upper and lower estimates. This characterization of area, in particular, is an example of the general limiting process called integration, and the corresponding limit is called an integral.

A good way to see how this general approach works is to try it out on a specific function. For this purpose, we try to find the area of the shaded region in Figure 8. That is, we try to evaluate the integral A of $f : x \to \sqrt{x}$ from 0 to 1.

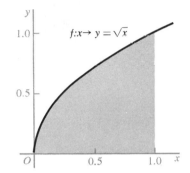

Figure 8

We observe that f is an increasing function. It follows that in any interval the minimum value of f occurs at the left endpoint and the maximum value at the right. Hence, for the entire interval $[0, 1]$, the minimum value of the function is $f(0) = 0$ and the maximum is $f(1) = 1$. The region is contained entirely in the rectangle of base 1 and height 1. Thus, as a preliminary estimate, we know that the area A we seek is between 0 and 1.

In order to refine the estimate, we subdivide the interval $[0, 1]$ into n parts and denote the successive endpoints of the n subintervals by $x_0, x_1, \ldots, x_n$ where $0 = x_0 < x_1 < \cdots < x_n = 1$. For computational simplicity in dealing with $f(x) = \sqrt{x}$, we choose the endpoints so that

$$\sqrt{x_1} = \frac{1}{n}, \quad \sqrt{x_2} = \frac{2}{n}, \quad \sqrt{x_3} = \frac{3}{n}, \ldots ; \quad \text{that is} \quad x_1 = \left(\frac{1}{n}\right)^2, \quad x_2 = \left(\frac{2}{n}\right)^2, \ldots .$$

We illustrate this procedure for $n = 2$ and $n = 3$ in Figure 9, and calculate lower and upper estimates of the integral A in each of these cases by adding areas of rectangles. The area of the stippled region in each figure is the difference between the upper and lower estimates

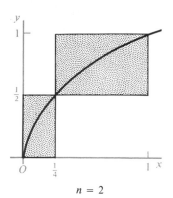

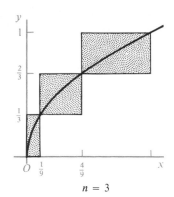

Figure 9

$n = 2$ $n = 3$

of the area A and represents the margin of error for the particular subdivisions.

For $n = 2$,

$$0 \cdot \tfrac{1}{4} + \tfrac{1}{2} \cdot \tfrac{3}{4} \le A \le \tfrac{1}{2} \cdot \tfrac{1}{4} + 1 \cdot \tfrac{3}{4},$$

or

$$\tfrac{3}{8} \le A \le \tfrac{7}{8}.$$

We have reduced the maximum error from 1, obtained for $n = 1$, to $\tfrac{7}{8} - \tfrac{3}{8} = \tfrac{1}{2}$.

Taking $n = 3$, we obtain, similarly,

$$0 \cdot \tfrac{1}{9} + \tfrac{1}{3} \cdot \tfrac{3}{9} + \tfrac{2}{3} \cdot \tfrac{5}{9} \le A \le \tfrac{1}{3} \cdot \tfrac{1}{9} + \tfrac{2}{3} \cdot \tfrac{3}{9} + 1 \cdot \tfrac{5}{9},$$

or

$$\tfrac{13}{27} \le A \le \tfrac{22}{27}.$$

In general, for n subdivisions with $x_k = \left(\dfrac{k}{n}\right)^2$ where $k = 0, 1, 2, \ldots, n,$

we estimate the area over the subinterval $[x_{k-1}, x_k]$ from above by $u_k = \sqrt{x_k}(x_k - x_{k-1})$ and from below by $v_k = \sqrt{x_{k-1}}(x_k - x_{k-1})$. We then have

$$v_1 + v_2 + \cdots + v_n \le A \le u_1 + u_2 + \cdots + u_n.$$

Observe, now, that $u_k = \dfrac{k^2 + k(k-1)}{n^3}$ and $v_k = \dfrac{k(k-1) + (k-1)^2}{n^3}.$

If we take the difference between the upper and lower estimates for A, we then obtain the estimate E_n of the maximum error for this subdivision, namely,

$$E_n = (u_1 - v_1) + (u_2 - v_2) + (u_3 - v_3) + \cdots + (u_k - v_k)$$
$$+ \cdots + (u_n - v_n)$$

$$= \frac{1}{n^3} \{(1 - 0) + (2^2 - 1) + (3^2 - 2^2) + \cdots + [k^2 - (k-1)^2]$$
$$+ \cdots + [n^2 - (n - 1)^2]\} \ .$$

Observe the pairwise cancellation across successive parentheses. With this cancellation, the error estimate becomes

$$E_n = \frac{n^2}{n^3} = \frac{1}{n} \cdot$$

We have shown for the given method of subdivision that we can bring the error below any given tolerance simply by taking n big enough: given a positive error tolerance ϵ, we simply take $n > \dfrac{1}{\epsilon} \cdot$

It may seem that we have not solved the problem of finding the number A. All we know is that we can approximate A within any given margin of error. Nonetheless, in describing the integral A of f from 0 to 1 as the limit of a set of approximations, we have left no room for ambiguity. We still may feel cheated. We would like to have a familiar representation for A like, say, $A = \frac{2}{3}$ (which, by the way, is exactly what A is in this case). Later, we shall see how to obtain such a number in cases like this. Still, it is important to know that we cannot always expect the solutions of our problems to take a familiar form; often the simplest and most comprehensible description of a number is its description as the limit of a set of approximations.

1.3 THE SCOPE OF THE CALCULUS

The calculus is the study of the derivative and the integral, the relationship between these concepts, and their applications. The derivative and the integral may be interpreted geometrically as slope and as area, but these are only two among a wide range of interpretations and applications. In the preceding sections, we emphasized slope and area in order to introduce the basic concepts in an intuitive, geometrical way. However, the concepts of derivative and integral are universal, and their incorporation into a calculus, a system of reckoning, enables us to solve significant problems in all branches of science. The intuitive approach followed to this point is useful and suggestive, but it needs to be, and will be, supplemented by a more careful investigation of the broad range of application of these methods as well as their limitations. Before starting a systematic development of the subject, we want to emphasize the universality of the concepts derivative and integral. We also want to stress that the problems considered thus far are primarily vehicles for the development of theory; they do not begin to suggest the full scope of applications of the calculus.

The steps by which we introduced the ideas of derivative and integral are so familiar that it may not seem they could lead to entirely new methods for solving problems completely different from those met in earlier courses. With the calculus, we are able to attack the problem of describing phenomena ranging from the dissemination of a rumor to the motion of a planet.

Who hasn't heard of that "Helen of Argos . . . for whose sake many Achaians lost their lives in Troy far from their own native country"? Three thousand years after the fall of Troy, passed on by word of mouth, transcribed on perishable materials, how did the story ever make its way to us? To frame such a question mathematically, we must first isolate the essential features of the process by which a story is passed on. Some stories spread like diseases; others die out. If the story is dull, nobody bothers to repeat it. If the story is good, some of the people who hear it remember it and pass it along. Starting with these ideas could you get far by familiar methods?

The same mathematical concepts with which we explore the process of spreading a story may also be applied to the processes of learning and forgetting. Too much that we once stuffed into our heads to pass tests was never used again and seems to be lost. Facts that we have met repeatedly and worked with actively have become so much a part of ourselves that we can hardly remember not having known them.

The way that stories spread, the way in which we learn and forget facts, these processes illustrate a broad class of phenomena unified by the basic mathematical models for growth, decay, and competition. Besides helping to describe the spreading of rumors, and learning or forgetting, these same mathematical models describe and clarify such natural phenomena as radioactive decay, the attenuation of sunlight by a cloudy sky, the progress of chemical reactions, the growth of bacterial colonies, or the spread of disease through a city. For each of these processes, the essential feature is that the amount of some quantity is changing (with respect to time, or distance, or whatever) at a rate proportional to the amount already present. A process of this sort can be described by a certain type of equation (a differential equation) whose solutions are, typically, combinations of exponential functions.

Other processes of nature change in a cyclic or periodic way; they repeat in identical form each year, each day, perhaps each second. The planetary motions, the tides, the daily routine of life, the harmonious chords of music, the propagation of X-rays through crystals, even the colored sheen of butterfly wings, all depend on periodic phenomena. For such processes, the rate of change of the rate of change of some quantity is proportional to the negative of the quantity itself, and then our mathematical model leads to a different class of differential equations whose solutions are, typically, combinations of trigonometric functions.

With the calculus, we may also investigate more complicated natural processes which may involve a combination of growth or decay with some sort of cyclic behavior.

Some of the problems we may solve will be simpler: in what distance can a car travelling at a rate of 60 miles per hour be brought to a dead stop if its brakes are capable of reducing its speed at a maximum rate of 22 feet per second per second? At what upward angle should a golf ball be driven to make it travel as far as possible? In what direction with respect to the Sun is a given rainbow color strongest? All these questions involve *rates of change;* they lie in the province of the *differential calculus.*

The second broad class of problems which we shall consider involve *totality*, the summing of small effects, the final result of a process of change. If we know how a droplet of ink spreads in the rug, how do we predict what happens when we spill a whole bottle? If we record our speed against time in the course of a long trip, how far have we traveled? These problems are in the province of the *integral calculus.*

It is the concept of limit upon which the calculus bases its great advance beyond elementary algebra and geometry. The two fundamental limit ideas of the calculus, derivative as illustrated by slope, and integral as illustrated by area, may not appear to be related. Yet there is but one calculus: derivative and integral are complementary ideas. Given a function f, we may introduce the area A of the standard region under the graph of f over the interval $[a, x]$. The graph of the function $g : x \to A$ has as its slope at any point x_0 the function value $f(x_0)$. Starting from the function f, we use the integral to define a new function g; we take the derivative of g to obtain the original function f again. The limit concepts, integral and derivative, and the inverse relation between the two are the key ideas of the calculus.

We strongly emphasize applications, not only to show that the calculus provides useful methods and concepts for science, but because much of the calculus was developed to solve specific problems. Most of the applications of mathematics considered here differ from those of previous courses in that they emphasize the effects of variation or summation. The calculus was tailor-made to treat such problems. Except for the simplest problems of this type, the methods of arithmetic, geometry, and algebra are inadequate, and even for the simpler problems the methods of the calculus are more efficient.

The calculus was invented to treat physical problems; now it has grown into the larger branch of mathematics known as analysis and its range of application has expanded enormously. To analysis we owe much of the progress in the physical sciences and modern engineering, and, more recently, in the biological and social sciences. The concepts and operations introduced by the calculus provide the right language and the right tools for the major part of the applications of mathematics to the sciences.

We have tried to maintain a balance of topics and of viewpoints that will meet the requirements of students who will become mathematicians, others who will become scientists primarily interested in applications, and still others for whom mathematics will become simply one of the deep intellectual experiences of their education. For the student of science, a fluent intuitive grasp of the subject may often seem to be his primary need; for the student of mathematics, it may seem that a careful deductive development is more essential. Sometimes these different needs may conflict, but more often they supplement each other. Both the scientist and the mathematician gain by a complete appreciation of both attitudes, and we regard this as an ideal worth striving for; the serious student should carry away a command of both these views and of their interrelations.

Historically, the replacement of an intuitive basis for the calculus by a careful logical structure through the method of limits marked a vital phase in the development of mathematics. This phase is far from complete. We are still learning how to combine the inspired use of intuition in approaching new problems with the effective use of logic, not only to verify our intuition, but to permit generalizations of broader applicability. Today, most mathematicians appreciate the essential roles of both intuitive and deductive procedures, not only for creating the calculus but for learning it, and we have tried to make both equally available to you.

In summary, we wish to show you how the effort to solve important problems leads to the methods of the calculus; how the attempt to make the best use of these methods and to understand their full scope leads to the development of the calculus as an independent study; and how the products of this study in turn lead to deeper insight into the original problems. Just as science enriches mathematics by providing concrete models and significant problems, mathematics enriches science by providing system and organization, as well as solutions of problems.

2

The Idea of Derivative

It was to explain the concept of direction of a curve that we introduced a special kind of limit in 1.1, the derivative of a function at a point of its domain. The derivative was given a direct geometrical interpretation in terms of the slope of a graph at a point. In the sciences, as we indicated in 1.3, the idea of derivative has a myriad of interpretations in terms of rates of change. Typical of these is the concept of velocity, or the rate of change of position with respect to time.

2.1 VELOCITY, RATES OF CHANGE

Travel by automobile has made the idea of velocity commonplace. If the gauge is properly adjusted, the velocity of the car is indicated by the pointer on the speedometer dial. If the car is driven at a constant velocity of fifty miles per hour so that the pointer is held constant at 50 on the dial, then in one hour the car will move a distance of fifty miles along the road and the odometer (mileage gauge) will register an increase of 50.0. The relation between distance traveled and velocity is well understood when the velocity is constant: the velocity is simply the ratio of the total distance traveled to the elapsed time. When the velocity is not constant, the relation between velocity and distance traveled cannot be stated so simply; it must be phrased in terms of limits.

The motion of a car is a complicated affair. Even if we concentrate on some feature on the body such as the tip of the hood ornament and disregard the motions of parts such as the shuttling pistons and turning wheels, we shall still wish to ignore such aspects of the motion as the up and down bobbing of the body on its springs.

We shall not attempt to describe the motion of a car or any large body in all its complexity, but make simplifications which permit us to describe the gross features of the motion. We suppose that the body can be represented as a particle, namely that the extent of the body may be ignored, that the body may be treated as though it were localized at a point. To describe the motion of the body, then, we need only specify its point location at every moment of time.

We restrict ourselves to the motion of a particle along a fixed curve. We describe the particle's position by giving its displacement along the curve from some origin O fixed on the path. To make the description unambiguous, the path is oriented; that is, a sign is attached to the displacement from O: points on one side of O, like P in Figure 1, have a posi-

Figure 1

tive displacement, points on the opposite side, like Q, a negative displacement. We may then present a complete history of the motion by giving the displacement s of the particle at each time t, that is, by a function $\phi: t \rightarrow s$. (The function ϕ need not be monotone; the particle is allowed to reverse the direction of its motion along the path.) Since we have alleged that such a description of the motion is complete, it should be possible to determine the velocity at any time from the given data; our problem is to show how to do it.

Let $s_0 = \phi(t_0)$ and $s_1 = \phi(t_1)$ describe the positions of the particle at the times t_0 and t_1, respectively. The difference $s_1 - s_0$ gives the distance $|s_1 - s_0|$ of s_1 from s_0 and, through $\text{sgn}(s_1 - s_0)$, the direction of s_1 from s_0. The ratio $\dfrac{s_1 - s_0}{t_1 - t_0}$ of displacement to time elapsed is called the *average velocity* of the particle over the time interval. If the velocity were constant throughout the time interval, then average velocity would coincide with the velocity at every intermediate time. In general, the velocity is not constant, and departures from the average velocity may be large. For example, it is possible to drive from one place to another at an average velocity of 50 miles per hour and yet exceed a posted speed limit of 60 miles per hour for a major part of the time. The idea of *instantaneous* velocity rather than average velocity is the significant one for many questions, not only the question whether we are violating the law by exceeding the speed limit. For example, the grimly practical matter of how much damage is done in a collision depends on the velocity at the instant of impact and bears little relation to the average velocity throughout the course of the preceding motion.

Although we may not know the velocity of a particle at a specific instant t_0 (unless there is an extraordinary event like a collision at the precise time t_0), we may surmise that in a small time interval containing t_0 that the velocity does not change much and that the average velocity over the interval differs by little from the instantaneous velocity at t_0. In that event, for a motion given by $s = \phi(t)$ we may approximate the instantaneous velocity at t_0 by the average velocity

(1) $$q(t) = \frac{\phi(t) - \phi(t_0)}{t - t_0},$$

and it should be possible to bring the error of approximation below any fixed tolerance by taking t sufficiently close to t_0. We take this as the full expression of the idea of instantaneous velocity and define the velocity at t_0 as the limit of the ratio (1). This definition of velocity as a limit is formally identical with the definition of slope as a limit in 1.1. We recognize, then, that the velocity at t_0 is the derivative of the function ϕ at t_0.

Example 1. At time $t = 0$ the brakes are applied on a car moving at the velocity 60 mph and kept on until the car is brought to a stop. The subsequent displacement in feet is measured at various times t in seconds and found to satisfy the formula

(2) $$s = \phi(t) = 88\left(t - \frac{t^2}{10}\right)$$

before the vehicle stops. Since the initial speed of 60 mph is the same as 88 ft./sec., we expect if we take t close to 0 that the average velocity over the time interval $[0, t]$ will approximate 88 ft./sec. closely. This average velocity is

$$q_0(t) = \frac{\phi(t) - \phi(0)}{t - 0} = 88\left(1 - \frac{t}{10}\right).$$

Calculating the values of $q_0(t)$ for values of t successively closer to 0, we obtain the table

t	1	0.1	0.01	0.0001
$q_0(t)$	79.2	87.12	87.912	87.9912

In this respect, then, formula (2) appears to be entirely reasonable.

In general, we may wish to know the velocity at any time t_0 within the interval when the car is braked to a stop. We approximate the velocity at t_0 by the average velocity (1) which in this case is

$$(3) \qquad q(t) = \frac{\phi(t) - \phi(t_0)}{t - t_0} = \frac{88(t - t_0)\left[1 - \dfrac{(t + t_0)}{10}\right]}{t - t_0}$$

$$= 88\left[1 - \frac{t + t_0}{10}\right] \qquad\qquad (t \neq t_0).$$

We stress that $q(t)$ has no meaning when $t = t_0$; if $t = t_0$, the denominator in the expression for $q(t)$ is zero. Otherwise, when $t \neq t_0$, the ratio $\dfrac{t - t_0}{t - t_0}$ appears in the expression for $q(t)$ and has the value 1. Apart from the gap at t_0, the function q is linear, and we are tempted to fill the gap by defining the instantaneous velocity v_0 as the value obtained by setting $t_0 = t$ in the last expression for $q(t)$.

We may believe that the instantaneous velocity v_0, or the limit of the average velocity at t_0 is simply the number obtained if t is taken as t_0 in the last expression for $q(t)$, namely,

$$(4) \qquad\qquad v_0 = 88\left[1 - \frac{t_0}{5}\right].$$

Again, if we take values of t successively closer to t_0, as in the following table, we find grounds for faith in this belief.

t	$t_0 + 1$	$t_0 - \frac{1}{10}$	$t_0 + \frac{1}{100}$	$t_0 - \frac{1}{1000}$
$q(t)$	$v_0 - 8.8$	$v_0 + 0.88$	$v_0 - 0.088$	$v_0 + 0.0088$

Belief based on a critical appraisal of the evidence is an excellent way to approach a mathematical question; but no mathematical investigation is complete until the belief is substantiated by deductive logical proof. To prove that the velocity is actually given by (4), we must show that we can control the error in approximating the instantaneous velocity v_0 by the average velocity $q(t)$ by choosing t sufficiently close to t_0. Specifically, the error of approximation to v_0 by $q(t)$ is $|q(t) - v_0|$, and for any prescribed error tolerance ϵ ($\epsilon > 0$ is implied), we must be able to ensure that

(5) $$|q(t) - v_0| < \epsilon \qquad\qquad (t \neq t_0),$$

by keeping $|t - t_0|$ small enough. From (3) and (4), we have

$$q(t) - v_0 = 88 \left(-\frac{t + t_0}{10} + \frac{t_0}{5} \right)$$
$$= 8.8(t_0 - t) \qquad\qquad (t \neq t_0).$$

Condition (5) is then equivalent to

(6) $$0 < |t - t_0| < \epsilon/8.8$$

and, therefore, the error of approximation can be kept within the tolerance ϵ if we choose t closer to t_0 than $\epsilon/8.8$. We exclude $t = t_0$ because it defines no member of the set of approximations, the values of $q(t)$. We have verified that the motion (2) defines a definite velocity at each instant t_0 and in (4) we have found its value.

Our purpose in this example is to exhibit how the idea of expressing instantaneous velocity as a limit of average velocities can be put into practice in a specific case. It is nice to know that our results give useful information. For example, we can calculate the stopping distance of the car. The expression (4) for the velocity yields the time $t_0 = 5$ sec. when the vehicle is stopped, that is, when $v_0 = 0$. Inserting this time in (2), we see that the vehicle travels 220 ft. before it comes to a stop.

The idea of velocity is one special case of the idea of rate of change which is applicable in almost any area of scientific investigation where variation is studied — for example, in the study of the way the price of a commodity changes as its supply varies, or the change in the intensity of sunlight with depth under the surface of the ocean, or the variation of the population with time of some infectious bacillus in its host, or the variation in elevation of a mountain road in relation to horizontal distance. In each instance, there is a presumed functional relation between two numerical variables, $f : x \to y$ and the question of how $y = f(x)$ changes with x is at issue. We may wish to compare the change in y with the change in x over the interval between x_0 and x_1. Corresponding to the change in x, that is, the difference $x_1 - x_0$, we have the change $y_1 - y_0$, where $y_0 = f(x_0)$ and $y_1 = f(x_1)$. To compare the change in y with the change in x, we may form the ratio

(7)
$$\frac{y_1 - y_0}{x_1 - x_0} = \frac{f(x_1) - f(x_0)}{x_1 - x_0};$$

this is the *average rate*† of *change of y with respect* to *x*. This average rate is identical with the slope of the chord joining the points (x_0, y_0) and (x_1, y_1) of the graph of f. Average velocity as defined by (1) is just the average rate of change of position with respect to time.

The *instantaneous rate of change of y with respect* to *x* at *x = a* is defined, as for instantaneous velocity, to be the limit of the average rate

(8)
$$r(x) = \frac{f(x) - f(a)}{x - a}$$

at *x = a*. This limit is the derivative of f at *a* already seen in 1.1 and it is denoted by $f'(a)$. The geometrical interpretation of the derivative, as we recall from 1.1, is the slope of the graph of f at the point $(a, f(a))$. For brevity, we shall refer simply to "rates" rather than "instantaneous rates"; "average rates" will always be referred to in full.

We may consider not only rates of change, but also rates of change of rates of change. For example, acceleration, the rate of change of velocity with respect to time is a physically important concept; one of the fundamental laws of Newtonian mechanics (Chapter 12) is that the acceleration of a particle is proportional to the applied force.

Example 2. In Example 1, we considered the motion of a car being braked to a stop. The velocity of the car is decreasing in the course of the motion. We therefore expect the rate of change of the velocity to be negative; that is, we should obtain a negative acceleration. Example 1 was composed under the reasonable assumption that the braking force is constant. This should mean a constant negative acceleration. Let us verify this condition.

From (4) and the calculated stopping time, we know the velocity as a function of time $\psi : t \to v$ where, in feet per second,

(9)
$$v = \psi(t) = 88\left[1 - \frac{t}{5}\right].$$

The change in *v* over the interval from t_0 to *t* is

$$v - v_0 = -88(t - t_0)/5,$$

†The word "rate" in the sense of comparative measure means "ratio."

where $v = \psi(t)$ and $v_0 = \psi(t_0)$. It follows that the average rate of change over the interval is constant:

$$(10) \qquad \frac{v - v_0}{t - t_0} = -\frac{88}{5} = -17.6 \qquad (t \neq t_0).$$

If the average rate of change of velocity is constant, then all the approximations to the instantaneous rate have the same value. Thus, the acceleration at any time t_0 is -17.6 ft./sec.^{2}, the constant negative acceleration on the basis of which Example 1 was composed.

We may have seemed insanely cautious in Examples 1 and 2 in going from the average rate of change to its limit, the instantaneous rate. In each case, we obtained a simple formula for the average rate when $t \neq t_0$ and it would have been necessary only to set $t = t_0$ in the formula to obtain the correct instantaneous rate. Yet in each case, we insisted on the more complicated procedure of considering an instantaneous rate as the limit of approximations by average rates to justify our results. There are good reasons for this seemingly round-about approach. In the first place, we defined the instantaneous rate as the limit of average rates and, for the sake of logical conviction, we should verify that the obvious instantaneous rates are really such limits. Furthermore, there is a compelling reason other than the need for logical conviction for proceeding with care. The definition of instantaneous rate is general, applicable to any function, not just the examples we have considered. Without knowing the function f explicitly, we cannot tell whether we can obtain a "simple" expression which agrees with the average rate $r(x)$ given by (8) when $x \neq a$ and is meaningful when $x = a$, as well. In fact, in 2.3 we give an example of a function for which such a simplification is impossible. In the end, we shall have the best of both worlds; when algebraic simplification is possible it will be seen to yield the correct result; when it is not, other formal methods of calculating instantaneous rates are usually available.

Before going on to further explore the idea of derivative, we wish to make it clear that its application almost always involves some sort of idealization. As an instance, let us reconsider Example 1 and follow the motion of a point on the hood ornament of a car a little more carefully. We consider only the displacements in one dimension, that is, we ignore vertical and sidewise components of the motion. In the gross time scale of 5 seconds, (2) is an adequate description of the motion and the graphs of displacement and velocity present the appearance depicted in Figure 2. If we observe on a finer time scale, say in the time interval of $\frac{1}{10}$ sec. after $t = 4$, we may find that the hood is vibrating mechanically like a drum. Thus, if

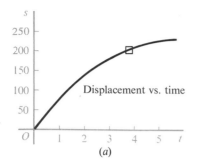

(a)

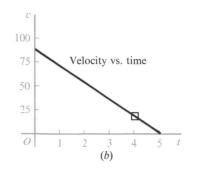

Figure 2

(b)

we magnify, as in Figure 3, the areas indicated by the boxes in Figure 2, we may find the actual motion (shown dark) to consist of an oscillation about the basic motion (shown light).

If we could refine our observations still further and study the motion of a single molecule, on a smaller time scale we might find an intense heat oscillation superimposed on the mechanical vibration, and the motion might appear as in Figure 4, where the heat motion of the molecule dominates the motion altogether and the molecule's average forward motion is not discernible. The motion appears as a sequence of rapid flights interrupted by impacts with adjacent molecules. The velocity scale is so large that the velocity of the vehicle described in Figure 2 is altogether negligible. When we are concerned with taking a ride out to the country, the scale of time of Figure 3 is clearly inappropriate to the concept of velocity. If, as automotive engineers, we should happen to care about the vibrations of the body, then the time scale of Figure 2 is too coarse and the scale of Figure 4 bears no imaginable relation to our concerns.

Clearly, the ideal of a velocity which can be approximated within any

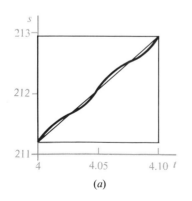

(a)

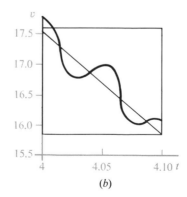

Figure 3

(b)

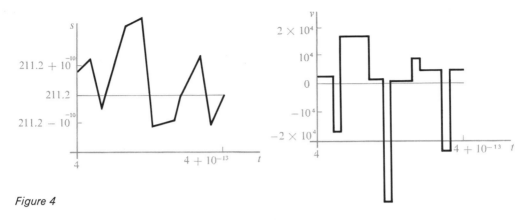

Figure 4

tolerance by taking a time interval small enough is a convenient fiction. Refinement of the time scale beyond a certain point may be expected to lead, in actual practice, into a regime where the original phenomena are lost. In fact, at the subatomic level the very ideas of particle position and velocity begin to come into question. Nonetheless, the idea of an infinitely refinable approximation to the limit is indispensable for the simplicity it produces in the way we think about such matters. The mathematics is likely to be useful to the extent that it takes into account only the minimum necessary amount of information. If we attempt to put into a mathematical analysis all the complexities of a real situation, we are likely to end with insoluble problems.

2.1 Exercises

1. Determine the average velocity of a car for a round trip if it averages 60 miles per hour going and 30 miles per hour returning.

2. As in Example 1, suppose that at time $t = 0$ the brakes are applied on a car moving at velocity 60 miles per hour, producing a constant deceleration (negative acceleration) of α ft./sec.^{2}, and kept on until the car is brought to a stop. Estimate what α ensures that the car will continue to travel only 100 feet after the brakes are applied.

3. Using the value of α from Exercise 2 determine the distance required to stop the car if it is traveling at 30 mph.

4. Let us assume that a pellet is projected straight up and after a while comes straight down via the same vertical path to the place from which it was launched. After t seconds the pellet is s feet above the ground. Some of the ordered pairs (t, s) are given in the following table.

t	0	1	2	3	4	5	6	7	8	9	10
s	0	144	256	336	384	400	384	336			0

We intentionally neglect complications like air resistance. Moreover, we use simple numbers rather than quantities measured to the degree of accuracy required for a practical engineering problem.

a. Interpolate between the given data to guess the height of the projectile at eight and nine seconds. (Use symmetry as your guide.) Does extrapolation to find values of s for $t = -1$ or $t = 11$ make sense on physical grounds? How long does it take the projectile to reach its maximum height? What seems to be the maximum height?

b. Does s appear to be a function of t? If so, discuss the domain and range, taking physical considerations into account.

c. If we were to plot a graph of $s = f(t)$, would it be plausible on physical grounds to restrict the plot to the first quadrant?

d. Do the data suggest that we choose the same scale on the s-axis (vertical) as on the t-axis (horizontal)?

e. Keeping in mind your responses to Parts c and d, plot the ordered pairs (t, s) from the table. Draw a smooth curve through the points. What kind of curve does the graph resemble? On physical grounds is it plausible that there is a real value of s for every real value assigned to t over the interval $0 \leq t \leq 10$? Are we justified in connecting the points?

f. Assuming that the equation $s = f(t) = At^2 + Bt + C$ was used to construct our table, find values for the constants A, B, and C.

g. Carefully plot the graph of the function $t \to 160t - 16t^2$ on the interval $0 \leq t \leq 10$. Draw the chord that connects the point where $t = 1$ with the point where $t = 2$. What is the slope of this chord? Estimate the slope of the curve at $t = 1$ and $t = 2$.

h. If the unit of s is the foot and the unit of t is the second, what is the unit of slope? What physical concept is commonly associated with this ratio of units? What are the physical interpretations of positive, zero, and negative values of this ratio?

i. Draw the graph $v = 160 - 32t$ over the interval $0 \leq t \leq 10$. Compare the values of v for $t = 1$ and $t = 2$ respectively with your estimates for the slopes of the graph of $s = 160t - 16t^2$ in Part g.

j. Average the values of v for $t = 1$ and $t = 2$ and compare this average with the slope of the chord connecting the points where $t = 1$ and $t = 2$ in Part g.

k. If the unit of v is the foot per second (ft./sec.) and the unit of t is the second, what is the unit of the slope of the line $v = 160 - 32t$? What physical concept is commonly associated with this ratio of units? What is the meaning of the negative value of this slope?

5. Find the velocity of an object whose position on its path is described by the equation $s = 128t - 16t^2$. Sketch the curves of s vs. t and v vs. t on the same set of axes.

a. During what time interval or intervals is the object moving toward the position $s = 0$?

b. What are the values of v and t when s is a maximum?

6. A ball is thrown upward with a velocity of 32 feet per second. Its height h in feet after t seconds is described by the equation $h = 32t - 16t^2$.

    a. What is the velocity of the ball when its height first reaches 12 feet? When it again reaches 12 feet?

    b. How high does it go, and at what time does the ball reach its highest position?

7. An object is projected up a smooth inclined plane in a straight line. Its distance s in feet from the starting point after t seconds is described by the equation $s = 64t - 8t^2$. After the object reaches its highest point it slides back along its original path to the starting point according to the equation $s^* = 8(t - t_1)^2$. Here s^* is the distance of the object from the highest point and t_1 is the time it takes the object to reach its highest point.

    a. Determine how long it takes the object to make the up-and-down trip.

    b. Sketch the s vs. t curve for the up-and-down motion using one set of coordinates. Do the same for the v vs. t curve.

8. The location of an object on a straight line is given by the formula

$$s = pt^2 + qt + r \qquad\qquad (p > 0),$$

where p, q, and r are real constants. Find all instants of time when the object is at rest, and show how the number of such instants depends on the constants p, q, and r.

9. For any but the simplest motions, the function ϕ describing the location at time t is unlikely to be expressible in terms of a single formula for the entire duration of the motion. Here is a more plausible description of a motion:

$$\phi(t) = \begin{cases} t^2/2, & \text{for } 0 \le t \le 1 \\ t - \frac{1}{2}, & \text{for } 1 \le t \le \frac{5}{2} \\ -\frac{1}{2}t^2 + \frac{7}{2}t - \frac{29}{8}, & \text{for } \frac{5}{2} \le t \le \frac{7}{2} \\ \frac{5}{2}, & \text{for } \frac{7}{2} \le t \le 6 \\ t^2 - 12t + \frac{77}{2}, & \text{for } 6 \le t \le 8 \\ \frac{21}{2} - 4(t-7)^{-1}, & \text{for } 8 \le t \le 10. \end{cases}$$

    a. Compute the function $t \to \psi(t)$ that describes the velocity of the motion with position given by $s = \phi(t)$.

    b. It is claimed that $s = \phi(t)$ and $v = \psi(t)$ are functions. What has to be checked to verify this? Does it check? Show the graph of each of these functions on the same axes.

    c. During what time intervals do you think the speed of the motion is increasing? decreasing?

    d. Does the object spend any time between $t = 0$ and $t = 10$ standing still? Does it have any other instants of zero velocity during the motion?

10. In this section we defined the velocity of an object whose location on a straight line at time $t = t_0$ is given by $s = \phi(t)$ as the limit of the ratio

$$\frac{\phi(t) - \phi(t_0)}{t - t_0}$$

and later we observed that this limit is the value of the derivative ϕ' at $t = t_0$. Experimentally it has been established that the distance covered in time t by a body falling freely from rest is proportional to t^2, and therefore can be represented by the function $\phi : t \to ct^2$, where c is a positive constant. Show that the velocity of a freely falling body is directly proportional to the time of descent.

11. Suppose a projectile is ejected with initial velocity v_0 feet per second at a point P that is 20 feet above mean sea level. Neglect friction and assume that the projectile moves up and down in a straight line. Let $\theta(t)$ denote the height above P in feet that the projectile attains t seconds after ejection. Note that if gravitational attraction were not acting on the projectile, it would continue to move upward with a constant velocity, traveling a distance of v_0 feet pet second, so that its height at time t would be given by $\theta(t) = v_0 t$. We know that the force of gravity acting on the projectile causes it to slow down until its velocity is zero and then to travel back to earth. On the basis of physical experiments the formula $\theta(t) = v_0 t - \frac{1}{2} g t^2$, where g represents the force of gravity, is used to represent the height of the projectile above P, as long as it is aloft. Note that $\theta(t) = 0$ when $t = 0$ and when $t = 2v_0/g$. This means that the projectile returns to the initial 20-foot level after $2v_0/g$ seconds.

a. Find the velocity of the projectile at $t = t_0$ in terms of v_0 and g.
b. Sketch the curves of s vs. t and v vs. t on the same set of axes.
c. In terms of v_0 compute the time required for the velocity to drop to zero.
d. What is the velocity on return to the initial 20-foot level?
e. Assume that the projectile returns to earth at a point 30 feet below the initial take off point P. What is the velocity at impact?

2.2 DERIVATIVES OF QUADRATIC FUNCTIONS

In 1.1 and 2.1 we have introduced two concepts, the slope of the graph $y = f(x)$ at $(a, f(a))$ and the rate of change of y with respect to x when $x = a$. These are two different aspects of the one basic concept, the derivative of f at a. For linear functions, the derivative should coincide with our older algebraic conception of slope (see A3.4a in the appendix), and we shall shortly see that it does. For more complicated functions, the derivative, a limit, is the only appropriate way to define slope. The next more complicated class of functions consists of the polynomial functions of degree up to 2, namely, the functions of the form

$$(1) \qquad f : x \to Ax^2 + Bx + C.$$

When $x = a$, the graph of f passes through the point $(a, f(a))$; we propose to calculate the slope there. We are primarily concerned with the quadratic case $A \neq 0$ for which the concept of slope is essentially new. At the same time, we shall observe for the linear case $A = 0$ that the old and new ideas of slope do agree.

We calculate the slope of the graph at $(a, f(a))$ as the limit of the approximations that define it, namely the slopes

$$(2) \qquad\qquad r(x) = \frac{f(x) - f(a)}{x - a}$$

of chords through $(a, f(a))$ and $(x, f(x))$, with $x \neq a$. For the general quadratic function, we obtain from (1) and (2)

$$r(x) = \frac{Ax^2 + Bx + C - (Aa^2 + Ba + C)}{x - a} = \frac{A(x^2 - a^2) + B(x - a)}{x - a}$$

$$= \frac{x - a}{x - a}[A(x + a) + B] \qquad\qquad (x \neq a).$$

When $x \neq a$, the function r coincides with the simple linear function $x \to A(x + a) + B$. As in 2.1, we immediately guess that the slope at the point $(a, f(a))$ must be $m = 2Aa + B$. We verify this guess by prescribing a tolerance ϵ and showing that the error of our approximations can be brought within the tolerance. For x sufficiently near to a, the error in the approximation is $|r(x) - m|$, namely,

$$(3) \qquad\qquad |A(x + a) + B - (2Aa + B)| = |A(x - a)|.$$

When the original function f is linear, $A = 0$ and the error (3) is identically zero. Thus, our approximations are exact in the linear case, and we do have $m = B$ which establishes the identity of derivative and the earlier idea of slope for linear functions.

Next, let us verify our guess for the slope in the quadratic case, $A \neq 0$. In order to bring the error (3) within the tolerance ϵ, we see that we must choose x in a way that depends on the coefficient A of the quadratic function. To ensure that we stay within the tolerance, that $|r(x) - m| < \epsilon$, we restrict x to values for which $|x - a| < \dfrac{\epsilon}{|A|}$, so that

$$|r(x) - m| = |A(x - a)| = |A|\,|x - a| < |A|\frac{\epsilon}{|A|} \leq \epsilon.$$

This proves that the calculated value m is the correct slope, the limit of the chordal slopes.

Example 1. Consider the parabola given by $y = f(x) = \frac{1}{2}x^2 + x + \frac{5}{2}$, where $A = \frac{1}{2}$, $B = 1$, and $C = \frac{5}{2}$. The lowest point on this graph may be fonnd algebraically from the standard form $(x + 1)^2 = 2(y - 2)$ of the equation of the curve; it is the vertex $(-1, 2)$. Alternatively, using the idea introduced in the optimum value problem of 1.1, we may find the lowest point directly as a point of zero slope. The slope at $(a, f(a))$ is

$m = (\frac{1}{2})2a + 1 = a + 1$, and it is zero for $a = -1$, where $f(a) = f(-1) = 2$. (Note, however, that we do not as yet have a way to prove by the calculus that this *is* the lowest point; but the standard form indicates that y cannot go below 2 on the graph.)

2.2 Exercises

1. In the text we assert that when f is linear, $A = 0$ and the error (3) is identically zero. Thus our approximations are exact in the linear case, and we do have $m = B$. Find the slope for $x = a$ of the general linear function $f : x \rightarrow Bx + C$ (where B and C are any constants except that $B \neq 0$) and compare your result with that obtained from the standard slope-intercept form of the equation of a straight line in coordinate geometry.

2. Find the slope of $y = f(x) = x^2 - 1$ at the point $(3, 8)$ by constructing a table of values of $r(x)$ for x successively closer to 3. Verify that your answer is the limit of the slopes of the chords.

3. For the function given by $f(x) = x^2 - x + 1$ tabulate the slopes of the chords joining $(\frac{5}{7}, f(\frac{5}{7}))$ to $(x, f(x))$ for $x = \frac{5}{7} + \frac{1}{10}, \frac{5}{7} - \frac{1}{10}, \frac{5}{7} + \frac{1}{100}, \frac{5}{7} - \frac{1}{100}, \frac{5}{7} + \frac{1}{1000}, \frac{5}{7} - \frac{1}{1000}$, etc., as far as your time, energies, and inclinations permit. Can you predict the limit of the approximations from an inspection of the table?

4. a. At each of the points $(1, 7)$ and $(2, 16)$, find the slope of

$$y = g(x) = 3x^2 + 4$$

   by constructing a table of approximations by slopes of chords; then verify that your answer is the limit of such approximations.
   b. Find the slope of the graph $y = g(x)$ at the point $(a, g(a))$.
   c. Find the lowest point on the graph of g algebraically.
   d. Using the result of Part b, check your answer to Part c.
   e. What is the relationship between the slopes for the function g at the points $x = a$ and $x = -a$? Interpret this result graphically. Give examples of other functions having this property.

5. In Example 1 we said that the lowest point $(-1, 2)$ on the graph of

$$y = f(x) = \tfrac{1}{2}x^2 + x + \tfrac{5}{2}$$

   may be found algebraically from the standard form $(x + 1)^2 = 2(y - 2)$ of of the equation of the curve. Equivalently, we could have written

$$y = \tfrac{1}{2}(x - (-1))^2 + 2.$$

   If we write $y = Ax^2 + Bx + C$ as

$$x = \frac{-B \pm \sqrt{B^2 - 4A(C - y)}}{2A},$$

we can see algebraically that the minimum (or maximum, if $A < 0$) conceivable value of y is $(4AC - B^2)/4A$ and corresponds to

$$x = -B/2A .$$

Show that $Ax^2 + Bx + C = A(x - s)^2 + d$ if and only if $s = -B/2A$ and $d = (4AC - B^2)/4A$.

6. For what values of k does the line $y = k$ intersect the parabola

$$y = Ax^2 + Bx + C \qquad\qquad (A \neq 0):$$

   a. In no points?
   b. In 1 point?
   c. In 2 points?
   d. What is the lowest or highest point of the given parabola?

7. a. Using Exercise 6, find the highest point on the graph of

$$g : x \rightarrow 5 - 6x - x^2 .$$

   b. Explain geometrically why the point in Part a can be found where the slope of $y = g(x)$ is zero.

8. a. What is the greatest possible number of points where the graph of a quadratic function $x \rightarrow Ax^2 + Bx + C$ $(A \neq 0)$ may be horizontal?
   b. Is it possible for the graph to be horizontal at less than the maximum number of points, or nowhere horizontal?

9. a. Given $y = f(x) = 20x - 3x^2$, find the slope of the curve at the point $(a, f(a))$.
   b. Where is the slope zero? How can you use this information in plotting the graph of f?

10. Determine the maximum value of the function

$$f: x \rightarrow \frac{1}{x^2 - 6x + 10} .$$

2.3 DERIVATIVES IN GENERAL

Slope and velocity are two concepts with seemingly unrelated origins in geometry and physics; yet we have obtained each in the same way as a limit. We have abstracted from the ideas of velocity and slope a general analytical concept, the derivative of a function at a point, and now we frame this concept in a purely numerical way, independently of the problems from which it arises.

Let a be a value of x in the domain of a function f. We say that m is the *derivative* of f at a if, by taking x sufficiently near to a, we can approximate m by the difference quotient $\dfrac{f(x) - f(a)}{x - a}$

with an error less than any prescribed tolerance. We describe this situation briefly by saying that m is the *limit* of $\dfrac{f(x) - f(a)}{x - a}$ as x approaches a, or writing

(1)
$$m = \lim_{x \sim a} \frac{f(x) - f(a)}{x - a}.$$

The procedure of computing a derivative is called *differentiation*, and if f has a derivative at a, if the limit (1) exists, then we say that f is *differentiable* at a.

The preceding description gives no prescription for differentiating any particular function at any particular point. In fact, no universal technique for finding derivatives exists, although, with the assistance of the general methods of operation with limits to be developed in the next chapter, we shall be able to differentiate many of the functions of greatest interest. Here, we try to pursue a little further the technique which enabled us to find the derivatives of functions in 1.1 and 2.2.

Look again at the difference quotient

(2)
$$r(x) = \frac{f(x) - f(a)}{x - a}.$$

No matter what function f appears in the numerator, the denominator forbids us to evaluate r at $x = a$. In each earlier example, we avoided this difficulty by finding a simple formula for a function which had the same values as r for $x \neq a$, but which was also defined for $x = a$. Thus, if $f(x) = x^2$, for example, we have

$$r(x) = \frac{x^2 - a^2}{x - a} = \frac{(x - a)}{(x - a)}(x + a),$$

or

$$r(x) = x + a \qquad (x \neq a).$$

This formula suggests that the limit of $r(x)$ for x approaching a is $m = 2a$.

In finding the value of m, the crucial step was the representation of the numerator of $r(x)$ as a product containing the factor $(x - a)$. With the help of algebraic techniques, it is possible to find the derivatives of a number of simple functions in this way.

Example 1. Consider the function g defined by $g(x) = \dfrac{1}{x}$, whose derivative we wish to find at $x = a$. As yet, we cannot even guarantee the existence of a derivative without further investigation. (See, for instance, Exercise 1.) For the function g, we have

$$r(x) = \frac{g(x) - g(a)}{x - a} = \frac{\frac{1}{x} - \frac{1}{a}}{x - a} = \frac{-x + a}{ax(x - a)} = -\frac{1}{ax}\frac{(x - a)}{(x - a)},$$

or

$$r(x) = -\frac{1}{ax} \qquad (x \neq a).$$

Our natural guess for the derivative at a is $m = -\dfrac{1}{a^2}$. To test our

guess, we should set a tolerance $\epsilon > 0$, and check that the error in the approximation of m by $r(x)$ remains within that tolerance for x sufficiently close to a. That is, we should show that for such x, we have

$$|r(x) - m| = \left|r(x) + \frac{1}{a^2}\right| = \left|\frac{x - a}{a^2 x}\right| = \frac{|x - a|}{a^2|x|} < \epsilon \qquad (x \neq a).$$

The situation is not quite so simple as before The error is still a multiple of $|x - a|$, but the multiplier depends on both a and x; and we must keep x away from 0. Algebraic techniques for completing the verification are developed in 3.3. You are encouraged to try to complete it yourself. (Compare Exercise 21.) We repeat the result to be proved: the derivative at $x = a$ of $g : x \to \dfrac{1}{x}$ is $m = -\dfrac{1}{a^2}$.

Example 2. Another function whose derivative at a can be obtained with the aid of elementary algebra is the square-root function $h : x \to x^{1/2} = \sqrt{x}$. For the approximations to the derivative m, we now have

$$r(x) = \frac{h(x) - h(a)}{x - a} = \frac{\sqrt{x} - \sqrt{a}}{x - a} \qquad (x \neq a).$$

In order to obtain the factor $(x - a)$ in the numerator, we rationalize the numerator.

$$r(x) = \frac{(\sqrt{x} - \sqrt{a})(\sqrt{x} + \sqrt{a})}{(x - a)(\sqrt{x} + \sqrt{a})} = \frac{(x - a)}{(x - a)}\frac{1}{\sqrt{x} + \sqrt{a}} \qquad (x \neq a).$$

The value of $r(x)$ is $\dfrac{1}{\sqrt{x} + \sqrt{a}}$ for $x \neq a$, and $m = \dfrac{1}{2\sqrt{a}}$ is our guess for the derivative of h at $x = a$. The proof that this is the limit is similar to the verification for the preceding function, and is also left for later. (See Exercise 21.) For the present, we accept the result that the derivative at $x = a$ of $h : x \to \sqrt{x}$ is $\dfrac{1}{2\sqrt{a}}$.

Example 3. Lest you jump to the wrong conclusion that all derivatives may be obtained with nothing more than simple algebra, take a careful look at the sine function, $k : x \to \sin x$. Although the domain of the sine function consists of all real x, for simplicity we shall attempt to compute the derivative only at $x = 0$. We then need to find the limit as x approaches 0 of the ratio

$$r(x) = \frac{k(x) - k(0)}{x - 0} = \frac{\sin x - \sin 0}{x - 0} = \frac{\sin x}{x}.$$

How can we divide $\sin x$ by x? The answer, unfortunately for our attempt to differentiate $\sin x$, is that there is no method of algebra or trigonometry that enables us to carry out such a division. No formal trick will help, and we are forced to take a quite different route in order to find the derivative. After a more detailed study of limits, and the application of this study to a more systematic calculation of the derivatives of algebraic functions, we shall return to this problem and solve it.

The idea of derivative is an example of a general idea, that of limit of a function. The derivative (1) is the limit of the function r given by $r(x) = \dfrac{f(x) - f(a)}{x - a}$. For the general idea of limit, we do not insist that the function be expressed in this special form of ratio. The limit of a function ϕ as x approaches a is a number L which we can approximate by function values $\phi(x)$ with an error less than any prescribed tolerance just by taking x sufficiently close to a. In this, we make no presupposition about the form of ϕ. So far, we have only offered an intuitive notion of what a limit should be. In Chapter 3, we shall make the idea precise. Nonetheless, we can foresee some of the requirements which must be imposed. Since the idea of limit of a function is to include the idea of derivative, we must be sure that the definition of limit does not involve the value of ϕ at a, for it is precisely at the point where the limit is to be determined that the difference quotient (2) is undefined. Furthermore, the process of approximation is meaningful only if it is possible to approach a arbitrarily closely through points x in the domain of ϕ. We shall have to require that every neighborhood of a contains points of the domain of ϕ other than a itself.

2.3 Exercises

1. Each of the following curves passes through the origin. For each curve construct a table listing the slopes of chords with one endpoint at the origin and the other at nearby points $(x, f(x))$. As these points are taken successively closer to the origin (e.g., $|x| < 0.1$, $|x| < 0.01$, etc.), what information do you obtain about the slope of the curve? In your opinion, is it possible to define the slope of the graph at the origin? If so, what is the slope? If not, justify your answer.

   a. $y = f(x) = x^{1/3}$.
   b. $y = f(x) = x^{2/3}$.
   c. $y = f(x) = |x|^{3/2}$.

2. a. Find the slope of the graph $y = x^3$ at (a, b) where $b = a^3$.
   b. Is there any lowest point on the graph $y = x^3$? Is there any highest point? Is there any point where the graph is horizontal?

3. For the function $x \rightarrow x^3$ of Exercise 2 what is the relationship between the slopes of the graph when $x = a$ and $x = -a$? Interpret this result graphically. Give examples of other functions having this property.

4. a. Find the slope of the graph of $h : x \rightarrow 4x^3 - 3x^2$ at $(a, h(a))$.
   b. Find all points where the graph of h is horizontal. Can you characterize these points as "highest" or "lowest," perhaps in a restricted sense?

5. Find the derivative of f at a for $f : x \rightarrow f(x)$, given

   a. $f(x) = \dfrac{1}{x+1}$,   c. $f(x) = \dfrac{1}{x^2}$,   e. $f(x) = \dfrac{1}{\sqrt{x}}$,

   b. $f(x) = \dfrac{1}{Ax+B}$,   d. $f(x) = \dfrac{1}{x^3}$,   f. $f(x) = x^{3/2}$,

   where A and B are constants, $A \neq 0$.

6. For each of the functions of Exercise 5, and also for the functions

   $$x \rightarrow 1/x \quad \text{and} \quad x \rightarrow \sqrt{x}$$

   (Examples 1 and 2 of the text), list the following: the domain of the function; all points of zero slope (if any); the highest point on the graph of the function (if any); the lowest point on the graph of the function (if any).

7. For each of the following use the definition of derivative to differentiate f both at $a = -2$ and at $a = 2$.

   a. $f(x) = (x-2)^2$.   c. $f(x) = 3x - x^3$.

   b. $f(x) = \dfrac{1+x}{1-x}$.   d. $f(x) = x^2 - x - x^{-1}$.

8. For each function f whose value $f(x)$ is given below, find the derivative at a, where a is in the domain of the function.

   a. $5x - x^2$.   c. $x^3 - 2x$.   e. $\dfrac{2}{x-1}$.

   b. $3 - x - x^2$.   d. $\dfrac{2x}{x+1}$.   f. $\dfrac{x^2+x}{x^2-1}$.

9. a. Find the slope at the point $(1, 1)$ of the graph of each function

$$f : x \to x^3, \qquad g : x \to x^{1/3}.$$

b. Discuss the relationship between the two answers.

10. a. At what point on the graph of $f : x \to x^2 + 5x + 4$ is the slope the same as the value of x ?

b. Write an equation of the line with slope -5 which contains the point $(-5, 4)$.

11. The graph of f passes through the point $(1, -2)$ and for each number a its slope at $x = a$ is given by $f'(a) = 10a - 11$.

a. Find such a function f.

b. Let the line which passes through $(1, -2)$ with the same slope as f at that point be given by

$$y = mx + b,$$

find m and b.

c. Find the point on the graph of f at which the slope is 9.

d. Write an equation of the line which passes through the point $(2, 2)$ with the same slope as the graph of f at that point.

12. Show for $f : x \to Ax^2 + Bx + C$ where $A > 0$, that if

$$f(x_1) = f(x_2) = 0 \qquad\qquad (x_1 \neq x_2),$$

then f has a minimum at $x = \frac{1}{2}(x_1 + x_2)$.

13. Assume that $y = mx + a$ touches the graph of $f : x \to Ax^2 + Bx + C$ at exactly one point $(p, f(p))$ and the parallel line $y = mx + b$ meets the graph in two points with the abscissas x_1 and x_2 (see figure).

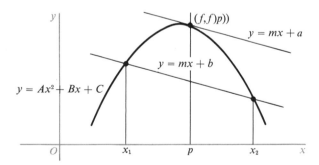

a. Show that $p = \frac{1}{2}(x_2 + x_1)$.

b. Determine m and a in terms of A, B, C, and p.

14. a. Find the points which the graph of $f : x \to 1 + x + x^2 - 2x^3$ has in common with the graph of $g : x \to 1 + x$.

b. Compare the slopes of the graphs of f and g at these points.

c. Write an equation of the line which has the same intercept and slope as the graph of f where it meets the y-axis.

15. Consider the function $f : x \to 2x^3 - 3x^2 - 12x + 13$.

a. Using the methods of this chapter find
- (i) $f'(a)$,
- (iii) $f'(3)$,
- (v) $f'(2)$.
- (ii) $f'(-2)$,
- (iv) $f'(-1)$,

b. Plot a few points and use the information you have gathered from computing slopes in Part a to sketch the graph of f.

c. Write an equation of the line which shares the point $(0, 13)$ with the graph of f and has the same slope as the graph of f at that point.

d. Write an equation of the line which has the same slope as the graph of f at $(\frac{1}{2}, \frac{13}{2})$ and passes through that point. Draw this line overlaying your sketch (Part b) of the graph. Compare the x- and y-intercepts of this line with the intercepts of the graph of f next on the right and left, respectively, of $x = \frac{1}{2}$.

16. a. Find the slope of the curve with equation $y = h(x) = Ax^3 + Bx^2 + Cx + D$ (the graph of the general cubic function) at $(a, h(a))$. Here A, B, C, D are any constants, except that $A \neq 0$.

b. What is the greatest possible number of points where the graph of a cubic function may be horizontal?

c. Is it possible for a cubic function to have its graph horizontal at less than the maximum number of points? If the answer is "Yes," give an example of such a function.

d. Is it possible for a cubic function to have its graph nowhere horizontal? If the answer is "Yes," give an example of such a function.

17. Show that the curve of Exercise 16 is symmetric to the point

$$(-B/3A, \ h(-B/3A)).$$

(See A3.6c.)

18. A function h is defined by

$$h(x) = \begin{cases} x^3, & x < 1, \\ -x^2 + 2x, & x \geq 1. \end{cases}$$

Find the slope of the graph of h for $x < 1$ and for $x > 1$. Is it possible in your opinion to define a slope for the graph at $(1, 1)$? Give an argument to support your answer. (A sketch may be helpful in answering the question.)

19. You probably know that large telescopes and automobile headlights use parabolic mirrors. A parabolic reflector can bring a bundle of parallel rays like those from a star† to a sharp focus (see figure). We are now able to demonstrate the focal property of the parabola.

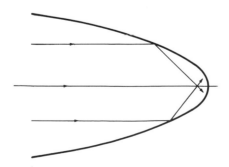

† At stellar distances the deviation from parallelism is negligible.

According to Heron's Law of reflection for a ray of light incident upon a smooth mirror, the incident ray and the reflected ray make equal angles with the mirror. Suppose the shape of the cross section through the axis of the mirror is given by the graph $y = x^2$. Prove for all incident rays parallel to the y-axis that the reflected rays have a common point of intersection as in the figure. This common point is called the focus of the parabola. It can also be shown that this property characterizes the parabola; i.e., if the curve is such that all parallel rays pass through a common point after reflection, then the curve must be a parabola.

20. A certain motion is described from time $t = 5$ until $t = 8$ by the equation

$$s = \phi(t) = 2t^3 - 39t^2 + 252t - 535 .$$

  a. Derive the velocity function for the motion.
  b. Sketch the graph $s = \phi(t)$ (called the world line) and the v vs. t curve (i.e., the graph of the velocity as a function of time).
  c. When the velocity $v = 0$, what features are exhibited by the graph of ϕ? Explain this physically.
  d. Given only that $\phi(6) = 5$ for the function ϕ that describes the motion, show that there is a second time t when $\phi(t) = 5$, and find that value of t. (This is *not* done by calculus.)
  e. Find the time of the greatest speed achieved between $t = 6$ and $t = 7$.

21. Prove that the derivative at $x = a$ of

$$g : x \to \frac{1}{x} \text{ is } -\frac{1}{a^2},$$

$$h : x \to \sqrt{x} \text{ is } \frac{1}{2\sqrt{a}} .$$

22. In Example 3, we expressed the derivative of $\sin x$ at $x = 0$ as the limit of the ratio $\dfrac{\sin x}{x}$ as x approaches 0. Using tables, compare values of x and $\sin x$ for x near 0 and guess the value of this limit.

23. Write the derivative of $f : x \to \cos x$ at $x = a$ as a limit, for $a = 0$ and for $a = \pi/2$, and show what limits must be evaluated before these derivatives can be obtained.

24. In Chapter 8 we shall define a function $f : x \to 2^x$ on the set $\mathfrak{R}$ of all real numbers that satisfies all the familiar laws of exponents valid for 2^n when n is a rational number. Compute the ratios $r(x)$ that serve to approximate the derivative of f at $x = a$ and $x = 0$, and show what limit problem must be solved before we can differentiate the function.

3

Limits and Continuity

3.1 INTRODUCTION

In the broad sense of Chapter 1, a limit is a number defined by a scheme of approximation. For a number L to be considered the limit in such a scheme, the scheme must yield some approximation A, for any given error tolerance ϵ, which lies within the distance ϵ of L:

$$|A - L| < \epsilon.$$

(In this text, an error tolerance is always positive.) Our concern here is with the idea of limit of a function at a point. The limit of a function f at a point x_0 is approximated, in a sense that will soon be made precise, by function values $f(x)$ where x approximates x_0. A simple case illustrates the idea.

Example 1. Consider the function $f : x \to \sqrt{x}$. We may be concerned with a particular value of this function, say $f(2) = \sqrt{2}$. Now, $\sqrt{2}$ is not rational (see A1.5 Ex. 1c), yet the purpose for which we are interested in this value of the function may require a rational approximation and an estimate of the error. A reasonable procedure is to attempt to approximate $\sqrt{2}$ by $\sqrt{x}$ where x approximates 2 and $\sqrt{x}$ is rational. For any natural number n we can find a natural number m so that

$$\frac{m}{n} < \sqrt{2} < \frac{m+1}{n}$$

(in terms of the integer part function of A2.2, $m = [\![n\sqrt{2}]\!]$). To determine the number m we need only compute the squares of the natural numbers in succession until we find two successive squares m^2 and $(m+1)^2$ that satisfy

$$m^2 < 2n^2 < (m+1)^2.$$

Since $\sqrt{2}$ lies between $\dfrac{m}{n}$ and $\dfrac{m+1}{n}$ the error in choosing either of these estimates for $\sqrt{2}$ must be less than $\dfrac{1}{n}$ (see Ex. 1). To obtain a rational approximation to $\sqrt{2}$ within the specified error tolerance ϵ, we take $\dfrac{1}{n} \leq \epsilon$; that is, we choose $n \geq \dfrac{1}{\epsilon}$.

For various error tolerances ϵ we tabulate appropriate values of m, n, $x = \dfrac{m^2}{n^2}$ (to five decimal places) and $\sqrt{x} = \dfrac{m}{n}$.

ϵ	0.1	0.01	0.001	0.0001
n	10	100	1,000	10,000
m	14	141	1,414	14,142
x	1.96000	1.98810	1.99940	1.99996
$\sqrt{x}$	1.4	1.41	1.414	1.4142

In this example, we have shown how to approximate $\sqrt{2}$ by $\sqrt{x}$ for special rational values of x which approximate 2. For $\sqrt{2}$ to be the limit of f at $x = 2$, we do not restrict ourselves to special rational values of x, but, for each error tolerance ϵ, admit all values of x in the domain of f contained in some open interval which contains the number 2. Since the function f is increasing (see A2.5 Example 2), it follows for all x that satisfy

$$\frac{m^2}{n^2} < x < \frac{(m+1)^2}{n^2},$$

that

$$\frac{m}{n} < \sqrt{x} < \frac{m+1}{n},$$

and we conclude that

$$|\sqrt{x} - \sqrt{2}| < \frac{1}{n}.$$

The function f of the preceding example has an important property; namely, the limit of f at any given point a of its domain is $f(a)$. Such a function is said to be continuous at a. For a function that is continuous at a, the idea of the limit at a may seem unimportant since the limit is only the function value at that point, but, in Example 1 we have already seen how practical necessity makes it convenient to think of the function value as the limit of approximations. We have also seen an important instance of the limit of a function at a point where the function is not even defined; this, the derivative, is regarded as the limit of a function in the form of a difference quotient which is meaningless at the point where the limit is to be calculated. Thus, we have good practical and theoretical reasons for investigating the idea of limit.

It is one of the triumphs of the calculus that an enormous variety of significant problems can be solved by straightforward formal operations which readily yield solutions in terms of derivatives or integrals, ideas defined as limits. In the formal calculus, the idea of limit and the process of approximation upon which it is based disappear. The formal methods enable us to find limits by a kind of algebra without apparent need for deductive reasoning about the concept of approximation upon which the idea of limit rests. As our mathematical horizons widen and we try to solve more complicated problems through the calculus, we soon exceed the potentialities of the formal methods. There are always problems for which the formal techniques fail; for these the underlying theory becomes essential and we must go back to first principles. Only a firm grasp of the theory of limits enables us to exploit the methods of the calculus fully. Our purpose in this chapter is to provide an adequate base for the calculus in the theory of limits.

It is unusual at first encounter to obtain a complete grasp of such a subtle concept as limit. The study of mathematics is a process of maturing, and you may be well satisfied simply to comprehend enough of the theory in this chapter to enable you to follow its later applications. As you gain mathematical skill and maturity, a more complete understanding will come; for the present, it is enough to see how we are able to use the theory for the practical purpose of developing a calculus — a scheme of rapid and efficient reckoning — of limits, derivatives, and later, integrals.

The most important use of the basic theory is to approximate solutions of complicated problems with simple functions. Such approximations have special interest in this day of high-speed computers. A problem may even have a complete formal solution by the methods of the calculus, yet, for the purpose of numerical computation it may save time, effort, and money to ignore the formal solution and treat the problem by approximation. More important, simple approximations play a fundamental role in science and engineering. A realistic model of a phenomenon may involve so many complexities that the problem is mathematically unmanageable. As we shall see in later chapters, a simplified model yielding an approximation to the complete solution is often more useful than a completely realistic one. Limits enter into approximations to the solution of the simplified problem when there is no formal explicit solution, and into estimation of the error when the unattainable solution of the realistic problem is replaced by the solution of the simplified problem.

3.1 Exercises

1. a. In Example 1 we use the proposition that

(i) $$a < x < b,$$

   implies $|a - x| < b - a$ and $|b - x| < b - a$.
   Show that this is true.
   b. Show that if $a < x < b$, then the average $\frac{1}{2}(a + b)$ approximates x within the error tolerance $\frac{1}{2}(b - a)$.

2. Consider $f: x \rightarrow [\![x]\!] + [\![-x]\!]$. ($[\![x]\!]$ is the integer part of x defined in A2.2.)
   a. Sketch the graph of f.
   b. To what number, if any, do the values of x approximate when x is near 1? When x is near 2?
   c. What would you say is the limit of $f(x)$ as x approaches n when n is any integer?

d. Evaluate $f(n)$, where n is an integer.

Check your answers to parts b through d. Do they agree with your graph?

3. For each of the following functions sketch the graph and, if possible, consider what should be the limit as x approaches 0.

a. $f: x \rightarrow \dfrac{x}{x}$.

b. $f: x \rightarrow \dfrac{1}{|x|}$.

c. $f: x \rightarrow \dfrac{x}{|x|}$.

d. $f: x \rightarrow \dfrac{x}{[\![x]\!]}$.

e. $f: x \rightarrow \dfrac{[\![x]\!]}{x}$.

f. $f: x \rightarrow \sin\dfrac{1}{x}$.

3.2 DEFINITION OF LIMIT OF A FUNCTION

In order to derive the laws that govern formal operations with limits, we need to define the concept of limit precisely. We first ask how such a definition should be worded. What relation must exist between a number L and a function f for us to say that the limit of $f(x)$ as x approximates a is L?

The first and most obvious condition is that it must be possible to approximate L by values $f(x)$ within any specified error tolerance; namely, given any positive ϵ there must be some x that satisfies

(1) $$|f(x) - L| < \epsilon.$$

Next, it must be possible to obtain such an approximation to L by taking x as a sufficiently close approximation to a: for each positive ϵ, there must be some neighborhood of a wherein each point of the domain of f, other than a, satisfies (1). We exclude a because we wish, in particular, to consider any derivative, that is, the limit of $f(x)$ as x approaches a for a function f given in the special form of a difference quotient

$$f: x \rightarrow \frac{\phi(x) - \phi(a)}{x - a}.$$

Usually, in this text, the domain of f will include an entire neighborhood of a except perhaps for a itself, but it is often useful to analyze the behavior of f on only one side of a. For example, the instant t_0 when the propellant is exhausted is a natural starting time in the motion of a projectile. It is essential to know the velocity of the projectile at this time in order to determine the rest of the trajectory.† This initial velocity is defined as a limit of approximations on the domain $t > t_0$. In any case, we must omit a from the neighborhood where (1) must be satisfied because we wish to employ the limit as x approaches a of functions which may not be defined at a, or which may have irrelevent values at a. Thus, for each positive ϵ, there must be a deleted neighborhood of a

$$(2) \qquad\qquad 0 < |x - a| < \delta$$

wherein every x that lies in the domain of f satisfies (1).

Finally, we must be sure that we can approximate a itself by points of the domain of f, otherwise the idea of limit as x approximates a would have no content. Therefore, we require that every deleted neighborhood of a contains points of the domain of f. If a point a has this property it is called a *cluster point*‡ of the domain of f. If a were not a cluster point of the domain of f, then there would be some deleted neighborhood of a which contained no point of the domain of f. Therefore, no point x of the domain could approximate a within the radius of this neighborhood and the basic idea of approximating L by $f(x)$ as x approximates a would be inapplicable.

We can now summarize the preceding ideas in a complete formal definition of limit of a function at a point.

Definition 1. A function f is said to have the *limit L at a*, and $f(x)$ is said to have the *limit L as x approximates* (or *approaches*) a, if and only if both of the following conditions are satisfied:

1. The point a is a cluster point of the domain of f.
2. For each positive number ϵ, there exists a positive number δ such that

$$|f(x) - L| < \epsilon$$

for every x in the domain of f which satisfies

$$0 < |x - a| < \delta .$$

If both conditions are satisfied, we write $\lim_{x \sim a} f(x) = L$.

It is also convenient to word this definition of limit geometrically in terms of neighborhoods: the number L is said to be the limit of f at

---

†In some texts this important case is covered by separate definitions of right and left limits. (See 3.4a Ex. 14.)

‡In general, a point a is called a cluster point of a set S if every deleted neighborhood of a contains points of S. A cluster point of S need not be an element of S. If a is an element of S but not a cluster point of S, then a is called an *isolated* point of S.

a if and only if a is a cluster point of the domain of f and for each positive ϵ there is at least one deleted δ-neighborhood of a where f maps the points of its domain into the ϵ-neighborhood of L.

Since the value $f(a)$ itself does not lie in the class of approximations considered in the definition of limit of f at a, it follows that any function that takes on the same values as f in some deleted neighborhood of a would have the same limit at a. For example, the following functions have the same limit at 0:

$$f : x \rightarrow x,$$
$$g : x \rightarrow x^2/x.$$

Although we do not rely upon pictures for our precise understanding of the concept of limit, it is desirable to have a geometrical interpretation of the idea.

Example 1. The graph of the function

$$f : x \rightarrow 2x - 2$$

is shown in Figure 1. We show that

$$\lim_{x \sim 2} (2x - 2) = 2.$$

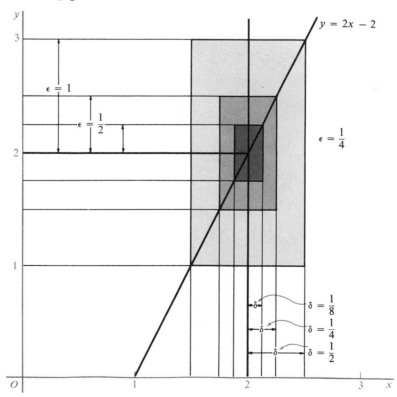

Figure 1

For this, given $\epsilon > 0$, we must show that there is a $\delta > 0$ so that

$$|(2x - 2) - 2| < \epsilon$$

for all x satisfying $0 < |x - 2| < \delta$. It is easy to see from Figure 1 how δ may be found. Given a horizontal band of width 2ϵ centered on the line $y = 2$, we can find a vertical band of width 2δ about $x = 2$ so that the graph of f lies entirely within the rectangle where the bands overlap. From the graph we infer that for $\epsilon = 1$ we may take $\delta = \frac{1}{2}$, for $\epsilon = \frac{1}{2}$, $\delta = \frac{1}{4}$, and for $\epsilon = \frac{1}{4}$, $\delta = \frac{1}{8}$. There seems to be no obstacle to finding a δ for any ϵ, no matter how small, but we clearly cannot rely on pictures to do so. Instead, we proceed analytically. If we require $0 < |x - 2| < \delta$, then

$$\begin{aligned}
|f(x) - 2| &= |(2x - 2) - 2| \\
&= |2x - 4| \\
&= |2(x - 2)| \\
&= 2|x - 2| \\
&< 2\delta.
\end{aligned}$$

Consequently, for any given ϵ, if we take $\delta = \dfrac{\epsilon}{2}$, then

$$|f(x) - 2| < \epsilon.$$

The preceding example was constructed to simplify the picture of the basic approximation scheme. To depict a limit in general, imagine a function f in the vicinity of a cluster point a of its domain. If $\lim_{x \to a} f(x) = L$, we may then confine the graph of f, except perhaps for the point $(a, f(a))$, to a strip of width 2ϵ centered about the line $y = L$ by restricting the domain to a neighborhood of a with a sufficiently small radius δ; see Figure 2.

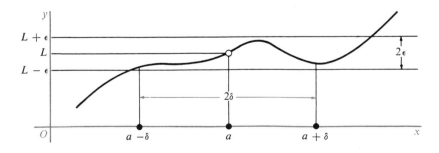

Figure 2

We now explore the concept of limit in some special situations.

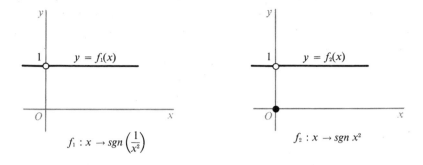

$$f_1 : x \rightarrow sgn\left(\frac{1}{x^2}\right) \qquad f_2 : x \rightarrow sgn\ x^2$$

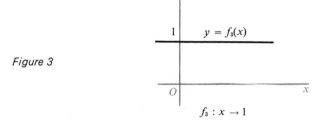

Figure 3

$$f_3 : x \rightarrow 1$$

Example 2. Figure 3 presents the graphs of the three functions given by $f_1(x) = sgn\left(\frac{1}{x^2}\right)$, $f_2(x) = sgn\ x^2$, $f_3(x) = 1$. Observe that $x = 0$ is a point in the domains of f_2 and f_3 but not of f_1. For each of these functions we wish to consider the limit, if it exists, as x approaches 0.

Since the three functions coincide when $x \neq 0$, and the value of the limits does not depend on how the functions are defined at $x = 0$, it is clear that all three functions have the same limit. In each case 1 is the obvious candidate for the limit.

Observe that there is a gap in the graphs of f_1 and f_2 at $x = 0$, and that the graph of f_3, having no gap, is continuous. The function f_1 has a limit at $x = 0$ but is not defined there, f_2 is defined at $x = 0$ but $f_2(0)$ is not its limit, f_3 has a limit at $x = 0$ and the limit is the function value. The concept of limit and the intuitive idea of a continuous or gapless function are closely related; we shall pursue this connection further in 3.5.

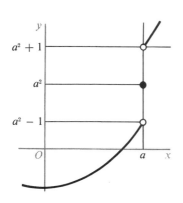 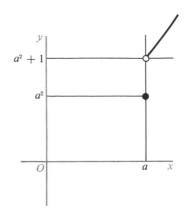

Figure 4

Example 3. Figure 4 presents the graphs of the two functions given by

$$g_1(x) = x^2 + \text{sgn}(x - a),$$
$$g_2(x) = x^2 + \text{sgn}\sqrt{x - a}.$$

The function g_1 is defined for all values of x. The domain of g_2 consists only of those values of x for which $x \geq a$ and on this domain it has the same values as g_1. It seems clear from the graph that there is no single number L which is approximated by the values $g_1(x)$ as x approaches a. On the contrary, within any positive distance of a it is possible to find values of x for which $g_1(x)$ approximates $a^2 - 1$ within any given error tolerance and other values which approximate $a^2 + 1$. Verify, then, that the conditions of Definition 1 cannot be satisfied, that g_1 has no limit at $x = a$.

For the function g_2, on the other hand, no matter what the error tolerance, there is a deleted neighborhood of a wherein $g_2(x)$ approximates $a^2 + 1$ within that tolerance for all x in the domain of the function. This is easily verified. In a deleted δ-neighborhood of a, we have

$$g_2(x) = x^2 + 1, \quad \text{for} \quad a < x < a + \delta.$$

We have for the absolute error of approximation

$$
\begin{aligned}
|g_2(x) - (a^2 + 1)| &= |x^2 - a^2| \\
&= |x - a| \cdot |x + a| \\
&< \delta(|x| + |a|) \\
&\leq \delta[(|a| + \delta) + |a|] \\
&< \delta(2|a| + \delta).
\end{aligned}
$$

This absolute error can be kept within any given error tolerance ϵ by restricting x to a small enough δ-neighborhood of a. For simplicity, we consider only neighborhoods with radius 1 or less. Taking $\delta \leq 1$ in the foregoing inequality, we obtain a simpler bound on the absolute error in terms of the radius δ :

$$|g_2(x) - (a^2 + 1)| < \delta(2|a| + 1).$$

Now, if

$$\delta \leq \frac{\epsilon}{2|a| + 1},$$

then

$$|g_2(x) - (a^2 + 1)| < \epsilon,$$

so that the error has been kept within the tolerance ϵ. Since this is a prescription for controlling the error within any tolerance ϵ, we have accomplished our purpose and proved

$$\lim_{x \sim a} g_2(x) = a^2 + 1$$

entirely in the analytic terms of Definition 1.

Observe that Definition 1 need not be framed in terms of the deleted neighborhood $\{x : 0 < |x - a| < \delta\}$, but may employ deleted open intervals about a, in general:

$$\{x : a - \delta_1 < x < a + \delta_2, x \neq a, \delta_1 \text{ and } \delta_2 \text{ positive}\}.$$

Suppose for every error tolerance ϵ there were such an open interval where the points of the domain of x satisfied $|f(x) - L| < \epsilon$; then there would also be a deleted neighborhood of a within the open interval which also has this property, namely, the neighborhood of radius $\delta = \min\{\delta_1, \delta_2\}$. Conversely, any deleted neighborhood is merely a special deleted open interval. Thus, we may reword Definition 1 in the equivalent form: The number L is said to be the limit of f at a if and only if a is a cluster point of the domain of f and for each positive ϵ there is at least one deleted open interval about a where f maps the points of its domain into the ϵ-neighborhood of L. From this form of the definition of limit it is clear that 3.1 Example 1 establishes $\lim_{x \sim 2} \sqrt{x} = \sqrt{2}$.

The statement $\lim_{x \sim a} f(x) = L$ simply means that L satisfies the conditions of Definition 1. It is conceivable that another number M might satisfy the same conditions. Then the statements $\lim_{x \sim a} f(x) = L$ and $\lim_{x \sim a} f(x) = M$ would both be true. If this could happen, the symbol

$\lim\limits_{x \sim a} f(x)$ by itself would have no meaning. In fact, the limit, if it exists, is unique.

Theorem 1. If L and M are limits of f at a, that is, if $\lim\limits_{x \sim a} f(x) = L$ and $\lim\limits_{x \sim a} f(x) = M$, then $L = M$.

Proof. Suppose $L > M$, take $\epsilon = \dfrac{L - M}{3} > 0$, then, by Definition 1 there are numbers $\delta_1 > 0$ and $\delta_2 > 0$ such that

$$-\epsilon < L - f(x) < \epsilon, \qquad \text{for} \quad 0 < |x - a| < \delta_1,$$

and

$$-\epsilon < f(x) - M < \epsilon, \qquad \text{for} \quad 0 < |x - a| < \delta_2.$$

Hence both inequalities hold for

$$0 < |x - a| < \min \{\delta_1, \delta_2\}.$$

Thus, $0 < L - M < 2\epsilon$. Since $L - M = 3\epsilon$, this yields the contradiction $3\epsilon < 2\epsilon$. ☐

3.2 Exercises

1. Prove if $S \subset T$ that every cluster point of S is a cluster point of T.

2. Show that every point and endpoint of an interval I is a cluster point of I.

3. Show that $\lim\limits_{x \sim a} f(x) = L$, if and only if $\lim\limits_{x \sim a} [f(x) - L] = 0$.

4. Show that if $0 < |x - a| < 1$, then $|x + 2a| < 1 + 3|a|$.

5. Show that if $0 < |x - a| < 1$, then

$$|x^3 - a^3| < (3|a^2| + 3|a| + 1) |x - a|.$$

6. Show that if $|x - a| < \frac{1}{2}|a|$, then $\dfrac{1}{x^2} < \dfrac{4}{a^2}$.

7. Show that if $0 < |x - 2| < 1$, then $\dfrac{1}{|x - 4|} < 1$.

8. Estimate how large $x^2 + 1$ can become if x is restricted to the open interval $-3 < x < 1$.

9. Use the axioms of order (see A1.2) to find a positive number M such that if $0 < |x - 1| < 3$, then $|3x^2 - 2x + 3| \leq M$.

10. a. Show that if $0 < |x - 3| < 1$ and $0 < |x - 3| < \frac{1}{7}\epsilon$, then

$$|x^2 - 9| < \epsilon.$$

b. Show that $\delta = \epsilon/(7 + \epsilon)$ satisfies the pair of inequalities $\delta \leq 1$ and $\delta \leq \frac{1}{7}\epsilon$ and the condition $\delta \leq \min\{1, \frac{1}{7}\epsilon\}$.

11. For each given positive ϵ, find a number δ such that if

$$0 < |x - 3| < \delta, \quad \text{then} \quad |x^2 - 9| < \epsilon.$$

a. $\epsilon = 0.1$.
b. $\epsilon = 0.01$.
c. $\epsilon = 10^{-6}$.

Is your choice of δ in Part c acceptable as an answer in Part a? Explain.

12. For each of the functions given below, find the limit L as x approaches a. For each positive ϵ, exhibit a number δ such that $|f(x) - L| < \epsilon$ whenever $|x - a| < \delta$.

a. $f(x) = 3x - 2$, $\quad a = \frac{1}{2}$.
b. $f(x) = mx + b$, $\quad (m \neq 0)$.
c. $f(x) = 1 + x^2$, $\quad a = 0$.

3.3 EPSILONIC TECHNIQUES

In approximation to a limit, it is customary to use the Greek letter *epsilon* for error tolerance. For this reason, techniques for error control are colloquially called *epsilonic*. We shall use epsilonic techniques in deriving the limit theorems which immediately follow this section. Skill in epsilonic techniques is extremely useful in applications, especially for making estimates when it is difficult to work with precise values. To develop this skill it is helpful to set up a routine pattern in which to present an epsilonic argument. We shall first describe the pattern in general and then, for several examples, carry out the proofs as indicated in the pattern.

Outline of the pattern.

Problem. To prove that $\lim\limits_{x \sim a} f(x) = L$.

Analysis. For each tolerance ϵ, seek a control δ to keep the error of approximation to L by $f(x)$ within the given tolerance ϵ.

Proof. Show that $0 < |x - a| < \delta$ implies $|f(x) - L| < \epsilon$.

This outline is based on 3.2 Definition 1. The proof merely verifies that condition 2 of the definition is satisfied.† The crucial effort is in the

---

†We need not usually be concerned about condition 1 because the point a will most often be contained in an interval within the domain of definition of f or will be an endpoint of such an interval. In either event, a is a cluster point of the domain, see 3.2 Ex. 2.

analysis which yields the desired δ ; the proof is essentially just a check that the analysis has been done correctly. The analysis consists of two steps, simplification and the choice of a control δ .

Step 1. Simplification.

In the step of simplification, the object is to replace $|f(x) - L|$, often a rather complicated expression, by something greater, but simpler in form. Typically, but not always, it is possible to find a positive number c such that $|f(x) - L| < c|x - a|$ in some deleted neighborhood of a . In that case, if δ is less than the radius of the neighborhood, the condition $0 < |x - a| < \delta$ implies $|f(x) - L| < c|x - a| < c\delta$; by taking δ small enough, we can bring the approximation $f(x)$ closer to L than any specified error tolerance. More generally, the analysis is directed at finding a convenient function g such that the condition $0 < |x - a| < \delta$ implies that

(1) $$|f(x) - L| < g(\delta)$$

where $g(\delta)$ can easily be made less than any given error tolerance by taking δ small enough.

In most of the following examples, the work of simplification is done in two stages:

a. $f(x) - L$ is expressed in terms of $x - a$.

b. From the inequality $0 < |x - a| < \delta$, there is derived an inequality of the form (1). If the simplification is successful, it will be easy to find a δ such that $g(\delta) \leq \epsilon$, or even to solve the equation $g(\delta) = \epsilon$ for δ . It is important to get the knack of throwing away excess information. We do not seek the largest possible value for δ ; if any given number δ works, any lesser positive number will work as well. The following examples illustrate the procedure.

Step 2. Choice of δ .

This is the reward for the work of Step 1. In the typical case, $g(\delta) = c\delta$, we choose $\delta = \epsilon/c$ to satisfy $|f(x) - L| < \epsilon$. Even if $g(\delta)$ is not quite so simple, if the work of Step 1 is done judiciously the choice of δ is an immediate step; see Example 3.

There is a final step, the proof. From the chosen expression for δ in terms of ϵ we must show directly that if $0 < |x - a| < \delta$, then $|f(x) - L| < \epsilon$. Typically, the proof starts from the conclusion of the analysis, the expression for δ, and retraces the steps of the analysis, showing for the given δ that each step is correct. The proof, which may be regarded as a check on the correctness of the analysis, is necessary to maintain the accuracy of mathematical thought. Anyone can verify the logical correctness of a fully written out mathematical proof by checking each link in the chain of argument. The proof is often the only thing recorded. Often the proof of a proposition contains no direct hint as to how the proposition was discovered. Sometimes the sequence of thoughts in a proof is actually the reverse of the order in which the thoughts occurred to the writer. In the following examples, the proof begins with the conclusion of the analysis, the expression for δ. Here, the analysis is the interesting material, and we shall give the proof perfunctory justice.

We first try the method for an example where no complications arise, the case of the general linear function.

Example 1.

Problem. To prove that

$$\lim_{x \to a} (mx + b) = ma + b \qquad\qquad (m \neq 0).$$

Analysis. For each tolerance ϵ, seek a control δ to keep the error $|(mx + b) - (ma + b)|$ within the tolerance ϵ.

Step 1. Simplification.

(a) $\quad f(x) - L = (mx + b) - (ma + b)$

$$= m(x - a).$$

(b) $\quad$ If $|x - a| < \delta$,

$$|f(x) - L| = |m(x - a)|$$
$$= |m| \cdot |x - a|$$
$$< |m|\delta.$$

As in (1), take $g(\delta) = |m|\delta$.

Step 2. Choice of δ.

For any positive ϵ, to make $g(\delta) \leq \epsilon$, set

$$\delta = \frac{\epsilon}{|m|}$$

(allowable, since $|m| \neq 0$ by assumption).

Proof. Enter the result $\delta = \dfrac{\epsilon}{|m|}$ in the statement of the problem. The verification follows the pattern of Step 1 with one additional step:

$$|f(x) - L| < |m|\delta$$
$$\leq |m|\frac{\epsilon}{|m|}$$
$$\leq \epsilon .$$

Since there is a strong inequality in this chain, we have

$$|f(x) - L| < \epsilon .$$

In the following examples we omit repetitious material.

Example 2.

Problem. To prove that $\displaystyle\lim_{z \sim 0} \frac{1}{1 + |x|} = 1$.

Analysis.

Step 1.

(a) $$\frac{1}{1 + |x|} - 1 = \frac{-|x|}{1 + |x|} .$$

(b)   If $0 < |x - 0| < \delta$,

$$\left|\frac{1}{1 + |x|} - 1\right| = \left|\frac{-|x|}{1 + |x|}\right|$$
$$= \frac{|x|}{1 + |x|}$$
$$< |x| \qquad (\text{since } 1 + |x| > 1\,|).$$
$$< \delta$$

Take $g(\delta) = \delta$.

Step 2.

For any positive ϵ, to make $g(\delta) \leq \epsilon$, set $\delta = \epsilon$.

Proof. Set $\delta = \epsilon$ in the statement of the problem. We carry out the proof following Step 1 where we set $\delta = \epsilon$ at the last line.

The next example shows that it is not always sufficient to choose δ proportional to ϵ.

Example 3.

Problem. To prove that $\lim_{x \sim a} \sqrt{x} = \sqrt{a}$ $\qquad$ $(a \geq 0)$.

Analysis. The choice $\delta = c\epsilon$, where c is a positive constant, cannot work when $a = 0$. In that case we observe that if $0 < x < \delta \leq c\epsilon$, then $\sqrt{x} < \sqrt{c}\sqrt{\epsilon}$. We must then make $\sqrt{c}\sqrt{\epsilon} < \epsilon$ for all ϵ, no matter how small. It follows that we must find a positive number c that satisfies $\sqrt{c} < \sqrt{\epsilon}$ or, equivalently, $c < \epsilon$ for all positive ϵ. By A1.3 Ex. 6b, no such positive number exists; hence, $\delta = c\epsilon$ cannot work.

Step 1.

From A1.3 (3),

$$|\sqrt{x} - \sqrt{a}| \leq |\sqrt{x} + \sqrt{a}| \, ;$$

whence, on multiplying by $|\sqrt{x} - \sqrt{a}|$, we obtain

$$|\sqrt{x} - \sqrt{a}|^2 \leq |x - a| \, ,$$

and, therefore,

$$|\sqrt{x} - \sqrt{a}| \leq \sqrt{|x - a|} \, .$$

Thus, if $0 < |x - a| < \delta$, then

$$|\sqrt{x} - \sqrt{a}| < \sqrt{\delta} \, .$$

Step 2.

For any positive ϵ, choose $\delta = \epsilon^2$.

Proof. Take $\delta = \epsilon^2$ in the statement of the problem. The verification is a recapitulation of Step 1 for this choice of δ.

It is often expedient to restrict δ by an auxiliary condition in Step 1. The following examples are typical.

Example 4.

Problem. To prove that $\lim_{x \sim 2} (x^3 - 5x - 1) = -3$.

Analysis.

Step 1.

(a) $\quad x^3 - 5x - 1 - (-3) = x^3 - 5x + 2$

$$= [(x-2)+2]^3 - 5[(x-2)+2] + 2$$
$$= (x-2)^3 + 6(x-2)^2 + 7(x-2).$$

(b) $\quad |x^3 - 5x - 1 - (-3)| = |(x-2)^3 + 6(x-2)^2 + 7(x-2)|$

$$= |(x-2)\{(x-2)^2 + 6(x-2) + 7\}|$$
$$= |x-2|\,|(x-2)^2 + 6(x-2) + 7|$$
$$\leq |x-2|\,\{|x-2|^2 + 6|x-2| + 7\}$$
$$< \delta(\delta^2 + 6\delta + 7).$$

(At the last line we used $\;|x-2| < \delta$.)

For definiteness, we restrict δ by requiring $\delta \leq 1$. Under this condition,

$$|x^3 - 5x - 1 - (-3)| < \delta(\delta^2 + 6\delta + 7)$$
$$\leq \delta(1 + 6 + 7)$$
$$\leq 14\delta.$$

In order to get an upper bound in the simple form $c\delta$, we imposed the constant bound 14 on $\delta^2 + 6\delta + 7$ by restricting δ. (The particular condition $\delta \leq 1$ and the particular bound 14 are inessential. We could have required $\delta \leq K$ where K is any positive constant.)

Step 2.

For any positive ϵ, we now wish to obtain a value δ which satisfies both conditions, $\delta \leq \dfrac{\epsilon}{14}$ and $\delta \leq 1$. One way of satisfying these conditions is to set

$$\delta = \frac{\epsilon}{14 + \epsilon}$$

where we have chosen the denominator simply as a convenient value which is greater than either 14 or ϵ. (See A1.3 Ex. 15.)

Proof. Set $\delta = \dfrac{\epsilon}{14 + \epsilon}$ in the statement of the problem. The verification follows Step 1 where we use $\delta \leq 1$ and $\delta \leq \dfrac{\epsilon}{14}$ at the end to obtain

$$|(x^3 - 5x - 1) - (-3)| < \epsilon.$$

Alternative Analysis.

Step 1.

(a) $\quad x^3 - 5x - 1 - (-3) = (x - 2)(x^2 + 2x - 1)$.

(b) $\quad |x^3 - 5x + 2| = |x - 2| \cdot |x^2 + 2x - 1|$
$$< \delta|x^2 + 2x - 1|$$
$$\leq 14\delta,$$

where, at the last line, imposing the condition $\delta \leq 1$, we use the result $1 < x < 3$ obtained from $|x - 2| < \delta \leq 1$.

Step 2.

Since we do not use the formula for δ in the verification but only the conditions $\delta \leq 1$ and $\delta \leq \dfrac{\epsilon}{14}$, it is natural to set

$$\delta = \min\left\{\frac{\epsilon}{14}, 1\right\};$$

see A1.3 Example 1.

Alternate Proof. Set $\delta = \min\left\{\dfrac{\epsilon}{14}, 1\right\}$ in the statement of the problem. The verification follows alternative Step 1.

From the preceding example, we see that we have great freedom in choosing the control δ. We can always use more stringent controls than necessary: given any deleted neighborhood of a wherein $|f(x) - L| < \epsilon$, we satisfy the same inequality for any subset of the neighborhood and, in particular, for any smaller deleted neighborhood of a. In other terms, given any δ which keeps the error within the specified tolerance, any smaller value of δ will certainly have the same effect. It follows that we may freely impose the condition $\delta \leq K$ where K is any convenient positive constant. Similarly, having found a δ for a particular ϵ, we know that the same δ will suffice for any larger error tolerance. Hence we need concern ourselves only with ϵ satisfying $\epsilon \leq M$, where M is any convenient positive constant.

We now apply the outlined techniques to prove that the conjectured values of the derivatives in 2.5 Examples 1 and 2 are, in fact, the correct limits.

Example 5.

Problem.

To prove for $a \neq 0$ that

$$\lim_{x \sim a} r(x) = \lim_{x \sim a} \frac{\frac{1}{x} - \frac{1}{a}}{x - a} = -\frac{1}{a^2} = L .$$

(Observe that $r(x)$ is not defined at $x = 0$ or $x = a$.)

Analysis.

Step 1.

(a) $r(x) - L = \dfrac{\frac{1}{x} - \frac{1}{a}}{x - a} + \dfrac{1}{a^2}$

$$= -\frac{1}{ax} \cdot \frac{x - a}{x - a} + \frac{1}{a^2}$$

$$= -\frac{1}{ax} + \frac{1}{a^2} \qquad\qquad (x \neq a)$$

$$= \frac{x - a}{a^2 x} .$$

(Note that we used $|x - a| > 0$ in setting $\dfrac{(x - a)}{(x - a)} = 1$ for $x \neq a$.)

(b) $|r(x) - L| = \left| \dfrac{x - a}{a^2 x} \right| ;$

whence,

(2) $$|r(x) - L| < \frac{\delta}{a^2 |x|} .$$

Our problem now is to obtain a constant upper bound for the factor $\dfrac{1}{a^2 |x|} = \dfrac{1}{a^2 |(x - a) + a|} .$ It is sufficient to bound the denominator away from 0 or to guarantee

$$|x| = |(x - a) + a| > c > 0$$

for some number c . We have from A1.3 (3),

$$|x| = |(x - a) + a| \geq |a| - |x - a| .$$

Entering $|x - a| < \delta$ in this relation, we obtain

$$|x| \geq |a| - |x - a| > |a| - \delta .$$

To obtain a positive lower bound c, we require† $\delta \leq \dfrac{|a|}{2}$. In that case,

$$|x| > |a| - \delta > \frac{|a|}{2} > 0$$

and $c = \dfrac{|a|}{2}$.

It follows from $|x - a| < \delta$ that $|x| > \dfrac{|a|}{2}$ and $\dfrac{1}{|x|} < \dfrac{2}{|a|}$. (See A1.3 Ex. 7.) Consequently, from (2), we have

$$|r(x) - L| < \frac{\delta}{a^2|x|}$$

$$< \delta \frac{2}{a^2|a|}$$

$$\leq \delta \frac{2}{|a|^3} .$$

Step 2.

For any positive ϵ, the value of δ is restricted by two conditions:

$$\delta \leq \frac{|a|}{2} \quad \text{and} \quad \frac{2\delta}{|a|^3} \leq \epsilon .$$

To satisfy both conditions we take

$$\delta = \min \left\{ \epsilon \frac{|a|^3}{2} , \frac{|a|}{2} \right\} .$$

Proof. Enter the above value of δ in the statement of the problem. The verification follows the pattern of Step 1. At the last line we use

$$\delta \leq \epsilon \frac{|a|^3}{2}$$

to obtain

$$|r(x) - L| < \epsilon .$$

---

†Of course, in general, we could have restricted δ in any convenient way so that $\delta < |a|$. For definiteness we took $\delta \leq \frac{1}{2}|a|$.

Example 6.

Problem.

To prove for $a > 0$ that $\lim_{x \sim a} r(x) = \lim_{x \sim a} \dfrac{\sqrt{x} - \sqrt{a}}{x - a} = \dfrac{1}{2\sqrt{a}} = L$.

(Observe that $r(x)$ is defined only for $x \geq 0$.)

Analysis.

Step 1.

(a) $r(x) - L = \dfrac{\sqrt{x} - \sqrt{a}}{x - a} - \dfrac{1}{2\sqrt{a}}$

$ = \dfrac{1}{\sqrt{x} + \sqrt{a}} - \dfrac{1}{2\sqrt{a}}$ $\qquad\qquad (x \neq a)$

$ = \dfrac{\sqrt{a} - \sqrt{x}}{2\sqrt{a}(\sqrt{x} + \sqrt{a})}$

$ = \dfrac{a - x}{2\sqrt{a}(\sqrt{a} + \sqrt{x})^2}$.

(Note that $\sqrt{x}$ is not defined for negative values and, therefore, we guarantee $0 \leq x$ by imposing the restriction $|x - a| < a$. For this purpose we require $\delta \leq a$.)

(b) $|r(x) - L| = \left| \dfrac{a - x}{2\sqrt{a}(\sqrt{a} + \sqrt{x})^2} \right|$

$ = \dfrac{|x - a|}{2\sqrt{a}(\sqrt{a} + \sqrt{x})^2}$

$ < \dfrac{\delta}{2\sqrt{a}(\sqrt{a} + \sqrt{x})^2}$ $\qquad$ (from $|x - a| < \delta$)

$ \leq \dfrac{\delta}{2\sqrt{a}(\sqrt{a})^2}$ $\qquad\qquad$ (from $\sqrt{x} \geq 0$)

$ \leq \dfrac{\delta}{2(\sqrt{a})^3}$.

Step 2.

For any positive ϵ, take $\delta = \min \{2\sqrt{a})^3\epsilon, a\}$.

Proof. For the above value of δ every expression used in Step 1 is defined for all x in the deleted δ-neighborhood $0 < |x - a| < \delta$.

(This requires $x \neq a$ and $x \geq 0$.) The verification follows Step 1. At the last line we use $\delta \leq 2(\sqrt{a})^3 \epsilon$ to obtain

$$|r(x) - L| < \epsilon.$$

In the preceding examples, we have not always followed the outline to the letter but used it only as a serviceable guide. Special difficulties are likely to appear in Step 1 and we cannot anticipate all contingencies. The only absolutely general pattern is the construction of a nondecreasing chain of expressions;

$$\phi_0 \leq \phi_1 \leq \phi_2 \leq \cdots \leq \phi_n$$

where $\phi_0 = |r(x) - L|$, $\phi_n = g(\delta)$, and $\phi_1, \phi_2, ..., \phi_{n-1}$ may involve both x and δ. To construct such a sequence in a particular case may require the greatest ingenuity.

In these examples, we have verified that a given number L is actually the limit but have not shown how the limit L was obtained. In the next section, we shall develop general theorems which will often enable us to discover the value of the limit and to prove that the discovered value is correct. Epsilonic technique will be necessary only to prove the theorems, not to apply them.

3.3 Exercises

In each of the following give the limit, and then prove that the given limit is correct: give an expression for $g(\delta)$ and find δ in terms of ϵ.

1. $\lim_{x \sim a} c$, c any constant.

2. $\lim_{x \sim a} x$.

3. $\lim_{x \sim a} kx$, k any constant.

4. $\lim_{x \sim 0} \dfrac{1}{1 + x^2}$.

5. $\lim_{x \sim 3} \dfrac{x^2(x - 3)}{x - 3}$.

6. $\lim_{x \sim 1} \dfrac{x + 1}{x^2 + 1}$.

7. $\lim_{x \sim 2} \dfrac{x^2 - 4}{x^3 - 8}$.

8. $\lim_{x \sim 0} \dfrac{x^3 - 3x - 1}{x + 2}$.

9. $\lim_{x \sim a} \dfrac{x^3 - a^3}{x - a}$.

10. $\lim_{x \sim -a} \dfrac{x + a}{x^3 + a^3}$.

3.4 THEORY OF LIMITS

If the epsilonic definition of limit were required in every calculation involving limits, the theoretical development of the calculus would be so disjointed and so burdened with elaborate detail that it would be mastered by only a few devoted specialists. We need and shall derive theorems that broadly cover most of the significant calculations involving limits. In the end, only the exceptional cases will require epsilonic techniques.

3.4a Limit theorems

The first general results apply to rational combinations of functions, that is, functions formed from the functions of a given set by the rational operations of addition, subtraction, multiplication, and division. We shall prove if each function of the set has a limit as x approaches a, that the limit of any rational combination of these functions is the same rational combination of the corresponding limits (with divisions by zero excluded).

There are certain special rational combinations of functions, called *linear combinations*, which often recur in different contexts. It is worth distinguishing them as a class because of their importance. A linear combination is built up by the addition of functions and multiplication by constants. Such a linear combination of functions $f_1, f_2, \dots, f_n$ can be put in the form

$$x \to c_1 f_1(x) + c_2 f_2(x) + \cdots + c_n f_n(x),$$

where $c_1, c_2, \dots, c_n$ are constants. In particular, a polynomial of degree less than or equal to n,

$$\phi(x) = c_0 + c_1 x + c_2 x^2 + \cdots + c_n x^n,$$

may be thought of as a linear combination of powers of x: $1, x, x^2, \dots, x^n$.

We first consider a special polynomial, the constant function $x \to c$.

Theorem 1. For a constant function† $f : x \to c$,

$$\lim_{x \sim a} f(x) = c.$$

Proof. We have

$$|f(x) - c| = |c - c| = 0 < \epsilon,$$

for every positive ϵ and every choice of δ. (The constant function is a trivial case, of course, but we include it for completeness.)   ⬚

---

†When we write

$$\lim_{x \sim a} c = c,$$

the interpretations of c on the right and left of the equation are slightly different. On the left, c stands for $f(x)$, where

$$f : x \to c$$

and on the right, c is the particular value assumed by the function for each value of x.

Theorem 2. If $\lim_{x \sim a} f(x) = L$, then for any constant c,

$$\lim_{x \sim a} cf(x) = c \lim_{x \sim a} f(x) = cL.$$

Proof. We may assume $c \neq 0$, for if $c = 0$, the theorem is a case of Theorem 1. Given any $\epsilon > 0$, we wish to make

$$|cf(x) - cL| < \epsilon$$

by restricting x to a deleted neighborhood

$$0 < |x - a| < \delta.$$

We must first prove the existence of such a δ corresponding to an arbitrary positive ϵ. From the hypothesis, we know that for any ϵ^* there exists a δ^* so that

$$0 < |x - a| < \delta^*,$$

implies that

$$|f(x) - L| < \epsilon^*,$$

and

$$|cf(x) - cL| = |c| \cdot |f(x) - L| < |c|\epsilon^*.$$

Accordingly, for any given ϵ, we choose $\epsilon^* = \dfrac{\epsilon}{|c|}$, obtain the appropriate value δ^* for this ϵ^*, and then set $\delta = \delta^*$. ☐

In the following theorems, we require that in some deleted neighborhood of a the domains of the functions appearing in the combination all coincide. This requirement eliminates nonsensical combinations such as $f(x) + g(x)$ when $f(x)$ is defined only for $x \geq a$ and $g(x)$ is defined only for $x \leq a$. The likelihood of ever making such a mistake is extremely small and, therefore, we do not mention this restriction on the functions explicitly in the statements or proofs of the theorems.

Theorem 3. If $\lim_{x \sim a} f(x) = L$ and $\lim_{x \sim a} g(x) = M$, then

$$\lim_{x \sim a} [f(x) + g(x)] = L + M.$$

Proof. We must show that for any given $\epsilon > 0$ there is some δ such that

$$|f(x) + g(x) - (L + M)| < \epsilon$$

for all x in the common domain of f and g which satisfy

$$0 < |x - a| < \delta.$$

From the hypothesis, we know that for any positive ϵ_1 and ϵ_2, no matter how small, there exist δ_1 and δ_2 such that

$$|f(x) - L| < \epsilon_1 \quad \text{when} \quad 0 < |x - a| < \delta_1,$$

and

$$|g(x) - M| < \epsilon_2 \quad \text{when} \quad 0 < |x - a| < \delta_2.$$

Now, when $0 < |x - a| < \min\{\delta_1, \delta_2\}$,

$$|f(x) + g(x) - (L + M)| = |f(x) - L + g(x) - M|$$
$$\leq |f(x) - L| + |g(x) - M| < \epsilon_1 + \epsilon_2.$$

To keep within the tolerance ϵ, we can choose ϵ_1 and ϵ_2 to be any positive quantities whose sum is ϵ. For convenience, we fix

$$\epsilon_1 = \epsilon_2 = \tfrac{1}{2}\epsilon.$$

Taking appropriate values δ_1, δ_2 for these values ϵ_1, ϵ_2, we set

$$\delta = \min\{\delta_1, \delta_2\}.$$

For this choice of δ, whenever

$$0 < |x - a| < \delta,$$

then

$$|f(x) + g(x) - (L + M)| < \frac{\epsilon}{2} + \frac{\epsilon}{2} \leq \epsilon. \qquad \square$$

Since a linear combination can be built up by successive operations of addition of two functions and multiplication by constants, we obtain:

Corollary a. The limit of a linear combination of functions is the same linear combination of the limits of the functions; i.e., if

$$\lim_{x \sim a} f_i(x) = L_i, \qquad\qquad i = 1, 2, \dots, n$$

then

$$\lim_{x \sim a} [c_1 f_1(x) + c_2 f_2(x) + \cdots + c_n f_n(x)]$$
$$= c_1 \lim_{x \sim a} f_1(x) + c_2 \lim_{x \sim a} f_2(x) + \cdots + c_n \lim_{x \sim a} f_n(x)$$
$$= c_1 L_1 + c_2 L_2 + \cdots + c_n L_n.$$

The proof is left to Exercise 16.

For general rational combinations, we have the further operations of multiplication and division, and must apply theorems concerning the limits of products and quotients.

Theorem 4. If $\lim\limits_{x \sim a} f(x) = L$ and $\lim\limits_{x \sim a} g(x) = M$, then

$$\lim_{x \sim a} [f(x) \cdot g(x)] = LM.$$

Proof. We estimate the difference $f(x)\,g(x) - LM$, using the differences $f(x) - L$ and $g(x) - M$:

$$
\begin{aligned}
f(x)\,g(x) - LM &= \{[f(x) - L] + L\}\,\{[g(x) - M] + M\} - LM \\
&= [f(x) - L]\,[g(x) - M] + M[f(x) - L] \\
&\quad + L[g(x) - M] ;
\end{aligned}
$$

hence,

(1)
$$
\begin{aligned}
|f(x)\,g(x) - LM| &\leq |f(x) - L|\,|g(x) - M| \\
&\quad + |M|\,|f(x) - L| + |L|\,|g(x) - M|.
\end{aligned}
$$

From the hypothesis, we know that for any positive numbers ϵ_1 and ϵ_2, there are corresponding controls δ_1 and δ_2 such that

$$|f(x) - L| < \epsilon_1 \quad \text{for} \quad 0 < |x - a| < \delta_1,$$

and

$$|g(x) - M| < \epsilon_2 \quad \text{for} \quad 0 < |x - a| < \delta_2.$$

Thus, if we choose $\delta = \min\{\delta_1, \delta_2\}$, it follows from (1) that when $0 < |x - a| < \delta$ then

(2)
$$|f(x)g(x) - LM| < \epsilon_1\epsilon_2 + |M|\epsilon_1 + |L|\epsilon_2.$$

In order to keep from exceeding the tolerance ϵ, we shall choose ϵ_1 and ϵ_2 so that

$$\epsilon_1\epsilon_2 + |M|\epsilon_1 + |L|\epsilon_2 \leq \epsilon ;$$

this will then determine our choice of δ_1 and δ_2, and, in turn, that of δ. For convenience, we require that $\epsilon_1 = \epsilon_2 = \epsilon^*$ and that $\epsilon^* \leq 1$. Then

(3)
$$\epsilon_1\epsilon_2 + |M|\epsilon_1 + |L|\epsilon_2 \leq \epsilon^*(1 + |L| + |M|).$$

We are now ready to choose ϵ^* and verify (3). Let

(4)
$$\epsilon^* = \left\{ \min 1, \frac{\epsilon}{1 + |L| + |M|} \right\}.$$

Choose δ_1 and δ_2 accordingly and set $\delta = \min\{\delta_1, \delta_2\}$. Then it follows from (2) and (4) when $0 < |x - a| < \delta$ that

$$|f(x)g(x) - LM| < \epsilon^*(1 + |L| + |M|) \leq \epsilon$$

as desired. □

Since a polynomial $p(x)$ is a linear combination of powers, and a power is a product,

$$x^k = x \cdot x \cdots x \qquad (k \quad \text{factors}, \quad k \geq 1),$$

we can now establish the following corollary.

Corollary a. For any polynomial function p,

$$\lim_{x \to a} p(x) = p(a).$$

The proof of this corollary is left to Exercise 17.

To prove the limit theorem for a quotient $\dfrac{f(x)}{g(x)}$, it is only necessary to prove the limit theorem for a reciprocal $\dfrac{1}{g(x)}$. The rule for general quotients then follows from

$$\frac{f(x)}{g(x)} = f(x)\left[\frac{1}{g(x)}\right].$$

First, we prove a useful preliminary result.

Lemma 1. If $\lim\limits_{x \to a} g(x) = M$ and $M > 0$, then there exists a neighborhood of a where $g(x) > 0$ for x in the domain of g.

Proof. Since g has the limit M at a, there is a δ-neighborhood of a wherein $g(x)$ is closer to M than to zero; namely,

$$|g(x) - M| < \frac{M}{2}.$$

In this neighborhood,

$$\frac{3M}{2} > g(x) > \frac{M}{2} > 0. \qquad \qquad \square$$

If a function ϕ has a negative limit at $x = a$ then, upon applying Lemma 1 to the function $-\phi$, we see at once that $\phi(x)$ is negative in some deleted neighborhood of a. As further consequences of Lemma 1 and its proof, we cite the following two corollaries.

Corollary a. If $\lim\limits_{x \to a} g(x) = M$ and $M \neq 0$, then there exists a neighborhood of a where $\left|\dfrac{3M}{2}\right| > |g(x)| > \left|\dfrac{M}{2}\right|$ for x in the domain of g.

Corollary b.   A limit of a function whose values are nonnegative is nonnegative.

The proofs of these corollaries are left to Exercise 1.

Theorem 5.   If $\lim\limits_{x \sim a} g(x) = M$ and $M \neq 0$, then

$$\lim_{x \sim a} \frac{1}{g(x)} = \frac{1}{M}.$$

Proof.   We have

(2)
$$\left| \frac{1}{g(x)} - \frac{1}{M} \right| = \left| \frac{M - g(x)}{Mg(x)} \right|$$
$$= \frac{|g(x) - M|}{|M|\,|g(x)|}$$

provided $g(x) \neq 0$. However, from Corollary (a) to Lemma 1 there is a δ-neighborhood of a wherein $|g(x)| > \dfrac{M}{2}$. Furthermore, for any ϵ^* the radius δ can be taken sufficiently small to insure that

$$|g(x) - M| < \epsilon^*.$$

From (2), therefore, we have

$$\left| \frac{1}{g(x)} - \frac{1}{M} \right| = \frac{|g(x) - M|}{|M|\,|g(x)|}$$
$$< \frac{\epsilon^*}{|M|\,\dfrac{|M|}{2}}$$
$$\leq \frac{2\epsilon^*}{M^2}$$
$$< \epsilon,$$

where, in the last line, we have taken

$$\epsilon^* = \frac{M^2 \epsilon}{2}.$$

To complete the proof, we choose the value of δ appropriate to this ϵ^*.   ☐

Corollary a.   If $\lim\limits_{x \sim a} f(x) = L$ and $\lim\limits_{x \sim a} g(x) = M$ where $M \neq 0$, then

$$\lim_{x \sim a} \frac{f(x)}{g(x)} = \frac{L}{M}.$$

Corollary b. If p and q are polynomial functions, and if $q(a) \neq 0$, then

$$\lim_{x \to a} \frac{p(x)}{q(x)} = \frac{p(a)}{q(a)}.$$

In connection with these corollaries, we observe that if $\lim_{x \to a} g(x) = 0$, the quotient $\dfrac{f(x)}{g(x)}$ may still have a limit. Under these conditions, $\lim_{x \to a} f(x) = 0$ is a necessary but not sufficient condition for existence of $\lim_{x \to a} \dfrac{f(x)}{g(x)}$. The primary example is the derivative of a function expressed as the limit of a ratio for which the numerator and denominator both approach zero. It is not possible to make any general statement about the existence of the limit of such a quotient; it is possible that $\lim_{x \to a} f(x) = 0$ and yet that the limit of $f(x)/g(x)$ does not exist $\left(\text{for example, } \lim_{x \to 0} \dfrac{x}{x^2}\right)$. (See Exs. 11 and 12.)

In estimating $\lim_{x \to a} f(x)$, we can often bound f below and above by functions g and h which have limits as x approaches a. In that case, we expect the limit of f to be bounded below and above by the limits of g and h. This result is a direct consequence of the following theorem.

Theorem 6. If $f(x) \leq g(x)$ in some deleted neighborhood of a, and $\lim_{x \to a} f(x) = L$ and $\lim_{x \to a} g(x) = M$, then $L \leq M$.

Proof. Since $g(x) - f(x)$ is nonnegative, it follows from Theorem 3 and Corollary (b) to Lemma 1 that

$$\lim_{x \to a} [g(x) - f(x)] = M - L \geq 0. \qquad \square$$

Corollary a. Sandwich Theorem. If, in some deleted neighborhood of a,

$$h(x) \leq f(x) \leq g(x)$$

and if

$$\lim_{x \to a} h(x) = K \quad \text{and} \quad \lim_{x \to a} g(x) = M,$$

then, if $\lim_{x \to a} f(x)$ exists,

$$K \leq \lim_{x \to a} f(x) \leq M.$$

If the functions g and h in the Sandwich Theorem have the same limit at a, we do not have to assume beforehand that the function f which is bounded between these two has a limit at a, but may use the information to prove that f has a limit, the same limit as g and h.

Theorem 7. Squeeze Theorem. If in some deleted neighborhood of a,

$$h(x) \le f(x) \le g(x)$$

and if

$$\lim_{x \sim a} h(x) = \lim_{x \sim a} g(x) = L,$$

then $\lim_{x \sim a} f(x)$ exists and

$$\lim_{x \sim a} f(x) = L.$$

Proof. Let I be the deleted neighborhood of a where

$$h(x) \le f(x) \le g(x).$$

By hypothesis, for every $\epsilon > 0$, I contains a deleted δ-neighborhood of a wherein $|h(x) - L| < \epsilon$ and $|g(x) - L| < \epsilon$. We then have

$$L - \epsilon < h(x) \quad \text{and} \quad g(x) < L + \epsilon$$

whenever $0 < |x - a| < \delta$. It follows that

$$L - \epsilon < f(x) < L + \epsilon,$$

or

$$|f(x) - L| < \epsilon,$$

whenever $0 < |x - a| < \delta$. □

3.4a Exercises

1. Prove the corollaries to Lemma 1.
   a. *Corollary a.* If $\lim_{x \sim a} g(x) = M$ and $M \ne 0$, then there exists a neighborhood of a where $|\frac{3}{2}M| > |g(x)| > |\frac{1}{2}M|$ for x in the domain of g.
   b. *Corollary b.* A limit of a function whose values are nonnegative is nonnegative.

2. Prove the corollaries to Theorem 5.
   a. *Corollary a.* If $\lim_{x \sim a} f(x) = L$ and $\lim_{x \sim a} g(x) = M$ where $M \ne 0$, then

$$\lim_{x \sim a} \frac{f(x)}{g(x)} = \frac{L}{M}.$$

b. *Corollary b.* If p and q are polynomials, and if $q(a) \neq 0$, then

$$\lim_{x \to a} \frac{p(x)}{q(x)} = \frac{p(a)}{q(a)}.$$

3. Find the following limits, giving at each step the theorem on limits which justifies it.

a. $\quad \lim_{x \to 3} (2 + x).$

b. $\quad \lim_{x \to -1} (5x - 2).$

c. $\quad \lim_{x \to 0} \left(\dfrac{a}{1 + |x|} - b\sqrt{|x|} \right),$ where a and b are constants.

d. $\quad \lim_{x \to 0} (x^3 + ax^2 + a^2 x + a^3),$ where a is constant.

4. Find the following limits, giving at each step the theorem which justifies it.

a. $\quad \lim_{x \to 1} \dfrac{x^3 - 1}{x^2 - 1}.$

b. $\quad \lim_{x \to 3} \dfrac{x^2 - 9}{x^3 - 27}.$

5. Find $\lim_{x \to 1} \dfrac{x^n - 1}{x - 1},$ for n a positive integer. (Note that

$$\frac{x^n - 1}{x - 1} = x^{n-1} + x^{n-2} + \cdots + x + 1, \quad \text{for} \quad x \neq 1 .)$$

6. Determine whether each following limit exists and, if it does exist, find its value.

a. $\quad \lim_{x \to 1} \dfrac{1 + \sqrt{x}}{1 - x}.$

b. $\quad \lim_{x \to a} (x^n - a^n),$ n a positive integer, a constant.

c. $\quad \lim_{x \to -1} \dfrac{\sqrt{2 + x} + 1}{x + 1}.$

d. $\quad \lim_{x \to 1} \dfrac{(x - 2)(\sqrt{x} - 1)}{x^2 + x - 2}.$

e. $\quad \lim_{x \to 1} \dfrac{1 - \sqrt{x}}{1 - x}.$

f. $\quad \lim_{x \to 0} \dfrac{\sqrt{1 + x} - \sqrt{1 - x}}{x}.$

7. Assume $\lim_{x \to 0} \sin x = 0$ and $\lim_{x \to 0} \cos x = 1$. Find each of the following limits, if the limit exists, giving at each step the theorem on limits which justifies it.

a. $\quad \lim_{x \to 0} \sin^3 x.$

b. $\quad \lim_{x \to 0} \tan x.$

c. $\quad \lim_{x \to 0} \sin 2x.$

d. $\quad \lim_{x \to 0} \dfrac{\sin x}{\tan x}.$

e. $\quad \lim_{x \to 0} \dfrac{1 - \cos x}{\sin x}.$

f. $\quad \lim_{x \to 0} \dfrac{\cos 2x}{\cos x + \sin x}.$

8. Prove Corollary 6a (Sandwich Theorem).

9. For what integral values of m and n does $\lim\limits_{x \to -a} \dfrac{x^m + a^m}{x^n + a^n}$ exist?

   Find the limit for these cases.

10. Prove that if $\lim\limits_{x \to a} f(x) = 0$ and $g(x)$ is bounded in a neighborhood of $x = a$, then $\lim\limits_{x \to a} f(x)\, g(x) = 0$.

11. a. Prove if $\lim\limits_{x \to a} \dfrac{f(x)}{g(x)}$ exists and if $\lim\limits_{x \to a} g(x) = 0$, that $\lim\limits_{x \to a} f(x) = 0$.

   b. Give examples of functions f and g for which $\lim\limits_{x \to a} f(x) = 0$ and $\lim\limits_{x \to a} g(x) = 0$ yet the limit of their quotient does not exist.

12. Prove that if $\lim\limits_{x \to a} g(x) = 0$ and $\lim\limits_{x \to a} f(x)$ does not exist, then the limit at a of the quotient f/g does not exist.

13. Consider the functions

$$ f : x \to x - [\![x]\!], \qquad g : x \to f\left(\frac{1}{x}\right). $$

   Prove that $\lim\limits_{x \to 0} g(x)$ does not exist, but that $\lim\limits_{x \to 0} x\, g(x) = 0$.

14. The *right* limit of a function at p is the limit of the function at p for a restricted domain $(p, p + \delta)$. Similarly, the *left* limit is the limit with respect to a restricted domain $(p - \delta, p)$. We denote these limits symbolically by $\lim\limits_{x \to p^+} f(x)$ and $\lim\limits_{x \to p^-} f(x)$, respectively. For example,

$$ \lim\limits_{x \to 2^+} [\![x]\!] = 2, \qquad \lim\limits_{x \to 2^-} [\![x]\!] = 1. $$

   For each of the following determine the indicated limit, if it exists.

   a. $\lim\limits_{x \to 2^+} \dfrac{[\![x]\!]^2 - 4}{x^2 - 4}$.

   b. $\lim\limits_{x \to 2^-} \dfrac{[\![x]\!]^2 - 4}{x^2 - 4}$.

   c. $\lim\limits_{x \to 3^+} (x - 2 + [\![2 - x]\!] - [\![x]\!])$.

   d. $\lim\limits_{x \to 3^-} (x - 2 + [\![2 - x]\!] - [\![x]\!])$.

   e. $\lim\limits_{x \to 0^+} \left(\dfrac{x}{a} \left[\!\left[\dfrac{b}{x} \right]\!\right] - \dfrac{b}{x} \left[\!\left[\dfrac{x}{a} \right]\!\right] \right), \qquad a > 0, \; b > 0.$

   f. $\lim\limits_{x \to 0^-} \left(\dfrac{x}{a} \left[\!\left[\dfrac{b}{x} \right]\!\right] - \dfrac{b}{x} \left[\!\left[\dfrac{x}{a} \right]\!\right] \right), \qquad a > 0, \; b > 0.$

   g. $\lim\limits_{x \to 0^+} \dfrac{\sqrt{x}}{\sqrt{4 + \sqrt{x}} - 2}$.

15. Prove if $\lim\limits_{x \to a^+} f(x) = \lim\limits_{x \to a^-} f(x) = L$ then the limit of f at a exists and is equal to L.

16. Prove Corollary 3a. The limit of a linear combination of functions is the same linear combination of the limits of the functions.

17. Prove Corollary 4a. For any polynomial function p, $\lim\limits_{x \to a} p(x) = p(a)$.

3.4b Limits at infinity

The idea of limit at "infinity" or "minus infinity" is a natural extension of the basic concept of limit of a function at a point.

Example 1. We consider the behavior of the function $f : x \to \dfrac{x + 2}{2x + 1}$ for large† positive values of x. We write $f(x)$ in the form

$$f(x) = \frac{1 + 2/x}{2 + 1/x}$$

and observe that the terms $2/x$ in the numerator and $1/x$ in the denominator both approximate zero for large x; we therefore expect that $f(x)$ approximates $1/2$. In other words, given an error tolerance ϵ, we expect to achieve

(1) $$|f(x) - \tfrac{1}{2}| < \epsilon$$

by taking x sufficiently large and positive. This is easily proved true. We have, for $x > 0$,

$$
\begin{aligned}
|f(x) - \tfrac{1}{2}| &= \left| \frac{x + 2}{2x + 1} - \frac{1}{2} \right| \\[2mm]
&= \left| \frac{3}{2(2x + 1)} \right| \\[2mm]
&= \frac{3}{4x + 2} \\[2mm]
&< \frac{3}{4x}.
\end{aligned}
$$

---

†The words "large" and "small" applied to a number x in this text refer to the distance $|x|$ of x from the origin. Thus, "x is larger than y" means that $|x| > |y|$. If we express the relation $x > y$ in words, we say, "x is greater than y." Thus, if x were positive and y negative, x would be greater than y, but could be "smaller" than y; for example $\tfrac{1}{2} > -1$, but $|\tfrac{1}{2}| < |-1|$. We shall not often use the comparative forms "larger" and "smaller," but will use "large" and "small" to indicate that we are considering neighborhoods of infinity (or minus infinity) and of the origin, respectively.

To keep within the tolerance ϵ, we need take only $x = 3/4\epsilon$ or greater. In this case, we say "f has the limit $\frac{1}{2}$ at infinity," and write,

$$\lim_{x \sim \infty} f(x) = \tfrac{1}{2}.$$

We define limits at infinity and minus infinity by direct analogy with ordinary limits. Infinity is said to be a cluster point† of the domain of f if for every real number M there exist points x of the domain of f which satisfy $x > M$.

Definition 1. We say that the *limit of f at infinity* is L and write

$$\lim_{x \sim \infty} f(x) = L$$

if and only if:
1. infinity is a cluster point of the domain of f;
2. for each positive number ϵ, there exists a real number N such that

$$|f(x) - L| < \epsilon$$

for every x in the domain of f which satisfies $x > N$.

At minus infinity, the limit of f could be defined similarly, but we may use Definition 1 for this purpose rather than repeat ourselves:

Definition 2. We say that the *limit of f at minus infinity* is L and write

$$\lim_{x \sim -\infty} f(x) = L$$

if and only if

$$\lim_{x \sim \infty} f(-x) = L.$$

We may define limit at infinity or minus infinity geometrically by introducing the idea of "neighborhood of infinity." A *neighborhood of infinity* is simply a ray of the type

$$(a, \infty) = \{x : x > a\};$$

see A1.4. Similarly, a *neighborhood of minus infinity* is a ray of the type

$$(-\infty, a) = \{x : x < a\}.$$

---

†In saying that "infinity is a cluster point" we do not imply that infinity is a point of the number line, that is, a real number. The word "infinity" and the symbol "∞" have no independent meaning in this text; both always appear in the context of a precisely defined usage.

A neighborhood of infinity or minus infinity is necessarily a deleted neighborhood. Furthermore, a neighborhood of infinity is a left neighborhood, a neighborhood of minus infinity is a right neighborhood, see 3.4a Ex. 14. Infinity (or minus infinity) is a cluster point of the domain of f if every neighborhood of infinity (or minus infinity) contains points of the domain of f.

In terms of these concepts, we now have a completely general definition for limit of a function:

A function f has the limit L at a cluster point of its domain if and only if for each positive ϵ there is at least one deleted neighborhood of the cluster point where f maps the points of its domain into the ϵ-neighborhood of L.

The limit theorems — 3.4a Theorems 1 to 7, 3.4a Lemma 1, and their corollaries, except 3.4a Corollaries 4a and 5b — may be taken over directly for limits at infinity. (Why except 3.4a Corollaries 4a and 5b? See Exs. 3, 4.)

Example 2. We prove the counterpart of 3.4a Theorem 3: If $\lim\limits_{x \sim \infty} f(x) = L$
and $\lim\limits_{x \sim \infty} g(x) = M$, then

$$\lim_{x \sim \infty} [f(x) + g(x)] = L + M.$$

Proof. From the hypothesis, we know that for each positive ϵ_1 and ϵ_2 there exist real numbers N_1 and N_2 such that

$$|f(x) - L| < \epsilon_1 \quad \text{when} \quad x > N_1,$$

and

$$|g(x) - M| < \epsilon_2 \quad \text{when} \quad x > N_2.$$

Now, when $x > \max\{N_1, N_2\}$,

$$|f(x) + g(x) - (L + M)| = |f(x) - L + g(x) - M|$$
$$\leq |f(x) - L| + |g(x) - M| < \epsilon_1 + \epsilon_2.$$

To keep within the tolerance ϵ, we fix $\epsilon_1 = \epsilon_2 = \tfrac{1}{2}\epsilon$ and choose N_1 and N_2 accordingly. For $N = \max\{N_1, N_2\}$, whenever $x > N$, we then have

$$|f(x) + g(x) - (L + M)| < \frac{\epsilon}{2} + \frac{\epsilon}{2} \leq \epsilon. \qquad \square$$

3.4b Exercises

1. Prove that each of the following functions has the limit zero at infinity.

a. $\quad x \to \dfrac{1}{x}.$ b. $\quad x \to \dfrac{1}{\sqrt{x}}.$

c. $x \to \dfrac{1}{[\![x]\!]}$.

d. $x \to \dfrac{1}{1+x}$.

e. $x \to \dfrac{1}{x^n}$, $(n,$ a natural number$)$.

f. $x \to \sqrt{x} - \sqrt{x-1}$.

g. $x \to \sqrt{x} - \sqrt{[\![x]\!]}$.

2. Find the limits at infinity for each of the following functions.

a. $x \to \dfrac{x+2}{x^2+x+1}$.

b. $x \to \dfrac{2x-3}{7x+2}$.

c. $x \to \dfrac{x^2+3x+2}{x^2-x-6}$.

d. $x \to \dfrac{6x^3-5x^2-4}{7x\,(3x^2+2)}$.

e. $x \to \dfrac{\sqrt{4x^2+4}}{x+2}$.

f. $x \to x\left[\!\!\left[\dfrac{1}{x}\right]\!\!\right]$.

g. $x \to \dfrac{x}{[\![x]\!]}$.

h. $x \to \dfrac{[\![x]\!]}{x}$.

3. a. Prove for any natural number n, that the power function $x \to x^n$ does not have a limit at infinity.
   b. Prove for a polynomial function p, that p is either a constant function or has no limit at infinity.

4. Let r be a rational function given in the form $r = p/q$ where p and q are polynomial functions.
   a. Prove that r has a limit at infinity if and only if $\deg p \le \deg q$, or p is the zero function.
   b. Prove that r has a nonzero limit if and only if $\deg p = \deg q$.
   c. Prove if r has a limit at infinity then it has the same limit at minus infinity.

5. Prove that $x \to |x|$ is not a rational function.

6. State and prove the counterpart of 3.4a Lemma 1 for limits at infinity.

⋏7. a. Let f be a function on the domain of all positive real numbers. Let g be the restriction of f to the set $\mathfrak{N}$ of natural numbers. Prove if

$$\lim_{x \sim \infty} f(x) = L \quad \text{then} \quad \lim_{x \sim \infty} g(x) = L.$$

   b. Let the domain of $n \to a^n$ be restricted to the set of natural numbers, $n \in \mathfrak{N}$. Prove if $0 < a < 1$, that $\lim_{n \sim \infty} a^n = 0$. If $a > 1$ show that a^n can be made greater than any given real number M by choice of a sufficiently large n.

3.5 THE IDEA OF CONTINUITY

The idea of continuity suggests a graph without gaps. Most of the functions which we have studied had graphs which appropriately are called continuous. It is intuitive that a moving object traces a continuous path:

the object cannot disappear at one place and instantaneously reappear at another. If we describe the path by $s = \phi(t)$, then the function ϕ is necessarily continuous.

We have also seen graphs with breaks or gaps, for example, the graph of $[\![x]\!]$ in A2.2 Figure 6. Such graphs may be the appropriate way to represent certain physical situations. For instance, light moves through air at a velocity of approximately $1.00c$ and through water at a velocity of approximately $0.75c$, where c is the velocity of light in a vacuum. If we use a function $s \rightarrow v$ to describe the velocity v at a distance s along a beam of light that penetrates a still body of water, the function is discontinuous at the water surface.

The figures of 3.2 show some ways in which a function can fail to be continuous, and they guide us to an informal definition of continuity. The function f_1 of 3.2 Figure 3 is merely undefined at $x = 0$, and, consequently, its graph has a break at that point. The function f_2 has a value at 0, but the point $(0, f_2(0))$ does not fill the gap in the graph: f_2 has the limit $L = 1$ at 0, so that the values of f_2 near $x = 0$ are successively better approximations to L; but $f_2(0)$ is not approximated by these values. For f_3, on the other hand, the function is defined at $x = 0$ and the values of $f_3(x)$ do approximate $f_3(0)$ as x approaches 0.

Until now, while investigating the limit of a function f as x approximates a, we have paid no attention to the value of f at a, or even to whether f was defined at a. As abstract concepts, the value of f at a and the limit of f at a are unrelated. The idea of continuity relates these two ideas: if $\lim_{x \sim a} f(x) = L$ then the graph of f will have no gap if $L = f(a)$.

Differentiation, the procedure for calculating derivatives, automatically creates discontinuous functions. For example, the derivative of $f : x \rightarrow x^2$ at a is the limit as x approximates a of the ratio

$$r(x) = \frac{x^2 - a^2}{x - a} = \frac{x - a}{x - a}(x + a).$$

There is a gap in the domain of r: the formula for r is meaningless at $x = a$. We observe that $r(x) = x + a$ when $x \neq a$ and that the value of $x + a$ when $x = a$ is the limit for $r(x)$. We may use the limit of r at a to fill the gap in the values of r, and thus define a continuous extension of r, the function

$$x \rightarrow \begin{cases} r(x), \text{ for } x \neq a, \\ \lim_{x \sim a} r(x), \text{ for } x = a. \end{cases}$$

The function g_1 of 3.2 Figure 4 shows that it is not always possible to redefine a function so as to make it continuous at a point, even when the point is contained in an interval of the function's domain. To fill the gap in the domain of g_1 we would have to choose a value for $g_1(a)$ which is a limit at a for the function on both restricted domains, one consisting of all x for which $x > a$, and the other, of all x for which $x < a$; see 3.4a Ex. 15. However, the two restrictions of the domain lead to different limits so that no single number is approximated as x approaches a. We are at liberty to redefine $g(a)$ as any real number we wish; but since g fails to have a limit as x approximates a, there is a tolerance within which the values of g cannot serve as approximations to $g(a)$ for *all* x in a deleted neighborhood of a. Therefore, these values cannot go over continuously into the value $g(a)$.

From the study of these examples, we can abstract an informal definition of the concept, continuity of the function f at a. To ensure that the function values have no break, f must satisfy three conditions:†

(1) $f(a)$ exists;
(2) $\lim_{x \sim a} f(x)$ exists;
(3) $f(a) = \lim_{x \sim a} f(x)$.

Continuity will fail at $x = a$ if f is undefined at a (e.g., f_1 of 3.2 Figure 3 at $x = 0$), if the limit fails to exist (e.g., g_1 of 3.2 Figure 4 at $x = a$), or if function value and limit both exist, but are not the same (e.g., f_2 of 3.2 Figure 3 at $x = 0$). If the limit of f exists but the value of the function is undefined, a new function defined to agree with f at points other than $x = a$ and to have the value $\lim_{x \sim a} f(x)$ at $x = a$ will be continuous at $x = a$ (e.g., f_1 of 3.2 Figure 3 replaced by f_3). If the limit of $f(x)$ as x approaches a fails to exist, then any function agreeing with f in a deleted neighborhood of a is doomed to be discontinuous there (e.g., g_1 of 3.2 Figure 4 at a).

Before establishing the properties of continuous functions, we supplement the preceding discussion with an analytical definition. For this purpose we express the relevant property, $\lim_{x \sim a} f(x) = f(a)$, in epsilonic terms by using 3.2 Definition 1.

Definition 1. The function f is defined to be *continuous at a point* a if and only if for every $\epsilon > 0$:

---

†If condition (3) holds then conditions (1) and (2) are implied. We shall, therefore, adopt (3) as the basic definition of continuity.

1. a is a point of the domain of f;
2. a is a cluster point of the domain of f;
3. there exists a $\delta > 0$ such that

$$|f(x) - f(a)| < \epsilon$$

for every x in the domain of f which satisfies the inequality

$$|x - a| < \delta.$$

We verify that Definition 1 is equivalent to the earlier informal definition. The value $f(a)$ is required to exist by Condition 1. If $|f(x) - f(a)| < \epsilon$ holds for all x such that $|x - a| < \delta$, then surely it holds for all x such that $0 < |x - a| < \delta$, so that $\lim\limits_{x \sim a} f(x)$ exists. Finally, because $f(a)$ appears in the inequality $|f(x) - f(a)| < \epsilon$ of the present definition in precisely the place where L appears in the inequality $|f(x) - L| < \epsilon$ of 3.2 Definition 1, we have $\lim\limits_{x \sim a} f(x) = f(a)$. All three ingredients of the informal definition are implied by Definition 1. Conversely, we arrive at the formal definition by replacing the terms of the three-part definition with their analytical expressions; therefore, the validity of the informal definition implies that of the formal one. The two definitions for the continuity of a function at a point of its domain are equivalent.

Note that to find a limit as x approaches a we examine deleted neighborhoods of the point, but to check continuity at a we include the point itself and examine an entire neighborhood, without deletion. It is because of this distinction that the inequality

$$0 < |x - a| < \delta$$

of 3.2 Definition 1 may be replaced by the inequality

$$|x - a| < \delta$$

in the definition of continuity; moreover, the value $f(a)$ at $x = a$ now plays the role of the limit L.

If the condition of the definition is met, then a is a *point of continuity* for f. A point a where this condition is not met is a *point of discontinuity* of f, and there, f is *discontinuous*.

Note particularly, that if $f(x)$ is defined by a formula which has no real value when $x = a$, then f is discontinuous at a. For example, the function f given by $f(x) = \dfrac{1}{x - a}$ is discontinuous at a. (It is also true by this definition that the function g given by $g(x) = \sqrt{x^2 - 1}$ is discontinuous at each point a satisfying $|a| < 1$, but points separated from the domain of f are of no interest here.)

Example 1. The absolute value function $f(x) = |x|$, A2.2 Figure 5, is defined by

$$f(x) = \begin{cases} x, & \text{if } 0 \leq x, \\ -x, & \text{if } x < 0. \end{cases}$$

We apply the criteria of Definition 1 to determine whether the function is continuous at $x = 0$, where the two intervals of definition meet. Given any $\epsilon > 0$, can we find $\delta > 0$ such that $|f(x) - f(0)| = ||x| - 0| = |x| < \epsilon$ for all x that satisfy the inequality $|x - 0| < \delta$? If $x > 0$, we wish to satisfy $|x| < \epsilon$ whenever $x < \delta$; while, if $x < 0$, we wish to satisfy $|-x| < \epsilon$ whenever $-x < \delta$; in either case, the choice $\delta = \epsilon$ clearly is sufficient to hold $|x|$ within the tolerance ϵ, and continuity at 0 is established.

Example 2. From the graph of the integer part function $f : x \to [\![x]\!]$ we expect to find discontinuity at the integers and continuity elsewhere. This is easily verified. If a is not an integer, $f(x) = [\![a]\!]$ whenever $[\![a]\!] \leq x < [\![a]\!] + 1$. Let δ be the distance from a to the closer of the two integers $[\![a]\!]$ or $[\![a]\!] + 1$. If $|x - a| < \delta$ then $|[\![x]\!] - [\![a]\!]| = 0$ which is less than any error tolerance. On the other hand, for an integer n we have $f(n) = n$ and $f(x) = n - 1$ for $n - 1 \leq x < n$. Consequently, if $\epsilon < 1$, then in any neighborhood of n there are always values of x on the left of n within the neighborhood for which

$$|[\![x]\!] - [\![n]\!]| = 1 > \epsilon$$

and the third criterion of Definition 1 cannot be satisfied.

3.5 Exercises

1. Use the formal definition of continuity to show that each of the following functions is continuous at $x = 1$.

   a. $\quad f : x \to \dfrac{x + 1}{x^2 + 1}$.

   b. $\quad g : x \to \dfrac{4x^2 - 3x - 1}{x + 2}$.

2. For what values of x is each of the following functions discontinuous? Justify your answer.

   a. $\quad f : x \to \dfrac{x}{x}$.

   b. $\quad f : x \to \dfrac{x^2}{x + 1}$.

3. Which of the following functions are discontinuous at $x = -1$? Justify your answer.

   a. $f: x \to \dfrac{x+1}{x^3+1}$.

   b. $g: x \to \dfrac{1}{1+x^2}$.

   c. $h: x \to \dfrac{1}{1-x^2}$.

4. Discuss the points of discontinuity of $f: x \to [\![x]\!] + [\![-x]\!]$. (See 3.1 Exercise 2.)

5. Prove that $f: x \to x - [\![x]\!]$ is continuous for every x which is not an integer and discontinuous for integral values of x .

6. For each of the following functions define a new function which agrees with the given one for $x \ne a$ and is continuous at $x = a$.

   a. $f: x \to \dfrac{x^3-1}{x^2-1}$, $a = 1$.

   b. $f: x \to \dfrac{x^2-4}{x^3-8}$, $a = 2$.

   c. $f: x \to \dfrac{x^n-1}{x-1}$, $a = 1$, n an integer.

   d. $f: x \to \dfrac{1-\sqrt{x}}{1-x}$, $a = 1$.

   e. $f: x \to \dfrac{(x-2)(\sqrt{x}-1)}{x^2+x-2}$, $a = 1$.

7. For each of the following functions, if possible, define a new function which agrees with the given one for $x \ne 0$ and is continuous at $x = 0$. If this is not possible, state why.

   a. $f: x \to \dfrac{x}{x}$.   b. $f: x \to \dfrac{x}{|x|}$.

   c. $f: x \to \dfrac{1}{|x|}$.   d. $f: x \to x - [\![x]\!]$.

8. For each of the following functions show that no function which agrees with the given one for $x \ne a$ can be so defined as to be continuous at $x = a$.

   a. $f: x \to \dfrac{1+\sqrt{x}}{1-x}$, $a = 1$.

   b. $g: x \to \dfrac{\sqrt{2+x}+1}{x+1}$, $a = -1$,

9. If f is a function whose domain is the set of all real numbers, and if f is not continuous at a , what can you say of

$$\lim_{x \to a} |f(x) - f(a)| ?$$

10. For every real x, let $N(x)$ denote the number of distinct real square roots of x, i.e., the number of distinct real solutions of $y^2 = x$. Where does N have a limit? What is the limit? Where is N continuous? Let $P(x) = [N(x) - 1]^2$. Where does P have a limit? What is the limit? Where is P continuous? How does P differ from the function $f : x \to 1$? from the function $g : x \to \dfrac{x}{x}$?

11. Each of the functions f, g, and h is defined for all real x. Which of the functions are not continuous at 0?

$$f(x) = \begin{cases} 0, & \text{for } x \text{ rational} \\ 1, & \text{for } x \text{ irrational.} \end{cases}$$

$$g(x) = \begin{cases} 0, & \text{for } x \text{ rational} \\ x, & \text{for } x \text{ irrational,} \end{cases}$$

$$h(x) = \begin{cases} 1, & \text{for } x \text{ rational} \\ -1, & \text{for } x \text{ irrational.} \end{cases}$$

12. Give an example of a function which is not continuous at 0 but whose absolute value is continuous at 0.

13. a. Show that the function f of Exercise 11 is periodic and determine all possible periods.
   b. Show that every nonconstant periodic function which is continuous, at least at one point, has a fundamental (smallest positive) period.
   c. If f is periodic with periods 1 and $\sqrt{2}$ (i.e., $f(x) = f(x + 1)$ and $f(x) = f(x + \sqrt{2})$) for all x, and if there is at least one point of continuity of f, show that f must be constant.

14. If $f(x) = \begin{cases} \dfrac{1}{q}, & x \text{ rational,} \quad x = \dfrac{p}{q} \ (p, q \text{ relatively prime, } q > 0) \\ 0, & x \text{ irrational,} \end{cases}$
   show that f is continuous for all irrational x, and discontinuous for all rational x.

3.6 PROPERTIES OF FUNCTIONS CONTINUOUS AT A POINT

3.6a Rational combinations of continuous functions

We have proved that limits are distributive over the elementary rational operations; namely, that the limit of a sum is the sum of the limits of its terms; that the limit of a product is the product of the limits of its factors; and that the limit of a quotient is the quotient of the limits of its numerator and its denominator, provided that the limit of the denominator is not zero. Thus, if two functions are continuous at $x = a$ then so are their sum, product, and quotient if no division by zero is involved.

In the following theorems, as for the corresponding theorems on limits, we presuppose that the domains of the functions appearing in a combination coincide in some neighborhood of a.

Theorem 1. If the functions f and g are continuous at $x = a$, so is the function h defined by $h(x) = f(x) + g(x)$; that is, the sum of two functions which are continuous at a point is also continuous there.

Proof. From 3.4a Theorem 3 on the limit of a sum and from the definition of continuous functions

$$
\begin{aligned}
\lim_{x \sim a} h(x) &= \lim_{x \sim a} \left(f(x) + g(x) \right) \\
&= \lim_{x \sim a} f(x) + \lim_{x \sim a} g(x) \\
&= f(a) + g(a) \\
&= h(a) .
\end{aligned}
$$

In precisely the same way, we obtain the following theorems.

Theorem 2. If the functions f and g are continuous at $x = a$, then so is the function h defined by $h(x) = f(x) \cdot g(x)$; that is, the product of two functions which are continuous at $x = a$ is also continuous there.

Theorem 3. If the functions f and g are continuous at $x = a$, and if $g(a) \neq 0$, the function h, defined for $g(x) \neq 0$ by $h(x) = \dfrac{f(x)}{g(x)}$, is continuous at $x = a$. In other words, the quotient of continuous functions is continuous if no division by zero is involved.

From these results it can be proved that any rational combination of continuous functions is continuous at points where the denominator does not vanish. In particular, since constant functions are continuous (3.4a Theorem 1), it can be proved that any linear combination of continuous functions is continuous. We have already proved that every polynomial is continuous (3.4a Corollary 4a); hence, a rational function is continuous at every point where the denominator is not zero.

3.6a Exercises

1. a. Prove Theorem 2 using the limit theorems as in the proof of Theorem 1.
   b. Prove Theorem 3 in the same way.

2. Prove Theorems 2 and 3 directly from 3.5 Definition 1.

3. a. If the function f is continuous at $x = a$ and the function g is not continuous at $x = a$, show that $f + g$ is not continuous at $x = a$.
   b. Can $f + g$ be continuous at $x = a$ if neither f nor g is continuous at $x = a$? Illustrate your answer by giving an example.
   c. Answer the same questions for the product $f \cdot g$.

3.6b Continuity and differentiability

The functions that concern us in the calculus are usually continuous, but we shall generally not need a separate proof of continuity, since these functions will usually be differentiable. If a function is differentiable at a point, it is also continuous at the same point.

Theorem 1. If the function f has a derivative at a, then f is continuous at a.

Proof. Let the derivative be

$$m = \lim_{x \sim a} \frac{f(x) - f(a)}{x - a}.$$

Observe that

$$\lim_{x \sim a} (x - a) = 0.$$

Using 3.4 Theorem 4, we obtain

$$\lim_{x \sim a} [f(x) - f(a)] = \lim_{x \sim a} \left[\frac{f(x) - f(a)}{x - a} \cdot (x - a) \right]$$

$$= \lim_{x \sim a} \frac{f(x) - f(a)}{x - a} \lim_{x \sim a} (x - a)$$

$$= m \cdot 0$$

$$= 0.$$

Finally, from 3.4a Theorem 3 and this result,

$$\lim_{x \sim a} f(x) = \lim_{x \sim a} [f(x) - f(a)] + \lim_{x \sim a} f(a) = f(a).$$

Therefore, f is continuous at a.   ▯

We have already proved (3.3 Example 6) that $\sqrt{x}$ has a derivative at a, for $a > 0$. As a consequence, we have:

Corollary a. The function $f : x \to \sqrt{x}$ is continuous at $x = a$, for $a > 0$.

The relation between differentiability and continuity is a one-way affair: a function may be continuous at a point without being differentiable there.

Example 1. In 3.5 Example 1 we demonstrated that $f : x \to |x|$ is continuous when $x = 0$. Does it have a derivative at $x = 0$? If we examine the graph A2.2, Figure 5, it seems most unlikely, because such a derivative would assign a slope to the graph of f at the origin. The graph consists of two rays having the slopes -1 to the left and $+1$ to the right of the origin, and it appears meaningless to talk of the direction of this graph at the origin. The proof that $|x|$ does not have a derivative at $x = 0$ is left to be worked out as an exercise (3.6b Ex. 1).

3.6b Exercises

1. Prove that $f : x \to |x|$ does not have a derivative at $x = 0$.

2. Let $f : x \to x^n$, where n is a positive integer.
   a. Use the binomial theorem to expand $(x + h)^n$.
   b. From the result of Part a derive a formula for

   $$r(x) = \frac{f(x + h) - f(x)}{h}$$

   c. From the result of Part b deduce

   $$m = \lim_{h \sim 0} \frac{f(x + h) - f(x)}{h} = nx^{n-1}.$$

   State which limit theorems you are using.
   d. Use 3.6b Theorem 1 to show that f is continuous at $x = a$, where a is any real number.

3. Consider $f : x \to \sqrt[n]{x}$, $(x > 0)$ where n is a natural number.
   a. Prove that f is continuous at a for any positive a.
   b. Express $x - a$ as the product of $\sqrt[n]{x} - \sqrt[n]{a}$ and a geometric sum by inverting the formula for the sum of a geometric progression.
   c. From the result of Part b derive a formula for the difference quotient

   $$\frac{f(x) - f(a)}{x - a}.$$

   d. From the result of Part c prove that the derivative of f at a is

   $$f'(a) = \lim_{x \sim a} \frac{f(x) - f(a)}{x - a} = \frac{\sqrt[n]{a}}{na}.$$

3.6c Composition of functions

The formation of rational combinations is one of the principal methods for construction of complicated mathematical functions from simpler ones, and we have proved that, in general, the existence of a limit and the property of continuity are preserved by rational combination. In the same spirit, we now examine whether the existence of a limit and continuity are preserved by composition.

Example 1. Let $f(x) = (1 + x)^{1/2}$, $g(x) = \dfrac{1}{x}$, and $h(x) = \cos x$. We have many possible compositions of f, g, and h, such as

(1)
$$gf(x) = \frac{1}{(1 + x)^{1/2}};$$

(2)
$$fgh(x) = \left(1 + \frac{1}{\cos x}\right)^{1/2};$$

(3)
$$gg(x) = \frac{1}{(1/x)}.$$

In composing functions, we must pay careful attention to their domains. Thus, in (1) although $x = -1$ is in the domain of f, it is not in the domain of gf since $f(-1) = 0$ is not in the domain of g. In a more complex composition such as (2), the difficulty may be somewhat disguised. Here we must exclude any point x for which $-1 < \cos x \le 0$; for example, $\dfrac{\pi}{2} \le x < \pi$ or $\pi < x \le \dfrac{3\pi}{2}$. For if x is such a point, then $\dfrac{1}{\cos x} < -1$, but the domain of f contains only -1 and greater numbers. Even such an elementary composition as (3) may have hidden dangers: we are tempted to say that $gg(x) = x$, but strictly speaking the composition has the value x only for $x \ne 0$, because $g(0)$ is undefined and, therefore, $gg(0)$ is meaningless.

We shall consider functions that can be built up by successive composition. For such functions, we shall obtain a general theorem, under certain restrictions to be stated; namely, that any function constructed by successive compositions of continuous functions is itself continuous. It is sufficient to prove the theorem for a single composition.

Theorem 1. Let g be a function whose range is contained in the domain of f. If g is continuous at a and f is continuous at $g(a)$, the composite function : $x \rightarrow fg(x)$ is continuous at a.

Proof. For any tolerance ϵ, we can choose a control $\delta^* > 0$ such that

$$|f(y) - fg(a)| < \epsilon$$

for

$$|y - g(a)| < \delta^*,$$

since f is continuous at $g(a)$. In particular, for $y = g(x)$, it follows that

(1) $$|fg(x) - fg(a)| < \epsilon$$

whenever

(2) $$|g(x) - g(a)| < \delta^*.$$

We now regard δ^* as a prescribed tolerance for the approximation of $g(a)$ by $g(x)$; then, because g is continuous at a, we can choose a control δ such that (2) holds for all x in the domain of g satisfying

$$|x - a| < \delta.$$

Since (1) holds for these values of x the composite function fg is continuous at a.   ⬜

Example 2. Given $f(u) = 1/u$, under the valid assumption that

$$g : x \rightarrow \sin x$$

is continuous for all x, we want to find all the discontinuities of fg, the cosecant function. We need not consider any point where Theorem 5 applies; that is, any point x where g is continuous and for which f is continuous at $g(x)$. The function g imposes no restrictions on the domain of the composite function since it is continuous for all x. The function f is continuous except when $u = 0$; here f is undefined and, consequently, discontinuous. The values x for which $g(x) = 0$ will be points of discontinuity for fg because the composition is undefined there. We conclude that the cosecant function is discontinuous for $x = 0$, $\pm\pi, \pm2\pi, \dots$, namely, whenever x is an integral multiple of π.

3.6c Exercises

1. Let $f(x) = \sqrt{x}$, $g(x) = 1/(x-1)$, and $h(x) = \sin x$. Describe the domain of the function given by
   a. $fg(x)$,
   b. $gf(x)$,
   c. $hg(x)$,
   d. $gh(x)$,
   e. $hfg(x)$.

2. Assume that the functions $x \to \sin x$ and $x \to \cos x$ are continuous for all x. Find the discontinuities of the function f given by

   a. $f(x) = \sin \dfrac{1}{x}$,

   b. $f(x) = \tan x$,

   c. $f(x) = \dfrac{1}{4 - 3\sin^2 x}$,

   d. $f(x) = \sin \cos x$,

   e. $f(x) = \tan \dfrac{x^2 - 1}{x + 1}$,

   f. $f(x) = \tan \cos x - \cos \tan x$.

3. a. Determine where the function $f : x \to [\![x]\!] + \sqrt{x - [\![x]\!]}$ is continuous.
   b. Sketch the graph of f.

4. Prove that if $\lim\limits_{x \to a} f(x) = L$ and $\lim\limits_{x \to a} g(x) = M$, then

$$\lim_{x \to a} \sqrt{f(x)^2 + g(x)^2} = \sqrt{L^2 + M^2}.$$

5. Prove, if $\lim\limits_{a \to x} g(x) = b$ and f is continuous at b, then the composite function $x \to fg(x)$ has a limit as x approaches a and

$$\lim_{x \to a} fg(x) = f(\lim_{x \to a} g(x)) = f(b).$$

3.6d Continuity of the inverse function

From the geometrical relation between the graph of a function and its inverse it may seem evident that continuity at a point of the domain of the function implies continuity at the corresponding point of the graph of its inverse; that is, if f is continuous at a then its inverse g is continuous at $b = f(a)$. This statement is not quite true (see 3.7a Ex. 17), but the result holds under an extra condition.

Theorem 1. Let f be a strongly monotone function and let g be its inverse. If f is continuous at a then g is continuous at

$$b = f(a) \,.$$

Proof. Since f is strongly monotone the existence of the inverse g is not at issue (see A2.5 Theorem 1). To prove continuity of g at b, we need to establish two things: (1) b is a cluster point of the domain of g; (2) given any ϵ-neighborhood of $a = g(b)$, there is a δ-neighborhood of b wherein g maps the points of its domain into the ϵ-neighborhood of a.

Since the domain of g is the range of f, we prove that $b = f(a)$ is a cluster point of the domain of g by demonstrating that b is a cluster point of the range of f. For this purpose, we must show that any deleted ϵ^*-neighborhood of b contains points of the range of f. Since f is continuous at a, there is a δ^*-neighborhood of a where f maps the points of its domain into the ϵ-neighborhood of b. Now, the mapping f is one-to-one, and $b = f(a)$; therefore, a is the only antecedent of b in the mapping. It follows that f maps the part of its domain in the deleted δ^*-neighborhood of a into the deleted ϵ^*-neighborhood of b. Furthermore, since a is a cluster point of the domain, the deleted δ^*-neighborhood of a contains points of the domain of f and, therefore, the deleted ϵ^*-neighborhood of b contains points of the range of f. We conclude that b is a cluster point of the range of f, hence, of the domain of g.

To complete the proof, we must show for any $\epsilon > 0$ that there is a δ-neighborhood of b wherein

$$|g(y) - g(b)| = |g(y) - a| < \epsilon \,.$$

Now, if $\mathcal{D}$ is the domain of f, let $\mathcal{D}_1$ and $\mathcal{D}_2$ be the subsets of $\mathcal{D}$ in the left and right ϵ-neighborhoods of a, namely,

$$\mathcal{D}_1 = \{x : x \in \mathcal{D}, a - \epsilon < x < a\} \,,$$
$$\mathcal{D}_2 = \{x : x \in \mathcal{D}, a < x < a + \epsilon\} \,.$$

Since a is a cluster point of $\mathcal{D}$, at least one of the sets $\mathcal{D}_1$ or $\mathcal{D}_2$ is not empty, say $\mathcal{D}_1$. Let x_1 be any point of $\mathcal{D}_1$. If $\mathcal{D}_2$ contains a point x_2 closer to a than x_1 (see Figure 1a), set

$$\delta = |f(x_2) - f(a)| = |f(x_2) - b| \,;$$

if no point of $\mathcal{D}_2$ is closer to a than x_1 (see Figure 1b), set

$$\delta = |f(x_1) - f(a)| = |f(x_1) - b| \,.$$

In either case, whether f is increasing or decreasing, g maps the values of f in the δ-neighborhood of b into the ϵ-neighborhood of a; hence, g is continuous at b.   ☐

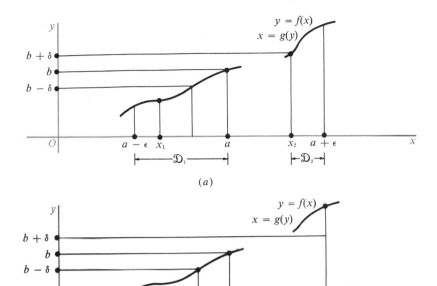

(a)

Figure 1

(b)

3.7 CONTINUITY ON AN INTERVAL

We are interested in curves, in motions, in processes that are continuous, and we wish to represent them by functions. Therefore, we are interested in functions that are continuous not at one point alone but at every point of an interval I. Such a function is said to be *continuous on the interval* I. It is possible to construct a function continuous at every point of its domain, yet not continuous on any interval; for such a function, every interval must contain points where the function is not defined. It is even possible to find a function continuous at every point of its domain, having an inverse that is discontinuous at every point of its domain (see 3.7a Ex. 17). From 3.6d Theorem 1, such a function could not be strongly monotone.

Since the concept of continuity at a point (given in 3.5 Definition 1) is a local property of a function — a property which is determined by the values of the function within any neighborhood of the point, however small — it is not at all obvious that the properties which intuition would ascribe to functions that are continuous on an interval can, in fact, be derived from the definition.

3.7a Properties of functions continuous on an interval

Extreme and intermediate value theorems. Many aspects of our intuitive picture of continuity are implicit in the precise definition. For example, we may think of the graph of a continuous function f passing through points $(a, f(a))$ and $(b, f(b))$ as the path of a walk over hilly terrain (Figure 1). It seems clear that such a path in passing from the elevation $f(a)$ to the

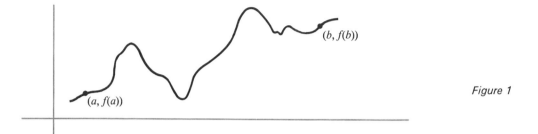

Figure 1

elevation $f(b)$ must pass through every elevation between. This idea is expressed by the following theorem:

Theorem 1. Intermediate Value Theorem. Let f be continuous on the closed interval $[a, b]$. Let v be any number between $f(a)$ and $f(b)$. Then there exists some value u in the interval such that $f(u) = v$.

Example 1. The Intermediate Value Theorem can be used to locate zeros of a continuous function. For example, consider the polynomial function p given by

$$p(x) = x^3 - x^2 - 1 .$$

We know that polynomials are continuous (see 3.4 Corollary 4a). We observe that $p(0) = -1$ and that $p(x)$ is positive for sufficiently large positive x; for example, $p(2) = 3$. From Theorem 1, it follows that there is a number r in $(0, 2)$ for which $p(r) = 0$. We can locate a zero more precisely in one of the halves of the interval $(0, 2)$ by calculating $p(x)$ at the midpoint of the interval: since $p(1) = -1$, there is a zero in $(1, 2)$. We may repeat the process: $p(\frac{3}{2}) = \frac{1}{8}$ yields a zero in $(1, \frac{3}{2})$; $p(\frac{5}{4}) = -\frac{39}{64}$ yields a zero in $(\frac{5}{4}, \frac{3}{2})$, and so on. Clearly, in this way, we can locate a zero of p to any desired accuracy. We need not take the midpoint of the interval at each stage, but may choose any interior point; if the choice is adroitly made, the process of locating a zero accurately can be greatly expedited.

Again, intuitively, there is at least one point on a continuous path, possibly an endpoint where the highest elevation on the interval is reached and another (or others) where the lowest elevation is reached. This property is expressed formally in the following theorem.

Theorem 2. Extreme Value Theorem. If f is continuous on the closed interval $[a, b]$, then f has a maximum and a minimum in the interval. Specifically, within the interval, there exists at least one value x_M for which $f(x_M)$ is the maximum $(f(x_M) \geq f(x)$ for all x in the interval), and at least one value x_m for which $f(x_m)$ is the minimum $(f(x_m) \leq f(x)$ for all x in the interval).

The restriction to a closed interval is essential in Theorem 2; for example, the function given by $g(x) = x$ on the open interval $0 < x < 1$ has neither a maximum nor a minimum in the interval. The same remark applies to the function given by $h(x) = \dfrac{1}{x}$ on the same interval.

If $f(x_M)$ is the maximum of f on an interval, and $f(x_m)$ the minimum, then it is clear from the Intermediate Value Theorem that f on the interval from x_m to x_M takes on every value between $f(x_M)$ and $f(x_m)$. Hence we can combine the extreme and intermediate value theorems in a single statement:

Corollary a. On a closed interval, the range of a continuous function contains a maximum, a minimum, and all values between.

This statement can be put more briefly as follows: A continuous function maps a closed interval onto a closed interval. The upper and lower endpoints of the image are, of course, the maximum and minimum of the function values.

(The proofs of these theorems involve the completeness of the real number system; see A1.5. For reference, Theorem 1 is proved in 3.7b and Theorem 2 in 3.7c.)

Monotone continuous functions. For strongly monotone functions the property of continuity is equivalent to the property of the preceding corollary, namely:

Theorem 3. Let f be a strongly monotone function and let the domain of f be an interval I. If f is continuous on I then, by the preceding corollary, the range of f is an interval. Conversely, if the range of f is an interval, then f is continuous on I.

Proof. We only need to prove the converse: if f is strongly monotone and the range R of f is an interval, then f is continuous. Let x_0 be an interior point of I. Since f is strongly monotone and R is an interval, $f(x_0)$ is an interior point of R. Consequently, for any sufficiently small ϵ the values $f(x_0) - \epsilon$ and $f(x_0) + \epsilon$ are in R; that is, there exist points c and d in I for which $f(c) = f(x_0) - \epsilon$ and $f(d) = f(x_0) + \epsilon$. Since f is strongly monotone, if x is between c and d, then $f(x)$ is between $f(x_0) - \epsilon$ and $f(x_0) + \epsilon$. Hence, to assure

$$|f(x) - f(x_0)| < \epsilon$$

it suffices to require

$$|x - x_0| < \delta,$$

where $\delta = \min\{|x_0 - c|, |x_0 - d|\}$.

A slight modification of this argument suffices to prove the result when x_0 is an endpoint of I. □

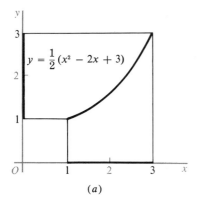

(a)

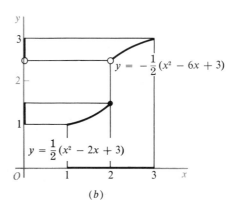

(b)

Figure 2

Figure 2a depicts the graph of the continuous monotone function $f : x \rightarrow \frac{1}{2}(x^2 - 2x + 3)$ for $1 \le x \le 3$ and Figure 2b, the graph of the discontinuous increasing function g given by

$$g(x) = \begin{cases} \frac{1}{2}(x^2 - 2x + 3), & 1 \le x \le 2, \\ -\frac{1}{2}(x^2 - 6x + 3), & 2 < x \le 3. \end{cases}$$

In both cases, the projection of the graph on the x-axis, the domain of the function, is the interval $1 \le x \le 3$. For the continuous function f, the projection on the y-axis, the range of the function, is an interval $1 \le y \le 3$. For the discontinuous function g, the range consists of two separated intervals $1 \le y \le \frac{3}{2}$ and $\frac{5}{2} < y \le 3$. This situation is typical.

In the preceding theorems we have evidence that the formal definition of continuity on an interval does agree with various aspects of the intuitive idea of continuity. Yet, a precise formal definition does not necessarily correspond in every respect to the intuitive idea from which it springs. In this respect, the idea of continuity is particularly revealing. You have seen that a continuous function need not have a derivative at every point of its domain (e.g., $x \rightarrow |x|$). It is not obvious, but it is true, that there are functions continuous on an interval which do not have a derivative at any point of their domains. If you think of functions in terms of graphs which can be plotted, this fact may be surprising; certainly no pen can follow the infinitely sinuous wiggles of such a graph.

In the early 19th century some mathematicians argued that a continuous function must also have a derivative, except perhaps at isolated points. In part, this feeling probably stemmed from the earlier concept of function as a relation defined by a formal expression; the idea of function as we know it (then called "single-valued" function) had not been thoroughly explored. The formal expressions familiar to the mathematicans of that time would not be likely to suggest the peculiarities of nondifferentiable continuous functions. In 1872 Weierstrass proved definitely that a certain function was just such a nondifferentiable continuous function. There is a persistent misconception that the mathematical community was deeply shocked by the example of Weierstrass. In fact, in 1834, thirty-six years prior to the paper of Weierstrass, Bolzano gave an example of such a function.[†‡] However, Bolzano did not completely prove that his function had all of the required properties. The story of the rediscovery of Bolzano's example and a proof is given by G. Kowalewski. According to Weierstrass,[*] around 1861 Reimann also proposed an example of such a function. Weierstrass found it too difficult to verify that the example of Reimann was correct, and it is unclear whether Reimann was able to verify this. Thus Weierstrass was the first to prove that a specific example actually was nowhere differentiable.

In 3.7d we present an example of a continuous but nowhere differentiable function whose properties can be demonstrated by elementary means.

[†] C. B. Boyer, *Concepts of the Calculus.*

[‡] G. Kowalewski, "Uber Bolzano's Nichtdifferenzierbare Stetige Funktion." *Acta Mathematica*, 44. 1923, pp. 315–319.

[*] Weierstrass, *Werke*, Vol. 2, pp. 71–74.

3.7a Exercises

1. Exhibit a discontinuous function for which the range of the function is an interval.

2. On which of the following intervals is the function $f : x \to \sin x$ increasing? decreasing? In each case locate the maximum and minimum values if any.

   a. $\left(-\dfrac{\pi}{2}, \pi\right)$.

   b. $\left[-\dfrac{\pi}{2}, \pi\right]$.

   c. $\left[-\dfrac{\pi}{2}, 0\right]$.

   d. $\left(-\dfrac{\pi}{2}, \dfrac{\pi}{2}\right)$.

   e. $[-\pi, \pi]$.

3. In which of the following intervals does $f : x \to |x|$ have a maximum?

   a. $-1 < x < 1$.
   b. $-1 \le x < 1$.
   c. $-1 < x \le 1$.
   d. $-1 \le x \le 1$.

4. Assume that $f : x \to \sin x$ is continuous for all x in $\left[-\dfrac{\pi}{2}, \dfrac{\pi}{2}\right]$.

   a. Prove that f is increasing. Hint: Use the identity

   $$\sin y - \sin x = 2 \sin \tfrac{1}{2}(y - x) \cos \tfrac{1}{2}(y + x).$$

   b. Show that the range of f is an interval. Show that the domain of the inverse of $f : x \to \sin x$ is an interval.

5. a. Assume that the function $f : x \to \tan x$ is continuous on the closed interval $[-\tfrac{1}{4}\pi, \tfrac{1}{4}\pi]$ and show that there is some number x where $-\tfrac{1}{4}\pi < x < \tfrac{1}{4}\pi$ such that $\tan x = \tfrac{1}{4}\pi$. Can there be more than one such number?

   b. Prove that if f is continuous on the closed interval $[a, b]$ and all values of f are in $[a, b]$, then there is an x in $[a, b]$ for which $f(x) = x$.

6. Show that the equation $x^4 + x - 10 = 0$ has at least one solution between $x = -2$ and $x = -1$ and obtain an approximation to the solution within a tolerance of $\tfrac{1}{2}$.

7. Isolate each real root of the given equation by exhibiting an interval containing this root and no others. (Each equation has four roots.)

   a. $x^4 - x^3 - 9x^2 + 2x + 14 = 0$.
   b. $2x^4 + 2x^3 - 3x^2 - x + 1 = 0$.

8. a. Show that the equation $\cos^2 x = \sqrt{|x|}$ has at least one positive root x, where $x < \tfrac{1}{4}\pi$.

   b. Find the maximum and the minimum value of $f : x \to \cos^2 x - \sqrt{|x|}$ on the closed interval $[0, \tfrac{1}{2}\pi]$.

9. The temperature T at any point of a thin circular ring is a continuous function of the point's position θ. Show that there is a pair of antipodes (points at opposite ends of a diameter) having the same temperature.

10. Sketch the graphs and determine how many points of discontinuity there are in the interval $[0, 2\pi]$ of the following functions:
   a. $f : x \to [\![\sin x]\!]$.
   b. $f : x \to [\![2 \sin x]\!]$.
   c. $f : x \to [\![a \sin x]\!]$.

11. Can a discontinuous function have the intermediate value property? Give examples.

12. a. Give an example of a monotone function on $[0, 1]$ with exactly n points of discontinuity.
   b. Can a monotone function on $[0, 1]$ have infinitely many points of discontinuity? Justify your answer.

13. Prove that $f : x \to x^r$ is increasing for $x > 0$ and ranges over the positive reals (r rational and positive).

14. a. Prove that $x \to \sqrt{f(x)}$ is continuous and increasing wherever f is positive, continuous, and increasing.
   b. Prove that $x \to \sqrt[3]{f(x)}$ is continuous wherever f is continuous.

15. Give an example of a function f defined on $[0, 1]$ such that f takes on every value between 0 and 1 once and only once but is discontinuous for all x.

16. If g is continuous with $g(0) = g(1) = 1$ and, in the interval $[0, 1]$, $g(x^2) = [g(x)]^2$, show that $g(x) = 1$ on $[0, 1]$.

17. Consider the function f given by

$$f(x) = \begin{cases} x, & \text{for } x \geq 1 \text{ and } x \text{ rational,} \\ -x, & \text{for } x \leq -1 \text{ and } x \text{ irrational.} \end{cases}$$

Prove that f is continuous at every point of its domain and one-to-one. Show, nonetheless, that the inverse of f is nowhere continuous.

E3.7b Proof of the Intermediate Value Theorem

The idea of continuity as expressed in the first paragraph of 3.5 is simple and intuitive. However, in order to attain a precise and workable definition, we abstracted what we thought was the essential property of continuity to formulate 3.5 Definition 1. How do we know that our definition agrees with our intuitive idea of continuity? We must prove that the functions which satisfy our precise definition have the properties we want continuous functions to have. Whenever we construct a precise definition of an intuitive idea, we must verify its appropriateness by "proving the obvious" — obvious in that the property is perceived directly from the intuitive idea, and proven in the sense that it is logically implied by our precise definition. In 3.7a we saw that the intermediate value property of continuous functions is obvious. Now we shall prove it. The proof uses the Least Upper Bound Principle of A1.5.

Intermediate Value Theorem. Let f be continuous on the closed interval $[a, b]$. Let v be any number between $f(a)$ and $f(b)$. Then there is a number u in $[a, b]$ such that $f(u) = v$.

Proof. Suppose $f(a) < v < f(b)$. Let

$$S = \{x : x \in [a, b] \text{ and } f(x) < v\}.$$

The set S has the upper bound b and S is not empty since $a \in S$. Consequently, S has a least upper bound u in $[a, b]$. We proceed to show that $f(u) = v$. First, u cannot be an endpoint of $[a, b]$ since, by 3.4a Lemma 1, the continuity of f implies that $f(x) < v$ in a neighborhood of a and $f(x) > v$ in a neighborhood of b. Next, every neighborhood of u contains points such that $f(x) < v$ (since u is the least upper bound of the set of such points) and points such that $f(x) \geq v$ (all points to the right of u). It follows that $f(u) = v$, for if $f(u)$ were greater than v then, by 3.4a Lemma 1, all points x of some neighborhood of u would satisfy $f(x) > v$ and, similarly, if $f(u) < v$ there would be a neighborhood of u where $f(x) < v$. $\quad\square$

3.7b Exercises

1. a. Sketch the curves $y = x^n$ and $y = x^{1/n}$, $n = 0, 1, 2, \ldots$, using the same set of axes.

 b. Prove that if $p(x)$ is a polynomial of odd degree (with real coefficients), then the equation $p(x) = 0$ has a real root.

 c. Prove that the equation $x^n = a$ has exactly one negative root if n is an odd positive integer and $a < 0$.

2. The real roots of the equation $x^n + ax + b = 0$ (n a positive integer) can be determined by finding the intersections of the curves $y = x^n$ and $y = -ax - b$.

 Verify for the number of real roots of $x^n + ax + b = 0$ that

 a. If n is odd, and $\begin{cases} a > 0, & \text{there is one,} \\ a < 0, & \text{there are three or one.} \end{cases}$

 b. If n is even, and $\begin{cases} b > 0, & \text{there are two or none,} \\ b < 0, & \text{there are two.} \end{cases}$

 Give numerical examples to illustrate each of the four cases.

3. For the semicircle $y = \sqrt{1 - x^2}$, it can be shown that chords parallel to the x-axis of length $1/n$ exist where n is any positive integer. This result can be generalized to the graph of any continuous function on $[0, 1]$ which

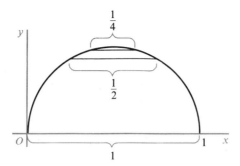

has the same value at 0 and at 1. Prove this. Give an example to show for some such function on $[0, 1]$ that for some real values r where

$$0 < r < 1,$$

the graph may have no chords parallel to the x-axis of length r .

4. A rigid planar motion is defined for each value of a parameter t in a given interval as an isometry (see A3.6d) that is continuous and maps the plane onto itself. Such an isometry is defined by equations of the form A3.6d(1) where the coefficients are continuous functions of t :

$$\begin{cases} x' = \alpha(t)x + \beta(t)\, y + \xi(t) \\ y' = \gamma(t)x + \delta(t)\, y + \eta(t) . \end{cases}$$

Show that no such motion will move the basis of perpendicular unit vectors $\mathbf{i}$, $\mathbf{j}$ onto the oppositely oriented basis consisting of the vectors $\mathbf{i}$ and $-\mathbf{j}$, respectively; that is, there is no rigid motion in which $\mathbf{i} \rightarrow \mathbf{i}$ and $\mathbf{j} \rightarrow \mathbf{j}$ at $t = t_0$ and $\mathbf{i} \rightarrow \mathbf{i}$ and $\mathbf{j} \rightarrow -\mathbf{j}$ at $t = t_1$, where

$$t_1 > t_0 .$$

E3.7c Proof of the Extreme Value Theorem

The range of a function may include arbitrarily large numbers. For example, the function defined by $f(x) = \dfrac{1}{x}$ on the domain

$$\{x : 0 < x \le 1\}$$

has the property that for any positive number $z > 1$ there is at least one value of f, e.g., $f\!\left(\dfrac{1}{z+1}\right) = z + 1$, which is greater than z. This cannot occur for a continuous function whose domain is a closed interval.

Theorem 1. If f is continuous on the closed interval $[a, b]$ then f has an upper bound on the interval; that is, there exists a number N for which $f(x) < N$ for all x in $[a, b]$.

Proof. Suppose that the theorem is false. Then $f(x)$ has no upper bound on $[a, b]$. It follows that f lacks an upper bound on at least one of the "half-intervals" $\left[a, \dfrac{a+b}{2}\right]$ or $\left[\dfrac{a+b}{2}, b\right]$. Let $[a_1, b_1]$ be a half-interval where $f(x)$ lacks an upper bound. The same argument, applied again, yields a half-interval $[a_2, b_2]$ of $[a_1, b_1]$ where f has no upper bound. Applying the argument repeatedly, we obtain a nested set of intervals $\{[a_n, b_n]\}$ where $[a_{n+1}, b_{n+1}]$ is a half-interval of $[a_n, b_n]$, and f has no upper bound on any interval of the set. From the Nested Interval Principle of A1.5 there exists at least one point ξ common to all the intervals $[a_n, b_n]$.

Since ξ is a point of $[a, b]$, f is continuous at ξ. Consequently, for any positive ϵ there is a δ-neighborhood of ξ wherein

$$|f(x) - f(\xi)| < \epsilon$$

for x in the domain of f. In the δ-neighborhood of ξ, then, $f(x)$ is bounded above:

$$f(x) < f(\xi) + \epsilon.$$

But since $b_n - a_n = \dfrac{b-a}{2^n}$ and ξ lies in $[a_n, b_n]$, it follows that $[a_n, b_n]$ is contained in the δ-neighborhood of ξ for all n satisfying $\dfrac{b-a}{2^n} < \delta$. This contradicts our earlier conclusion that $f(x)$ has no upper bound in $[a_n, b_n]$; hence, our original supposition that f has no upper bound on $[a, b]$ is false.   □

Corollary a. If f is continuous on the closed interval $[a, b]$, then f has a lower bound on the interval; that is, there is a number N such that for all x in $[a, b]$, $f(x) > N$.

Corollary b. A function continuous on a closed interval is bounded on the interval; that is, the function is bounded above and below.

The sharpest upper (lower) bound for a function is, of course, the least upper bound, M (greatest lower bound, m) of the range of the function. Considering the fact that there are function values arbitrarily close to M, we might hope and expect that M is actually a function value. That this need not happen can be seen in the following example.

Example 1. Consider the graph defined by the function f on the closed interval $[0, b]$ which is linear on the subintervals $[0, z]$ and $[z, b]$ and satisfies $f(0) = a$, $f(z) = 0$, and $f(b) = 0$, see Figure 1. Is

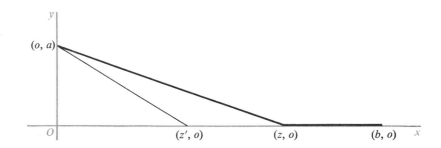

Figure 1

there a value of z for which the sum of the length of the line segments that compose the graph is maximal? That is, does the function $L : z \rightarrow b - z + \sqrt{a^2 + z^2}$ have a maximum value? If $z' < z$, then the sum of the lengths of the segments joining $(0, a)$ to $(z', 0)$ and $(z', 0)$ to $(z, 0)$ is greater than the length of the segment joining $(0, a)$ to $(z, 0)$. We conclude that $L(z') > L(z)$ whenever $z' < z$. Since z cannot equal 0 (we would not have the graph of a function), the function $L : z \rightarrow L(z)$, though bounded by $a + b$, does not have a maximum value.

The next theorem gives conditions under which this difficulty cannot occur.

Extreme Value Theorem. If the function f is continuous on the closed interval $[a, b]$, then there are numbers x_m and x_M in $[a, b]$ such that

$$f(x_m) \leq f(x) \leq f(x_M)$$

for all x in $[a, b]$.

Observe that the theorem does not apply to Example 1, the function L being defined on a half-open interval.

Proof 1. Let M be the least upper bound of f on $[a, b]$; then for any number L smaller than M, there is a value of f greater than L. In particular, for every positive integer k, there is a point x_k in $[a, b]$ for which $f(x_k) > M - \dfrac{1}{k}$. Next, consider the half-intervals $\left[a, \dfrac{a+b}{2}\right]$

and $\left[\dfrac{a+b}{2}, b\right]$. At least one of the half-intervals must contain such values x_k for infinitely many integers k. (If both intervals contained x_k for only a finite set of integers k, then the whole interval could contain such x_k for only a finite set of k's.) Let $[a_1, b_1]$ be such a half-interval. Now, repeat the process and take for $[a_2, b_2]$ a half-interval of $[a_1, b_1]$ which contains such values x_k for infinitely many integers k. In general, given $[a_n, b_n]$, we take for $[a_{n+1}, b_{n+1}]$ a half-interval of $[a_n, b_n]$ which contains such values x_k for infinitely many integers k.

Observe that $\{[a_n, b_n]\}$ is a nested set of closed intervals. Consequently, there is a point ξ common to all the intervals of the set, and, as in the proof of Theorem 1, any neighborhood of ξ contains $[a_n, b_n]$ for sufficiently large n. We now show that $f(\xi) = M$. Since f is continuous, for each $\epsilon > 0$ there exists a $\delta > 0$ such that

$$|f(x) - f(\xi)| < \epsilon$$

for all points x of the domain of f within the δ-neighborhood of ξ. The δ-neighborhood contains some interval $[a_n, b_n]$ of the nested set and, therefore, contains the values x_k for infinitely many integers k. In particular, the δ-neighborhood must contain some value x_ν for which $\nu > \dfrac{1}{\epsilon}$, otherwise the δ-neighborhood could contain only the values x_k for the finite set of integers satisfying $k \leq [\![1/\epsilon]\!]$. Since

$$|f(x_\nu) - f(\xi)| < \epsilon$$

and

$$f(x_\nu) > M - \frac{1}{\nu} > M - \epsilon,$$

it follows that

$$M - 2\epsilon < f(\xi) \leq M.$$

Since this inequality holds for any positive ϵ, we conclude that $f(\xi) = M$; thus the range of the function contains a maximum value. $\square$

Proof 2. Since M is the least upper bound of the range of f, for every number M' smaller than M there is a value of f greater than M'. Thus, for every positive integer j there is a point x_j in $[a, b]$ such that $f(x_j) > M - \dfrac{1}{j}$. Suppose that M is not in the range of f.

Then the function $\phi : x \to \dfrac{1}{M - f(x)}$ is continuous in $[a, b]$ (by 3.6 Theorem 3), hence, by Theorem 1, ϕ is bounded. But

$$\phi(x_j) = \frac{1}{M - f(x_j)} > j,$$

hence ϕ is not bounded. Contradiction.   □

3.7c Exercises

1. a. Is the continuity of f essential to the hypothesis of the boundedness theorem?
   b. Can a discontinuous function whose domain is a closed interval be bounded?
   c. Do Parts a and b amount to the same question?

2. Can a nonconstant function whose domain is the set of real numbers be bounded?

3. a. Give an example of a bounded function f defined on $[0,1]$ such that f has no extreme values.
   b. Repeat Part a with the extra condition that f have an inverse.

4. Give an example of a function f defined in the interval $[0,1]$ such that:
   a. f has neither an upper or lower bound.
   b. f has a lower bound but no upper bound.
   c. f takes on maximum and minimum values infinitely often, but is not constant.

5. Show that any nonconstant function f cannot be continuous at a if it takes on its maximum and minimum values infinitely often in every neighborhood of a.

6. Show that a function which is increasing on some neighborhood of each point of an interval (a,b) is increasing on (a,b).

7. A function ϕ is said to be *weakly increasing on the right of a* if

$$\phi(x) \geq \phi(a)$$

   for all x in an interval $[a, a + \delta]$.
   a. Show that if ϕ is continuous and weakly increasing on the right of all points in (b,c), then ϕ is weakly increasing on (b,c).
   b. Show by a counter-example that the result of Part a does not necessarily hold if ϕ is discontinuous.

8. A function has the property that there is a neighborhood of each point of an interval in its domain where the function is bounded. Show that the function is bounded over the whole interval. (This is an example for which a local property implies a global one. It is clear that the global property implies the local one.)

9. Give an example of a function defined everywhere on a closed interval but unbounded in a neighborhood of every point of the interval. (Suggestion: See 3.5 Exercise 14.)

E3.7d A nowhere differentiable continuous function†

Here we exhibit a *Weierstrass Function*, that is, an everywhere continuous but nondifferentiable function. The idea is to take a smooth curve and "roughen" it in successive stages of approximation to a curve that is still continuous but everywhere rough.

We shall use polygonal approximations. We roughen the line segment joining two consecutive vertices (a_1, b_1) and (a_2, b_2), where $a_1 < a_2$, by the following construction. We set $h = (a_1 - a_2)/3$ and $k = \lambda(b_2 - b_1)$, where $0 < \lambda < 1$. Then we replace the original segment by the zigzag line joining the consecutive vertices

$$(a_1, b_1), \quad (a_1 + h, b_2 - k), \quad (a_2 - h, b_1 + k), \quad (a_2, b_2);$$

see Figure 1.

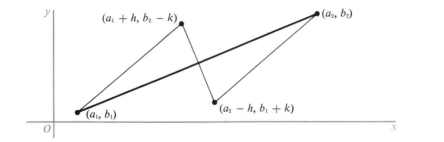

Figure 1

The differences in height of the successive vertices are, in order,

$$(1 - \lambda)(b_2 - b_1), \quad (2\lambda - 1)(b_2 - b_1), \quad (1 - \lambda)(b_2 - b_1).$$

We choose λ so that the absolute difference in height between consecutive vertices is no greater than $(1 - \lambda)(b_2 - b_1)$. Thus, in going from one step of approximation to the next, we reduce the absolute difference in height between two consecutive vertices by a factor no greater than $1 - \lambda$ which is less than 1. This is the property which will yield continuity in the limit. For this purpose, we require $0 < 1 - 2\lambda < 1 - \lambda$ or $0 < \lambda < \frac{1}{2}$.

The three consecutive segments of the zigzag line have as their respective slopes, in order,

$$3(1 - \lambda)m, \quad 3(2\lambda - 1)m, \quad 3(1 - \lambda)m$$

where $m = (b_2 - b_1)/(a_2 - a_1)$ is the slope of the original segment.

†Adapted from A. A. Blank, "A simple example of a Weierstrass function," Am. Math. Monthly 73, No. 5. (1955), pp. 515–519.

We further restrict λ so that the steepness or absolute value of the slope m is multiplied here by a factor no less than $3(1 - 2\lambda)$ which is greater than 1. The increase in steepness of the segments is the property which will yield nondifferentiability in the limit. For this we observe that it is sufficient to require $0 < \lambda < \frac{1}{3}$.

Note that as we pass from the segment to the zigzag line, the endpoints and midpoint of the original segment remain fixed.

For the construction of the Weierstrass function f, we begin with the segment of the line $y = x$ on the interval $0 \leq x \leq 1$. The next step is to apply the foregoing construction to replace this segment by a zigzag (solid curve in Figure 2). Next, we replace the segment over each third of the interval by a further application of the construction, and all succeeding steps are simply iterations of this procedure. The first five iterations are shown in Figures 2 to 6 for $\lambda = 0.3$.

First, we observe that at the n-th step all vertices of the polygonal curve, namely, the points with abscissas

$$\frac{j}{3^n} \qquad\qquad (j = 0, 1, 2, ..., 3^n),$$

are again vertices at the next step. It follows that these points lie on all the approximating polygons from the n-th step on, and, hence, are points of the prospective limit curve. Therefore, if we let f denote the Weierstrass function, we observe that this construction defines f unambiguously for all the ternary fractions, that is, for all values $x = j/3^n$, for $n = 1, 2, 3, ...$ and $j = 0, 1, 2, ... , 3^n$. We shall use this result to define f unambiguously as the continuous extension to all real values of the function that is defined only for ternary values.

From our discussion of the zigzag construction, we observe for two successive vertices x_j and x_{j+1} of the polygon obtained at the n-th iteration that

(1) $$|f(x_{j+1}) - f(x_j)| \leq (1 - \lambda)^n$$

where $x_j = \dfrac{j}{3^n}$. This is the basis for the proof of continuity for the limit function. Moreover, for the slope of the chord joining $(x_j, f(x_j))$ to $(x_{j+1}, f(x_{j+1}))$,

(2) $$\left| \frac{f(x_{j+1}) - f(x_j)}{x_{j+1} - x_j} \right| \geq [3(1 - 2\lambda)]^n.$$

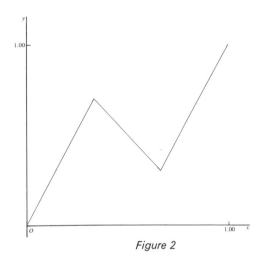

Figure 2

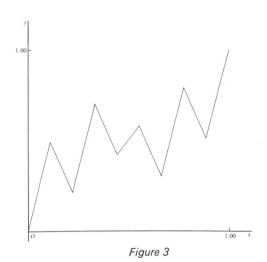

Figure 3

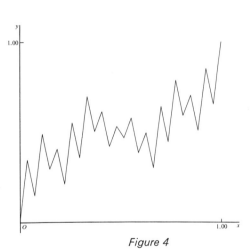

Figure 4

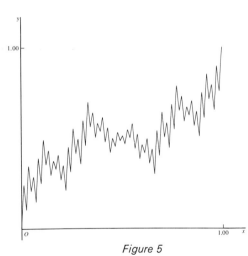

Figure 5

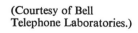

(Courtesy of Bell
Telephone Laboratories.)

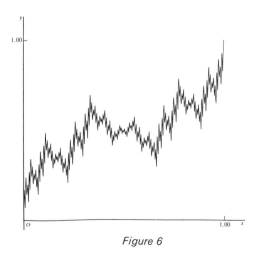

Figure 6

It is clear from (2) that in every subinterval, however small, we can find chords as steep as we please, see 3.4 Ex. 7b. We shall see that (2) implies that no derivative exists at any point.

Although we have fixed the values of the Weierstrass function at the ternary points, we have yet to define $f(x)$ when x is not such a point. For each n let j_n be chosen so that

$$a_n \leq x < b_n$$

where $a_n = \dfrac{j_n}{3^n}$ and $b_n = \dfrac{j_n + 1}{3^n}$. Observe that $a_{n+1} \geq a_n$ and $b_{n+1} \leq b_n$, and that $f(a_{n+1})$ and $f(b_{n+1})$ both lie between $f(a_n)$ and $f(b_n)$. Thus, the set of closed intervals $\{I_n\}$ where I_n has $f(a_n)$ $f(b_n)$ as endpoints is *nested* in the sense of A1.5. The one real number common to all the intervals I_n is taken as $f(x)$. From this way of defining $f(x)$ it is easy to prove continuity: for $\epsilon > 0$ we choose n so large that $2(1 - \lambda)^n < \epsilon$, see 3.4 Ex. 7b, and take $\delta = 4^{-n}$. If

$$|\xi - x| < \delta \quad \text{and} \quad \xi < x,$$

then by (1)

$$|f(\xi) - f(x)| \leq |f(\xi) - f(a_n)| + |f(a_n) - f(x)|$$
$$\leq 2(1 - \lambda)^n < \epsilon.$$

Similarly, if $|\xi - x| < \delta$ and $\xi > x$,

$$|f(\xi) - f(x)| \leq |f(\xi) - f(b_n)| + |f(b_n) - f(x)| < \epsilon.$$

Thus, continuity is established.

Now, we prove that the function f cannot have a derivative anywhere. For a ternary point $\alpha = \dfrac{p}{3^q}$, in particular, we find another ternary point in any neighborhood of α such that the chord joining $(\alpha, f(\alpha))$ to $(\beta, f(\beta))$ has arbitrarily large slope. For this purpose we take $(\alpha, f(\alpha))$ as a vertex on the n-th iterated polygon $(n \geq q)$, where we use

$$\alpha = \frac{p3^{n-q}}{3^n},$$

and we take

$$\beta = \frac{p3^{n-q} \pm 1}{3^n}.$$

Thus,

$$|\beta - \alpha| = \frac{1}{3^n}$$

and, by (2)

$$\left| \frac{f(\beta) - f(\alpha)}{\beta - \alpha} \right| \geq [3(1 - 2\lambda)]^n .$$

By taking n large enough, we can obtain a chord with slope as large as we please in any neighborhood of a; see 3.4 Ex. 7b. For any value r in the interval $0 < x < 1$ that is not a ternary point, we can find two successive ternary numbers x_j, x_{j+1} of the subdivision at the n-th step such that

$$x_j < r < x_{j+1}.$$

From (2) we know that $f(x_{j+1}) \neq f(x_j)$, say $f(x_{j+1}) > f(x_j)$ (the argument for $f(x_j) > f(x_{j+1})$ is similar). There are three possibilities (Figure 7):

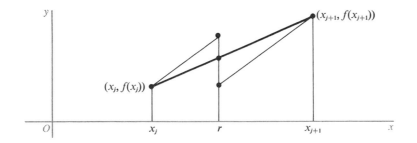

Figure 7

a. The point $(r, f(r))$ lies on the chord joining $(x_j, f(x_j))$ to $(x_{j+1}, f(x_{j+1}))$; then

$$\frac{f(x_j) - f(r)}{x_j - r} = \frac{f(x_{j+1}) - f(x_j)}{x_{j+1} - x_j} \geq [3(1 - 2\lambda)]^n .$$

b. The point lies above the chord; then

$$\frac{f(x_j) - f(r)}{x_j - r} > \frac{f(x_{j+1}) - f(x_j)}{x_{j+1} - x_j} \geq [3(1 - 2\lambda)]^n .$$

c. The point lies below the chord; then

$$\frac{f(x_{j+1}) - f(r)}{x_{j+1} - r} > \frac{f(x_{j+1}) - f(x_j)}{x_{j+1} - x_j} \geq [3(1 - 2\lambda)]^n .$$

Again, in any neighborhood of r we can find points for which the slope of the corresponding chords can be made as large as we please. Thus, the slopes of the chords can have no limit and nondifferentiability is proved.

3.7d Exercise

1. Show that the given Weierstrass function is not monotone in any interval.

4

Differentiation

4.1 INTRODUCTION

With the techniques developed in 3.3 for computing limits and the limit theorems of 3.4, we possess the means to compute some of the most important limits; the derivatives of powers, of the circular functions and of all functions obtained by rational combination, inversion, and composition of functions with known derivatives. The enormous practical value of the concept of derivative arises from the ease with which the derivatives of common functions and combinations of them are computed.

The derivative of a function f at a point a is defined in 2.3 as the limit, as x approximates a, of the difference quotient

$$r(x) = \frac{f(x) - f(a)}{x - a}.$$

For differentiability, as for continuity, the useful idea is not so much differentiability at one point as differentiability at every point of an interval. On such an interval, we define a function f' whose value at any point x in the interval is the derivative of f at x. In general, the *derivative* of f is defined as the function (in distinction to the derivative at a point, a number)

$$(1) \qquad f': \ x \rightarrow \lim_{z \sim x} \frac{f(z) - f(x)}{z - x},$$

where the domain of f' is that subset of the domain of f for which the limit exists. From the uniqueness of limits proved in 3.2, we know that (1) does define a function: there is at most one derivative at any point x of the domain of f.

It is often convenient for computation to set $z - x = h$ in (1) and to give f' by

$$(2) \qquad f'(x) = \lim_{h \sim 0} \frac{f(x + h) - f(h)}{h}.$$

It is useful, too, to have expressions for the derivatives of functions like $x \rightarrow x^2$ or $x \rightarrow \sin x$ without introducing a function symbol like f. For this purpose we shall find it convenient to use the prefix D_x where the subscript is the independent variable. Thus, for

$$f: x \rightarrow x^2 \quad \text{and} \quad g: x \rightarrow \sin x$$

we express the derivatives by

$$f'(x) = D_x x^2, \qquad g'(x) = D_x \sin x.$$

The subscript may be omitted if it is clear from context which symbol is the independent variable. Thus, we shall usually write Dx^2 and $D \sin x$; when there may be doubt, we retain the subscript, e.g., $D_x \sqrt{u^2 + x^2}$.

Example 1. For $f: x \rightarrow x^2$ we have

$$\frac{f(x + h) - f(x)}{h} = \frac{(x + h)^2 - x^2}{h}$$

$$= \frac{h}{h}(2x + h).$$

Consequently, by 3.4a Corollary 3a,

$$f'(x) = Dx^2 = \lim_{h \sim 0} \frac{f(x + h) - f(x)}{h} = 2x.$$

For ready reference, we list the few derivatives which have been found or are obtained easily from examples here and in Chapters 2 and 3. It will be the beginning of a catalog of functions whose derivatives you should learn. We shall add to the catalog in the following sections.

(3) $\qquad D_x c = 0, \quad c, \quad$ a constant. $\qquad$ (from 2.2).

(4) $\qquad Dx = 1 \qquad$ (from 2.2).

(5) $\qquad Dx^2 = 2x \qquad$ (from 2.2).

(6) $\qquad D\sqrt{x} = \dfrac{1}{2\sqrt{x}} \qquad$ (from 3.3 Example 6).

(7) $\qquad D\left(\dfrac{1}{x}\right) = -\dfrac{1}{x^2} \qquad$ (from 3.3 Example 5).

(8) $\qquad D|x| = \begin{cases} 1, & \text{for } x > 0, \\ -1, & \text{for } x < 0. \end{cases} \qquad$ (from (1)).

4.1 Exercises

1. If $f: x \to x^2$ show that $\displaystyle\lim_{z \to x} \dfrac{f(z) - f(x)}{z - x} = 2x$.

2. Using the two equivalent expressions (1) and (2) for the derivative find $f'(x)$ for $f: x \to 1 - x^3$.

3. Use either (1) or (2) to show that $D\sqrt{x} = \dfrac{1}{2\sqrt{x}}$ by a method other than that of 3.3 Example 6.

4. Using either definition of derivative, find $f'(x)$ for each of the following:

   a. $\quad f(x) = 2x^2 - x + 4$,
   b. $\quad f(x) = \dfrac{1}{\sqrt{x}} \quad (x > 0)$,

   c. $\quad f(x) = \dfrac{1}{x^2} \quad (x \neq 0)$,
   d. $\quad f(x) = x^3 - 3x + 4$,

   e. $\quad f(x) = \dfrac{1}{ax + b} \quad \left(a, b \text{ constants}, \ a \neq 0, \ x \neq -\dfrac{b}{a}\right)$,

   f. $\quad f(x) = ax^2 + bx + c \quad (a, b, c \text{ constants})$,

   g. $\quad f(x) = |x - 1|$,
   h. $\quad f(x) = ax + \dfrac{b}{x}$.

5. Find the slope of the graph of $x \to 3x + 2$ at the points $(-2, -4)$, and $(2, 8)$.

6. If $f(x) = 1 + 2x - x^2$, find the slope of the graph of f at

   a. $\quad x = 0$,
   b. $\quad x = \frac{1}{2}$,

   c. $\quad x = 1$,
   d. $\quad x = -10$.

7. If $f(x) = x^3 + 2x + 1$, find all x such that

   a. $\quad f'(x) = 4$,
   b. $\quad f'(x) = 20$,

   c. $\quad f'(x) = 0$,
   d. $\quad f'(x) = -1$.

8. Sketch the graphs of $f : x \to |x|$ and $g : x \to \dfrac{|x|}{x}$. How do f and g seem to be related?

9. Determine $f'(0)$ if $f : x \to x|x|$.

4.2 RATIONAL COMBINATIONS

By considering rational combinations of differentiable functions, we can extend the list of known derivatives greatly. We need consider only three basic kinds of combinations, namely, linear combinations, products, and quotients.

4.2a Linearity of differentiation

Theorem 1. Linearity of Differentiation. If f and g are both differentiable at x, then for any constants a and b

$$D_x \left[af(x) + bg(x) \right] = aDf(x) + bDg(x).$$

Proof. By linearity of limits (3.4a Corollary 3a)

$$\lim_{h \sim 0} \left[\frac{af(x+h) - af(x)}{h} + \frac{bg(x+h) - bg(x)}{h} \right]$$

$$= a \lim_{h \sim 0} \frac{f(x+h) - f(x)}{h} + b \lim_{h \sim 0} \frac{g(x+h) - g(x)}{h}$$

$$= aDf(x) + bDg(x). \qquad \square$$

Example 1. $D \left(3x^2 + 2\sqrt{x} - \dfrac{1}{x} \right)$

$$= 3Dx^2 + 2D\sqrt{x} - D\left(\frac{1}{x}\right) = 6x + \frac{1}{\sqrt{x}} + \frac{1}{x^2}.$$

4.2a Exercises

1. Evaluate $\lim\limits_{h \sim 0} \dfrac{1}{h} \left\{ \left[3(x+h)^2 + 2\sqrt{x+h} - \dfrac{1}{x+h} \right] - \left[3x^2 + 2\sqrt{x} - \dfrac{1}{x} \right] \right\}$.

2. Evaluate

    a. $D\left(4|x| + 6\sqrt{x}\right),$ b. $D\left(5x^2 + \dfrac{2}{x}\right),$

    c. $D\left(|7x| + \dfrac{3}{2x-1}\right),$ d. $D_x\left(|ax| - |bx|\right).$

3. Consider $g : x \to |x + 2| - |3 - x|$.

   a. Sketch the graph of g.

   b. Define $g(x)$ explicitly in terms of linear functions for all real x.

   c. For what values of x is the derivative not defined?

4. Consider $f : x \to [\![x]\!]$ (defined in A2.2), where $[\![x]\!]$ is the integer part of x.

   a. Find $f'(x)$, if it exists, for each of the values $x = -2.8$, $x = 0.6$, $x = 2$.

   b. Find the domain of the derivative f'.

5. Consider $f : x \to x - [\![x]\!]$.

   a. Draw the graph of f.

   b. Find $f'(-1.5)$ and $f'(2.3)$ and describe the domain of the derivative.

6. Extend 4.2a Theorem 1 to a general linear combination of functions

$$\phi : x \to c_1 f_1(x) + c_2 f_2(x) + \cdots + c_n f_n(x).$$

7. For each of the following functions, find the derivative and describe the domain of the derivative.

   a. $f : x \to |x^2 - 2|$.   b. $f : x \to [\![2x^2]\!]$.

   c. $f : x \to |[\![x + 1]\!]|$.   d. $f : x \to [\![|x + 1|]\!]$.

   e. $f : x \to \text{sgn}\,(1 - \sqrt[3]{x})$.   f. $f : x \to \max\,\{x^3, 4|x|\}$.

   g. $f : x \to \min\,\{[\![x]\!], \max\{x^3, 2x^2\}\}$.

   h. $f : x \to \text{sgn}\,\min\{x^3 - 1, 7\}$.

8. Right and left derivatives are defined in terms of right and left limits (see 3.4a Exercise 14) as follows:

   Right derivative: $D^+ f(x) = \lim\limits_{h \sim 0^+} \dfrac{f(x + h) - f(x)}{h}$.

   Left derivative: $D^- f(x) = \lim\limits_{h \sim 0^-} \dfrac{f(x + h) - f(x)}{h}$.

   In particular,

$$
\begin{array}{ll}
D^+|x| = D^-|x| = 1, & x > 0, \\
D^+|x| = D^-|x| = -1, & x < 0, \\
D^+|x| = 1 = -D^-|x|, & x = 0.
\end{array}
$$

   a. Show that $D^-|x^5| = D^+|x^5|$ for all x.

   b. For what values of x does $D^-|x^3 - 2| = D^+|x^3 - 2|$?

   c. Show that a function is differentiable at a point in the interior of its domain if and only if it has equal right and left derivatives at the point.

4.2b Derivatives of products and related functions

Theorem 1. If the functions f and g are differentiable at x, then the product function $F = f \cdot g$ given by

$$F : x \to f(x)g(x)$$

has the derivative at x given by

$$F'(x) = f(x)g'(x) + g(x)f'(x).$$

Proof. From the definition of F we have

$$\frac{F(x + h) - F(x)}{h}$$

$$= \frac{f(x + h)g(x + h) - f(x)g(x)}{h}$$

$$= \frac{f(x + h)g(x + h) - f(x + h)g(x) + f(x + h)g(x) - f(x)g(x)}{h}$$

$$= f(x + h)\frac{g(x + h) - g(x)}{h} + g(x)\frac{f(x + h) - f(x)}{h}.$$

Since f is differentiable at x, it is continuous there (3.6b Theorem 1) and

$$\lim_{h\sim 0} f(x + h) = f(x),$$

$$\lim_{h\sim 0} g(x) = g(x),$$

$$\lim_{h\sim 0} \frac{f(x + h) - f(x)}{h} = f'(x),$$

$$\lim_{h\sim 0} \frac{g(x + h) - g(x)}{h} = g'(x).$$

It follows from the limit theorems of 3.4 that

$$\lim_{h\sim 0} \frac{F(x + h) - F(x)}{h} = F'(x) = f(x)g'(x) + g(x)f'(x). \qquad \Box$$

Example 1. $Dx^{3/2} = D(x\sqrt{x}) = xD\sqrt{x} + \sqrt{x}Dx$

$$= x\frac{1}{2\sqrt{x}} + \sqrt{x} \cdot 1$$

$$= \frac{\sqrt{x}}{2} + \sqrt{x} = \tfrac{3}{2}\sqrt{x}.$$

Corollary a. If f' exists and if $F(x) = [f(x)]^2$, then

$$F'(x) = 2[f(x)]D_x f(x)$$

$$= 2f(x)f'(x).$$

The proof is left to Exercise 3.

Theorem 2. Power Rule for Positive Integers. If f' exists and if $F(x) = [f(x)]^n$, then

$$F'(x) = n[f(x)]^{n-1}f'(x)$$

for any positive integer n.

The proof is left to Exercise 6a.

Example 2. If $F(x) = (3x - 2)^5$, then

$$F'(x) = 5(3x - 2)^4(3)$$
$$= 15(3x - 2)^4 .$$

Corollary a. If $G(x) = x^n$, then $G'(x) = nx^{n-1}$ for any positive integer n.

The proof is left to Exercise 6b.

Since a polynomial

$$p(x) = a_0 + a_1x + a_2x^2 + \cdots + a_nx^n$$

is a linear combination of powers of x, Corollary 2a and 4.2a Theorem 1 enable us to differentiate any polynomial.

Corollary b. The polynomial function p, where

$$p(x) = a_0 + a_1x + a_2x^2 + \cdots + a_nx^n ,$$

has the derivative given for each real x by

$$p'(x) = a_1 + 2a_2x + \cdots + na_nx^{n-1} .$$

In general, by means of 4.2a Theorem 1 and Theorem 2 we can differentiate any polynomial function of a function whose derivative we know.

Corollary c. If p is a polynomial and f' exists, then

$$D_x pf(x) = D_u p(u)D_x u ,$$

where $u = f(x)$.

Example 3. We apply Corollary 2c:

a. $D_x[(3x - 2)^5 + 3(3x - 2)^4 - 5(3x - 2)]$
$$= [5(3x - 2)^4 + 12(3x - 2)^3 - 5] \cdot 3$$
$$= 15(3x - 2)^4 + 36(3x - 2)^3 - 15 .$$

b. $D[x^{7/2} + 4x^{5/2}] = D[(\sqrt{x})^7 + 4(\sqrt{x})^5]$

$$= [7(\sqrt{x})^6 + 20(\sqrt{x})^4]D\sqrt{x}$$

$$= (7x^3 + 20x^2)\frac{1}{2\sqrt{x}}$$

$$= \tfrac{7}{2}x^{5/2} + 10x^{3/2}.$$

c. $D_x\left[(x^2 + 3)^5 - 3\left(\frac{1}{x}\right)^2 + 2(\sqrt{x})^3\right]$

$$= 5(x^2 + 3)^4\,(2x) - 6\left(\frac{1}{x}\right)\left(-\frac{1}{x^2}\right) + 6(\sqrt{x})^2\,\frac{1}{2\sqrt{x}}$$

$$= 10x(x^2 + 3)^4 + \frac{6}{x^3} + 3\sqrt{x}.$$

4.2b Exercises

1. Find the derivatives of functions with the following values:

a. $x(2x - 3)$,

b. $(4x - 2)\,(4 - 2x)$,

c. $(x^2 + x + 1)\,(x^2 - x + 1)$,

d. $\sqrt{x}(ax + b)^3$,

e. $\frac{1}{x}\sqrt{x}$,

f. $\frac{1}{x}\,(5x + 2)$,

g. $|x|\,\frac{1}{x^2}$,

h. $x^{7/2}$,

i. $\left(3x^4 - \frac{1}{\sqrt{x}}\right)$ (Hint: see Part e),

j. $3x^2\,(x^2 - 5)$,

k. $|13x^2 - 36 - x^4|$,

l. $|x^4 + 5x^2 - 36|$.

2. Evaluate

a. $D(3x^2 + 5x - 1)^2$,

b. $D(3 - 5x)^3$,

c. $D(3 - 5x)^4$,

d. $Dx(\sqrt{x} - 1)^2$,

e. $D\left(x + \frac{1}{x}\right)^2$,

f. $D\left(\frac{x^{3/2}}{3} - \frac{x^{1/2}}{2} + x^{-1/2}\right)$,

g. $D\left(4\sqrt{x^3} - 2\sqrt{x} + \frac{1}{\sqrt{x}}\right)$,

h. $D([\![x^2 - 1]\!](x^2 - 3x + 1))$,

i. $D(x\,([\![x + 1]\!] - 1)^n)$.

3. Prove Corollary 1a.

4. Find each listed derivative by two methods: first, expand and then differentiate; second, use the product formula.

a. $D\,(x^2 + 1)^2$.

b. $D\,x^2(x^2 + 1)^2$.

c. $D\,(x + 1)\,(x^2 - x + 1)$.

d. $D\,[(ax^2 + bx + c)\,(dx^2 + ex + f)]$.

5. Find the derivative of each of the following functions in as many ways as you can and describe its domain. (Do not overlook the definition of the derivative.)

a. $f : x \to x \, |x|$.

b. $f : x \to |x|^2$.

c. $f : x \to x \, [\![x]\!]$.

d. $f : x \to [\![x]\!]^2$.

e. $f : x \to |x| \, [\![x]\!]$.

f. $f : x \to |x| \, [\![x]\!]^2$.

g. $f : x \to x \, [\![4 - x^2]\!]$.

h. $f : x \to x \max\{x, 2 - x^2\}$.

i. $f : x \to x \, [\![x]\!] \, |x|$.

j. $f : x \to [\![|x|]\!] \, |[\![x]\!]|$.

6. a. Prove Theorem 2.
   b. Prove Corollary 2a.
   c. Prove Corollaries 2b and 2c.

7. Evaluate

a. $D \, (x^5 - x^8 + x^{11})$,

b. $D \, (5 + x)^6$,

c. $D \, (3 - 2x^3)^5$,

d. $D \, (x - 3x^2 + 5x^3)^4$,

e. $D \, [x(1 - x^2)^3]$,

f. $D \, [(3 - 5x)^2 \, (1 - x^2)^3]$,

g. $D \left(1 - \dfrac{1}{x} \right)^3$,

h. $D \, (3x^{1/2} - 4x^{3/2})^6$,

i. $D \, (1 - \sqrt{x})^{10}$,

j. $D \, [(3 - 5x + x^2)^3 \, (1 + x^2)^{10}]$.

8. Consider the curves $y = ax^3 + 1$ and $y = bx^2$.
   a. Find two numbers a and b such that the curves have the same slope at $x = 1$ and that the sum of the slopes at $x = 2$ is 36 .
   b. Find values of a and b such that the curves have the same slope at a point of intersection.
   c. Sketch the curves in Part b for some allowable values of a and b .

9. a. Sketch the curves $y = x^3$, $y = \dfrac{3}{x}$ for $|x| \le 2$.

   b. What values of x satisfy $g'(x) = 0$, where $g(x) = x^3 + \dfrac{3}{x}$ for $|x| \le 2$?

   c. Find the discontinuities of g and g' .
   d. Using the results of Parts a, b, and c, sketch the graph of g for $|x| \le 2$.

10. Set $u = f(x)$, $v = g(x)$, and $w = h(x)$.
    a. Prove that if the functions f, g , and h are differentiable at x , then

$$D \, (uvw) = uv \, D_x w + uw \, D_x v + vw \, D_x u .$$

    b. Can you suggest a way to generalize your result to obtain a formula for the derivative of a product of n functions? Test your conjecture with the case $n = 4$.
    c. Use the above result to evaluate:
       (i) $D \, \{(5x - 2) \, (3 - 2x) \, (x^2 + 1)\}$,
       (ii) $D \, \{(2x^3 - 3x^2 + 1) \, (\sqrt{x} + 1)^2\}$,
       (iii) $D \, \{(3x - 2) \, (1 - x^2) \, (1 + x) \, (1 + x^2)\}$.

4.2c Derivatives of quotients

We have found the derivative $D\left[\dfrac{1}{x}\right]$ and, by the product rule, can obtain $D\left[\dfrac{1}{x^n}\right]$, but we still do not have a general rule for differentiating such functions as

$$f(x) = \frac{x-1}{x^2+3}, \qquad g(x) = \frac{\sqrt{x}}{x-2},$$

or, more generally, the quotient of any two functions whose derivatives we know. Since the derivative of a quotient $\dfrac{f(x)}{g(x)}$ can be obtained from that of the product

$$f(x)\left[\frac{1}{g(x)}\right],$$

we need only obtain the rule for the derivative of the reciprocal of $g(x)$.

Theorem 1. If $F(x) = \dfrac{1}{g(x)}$, then $F'(x) = \dfrac{-g'(x)}{[g(x)]^2}$ at each point x for which $g'(x)$ exists and $g(x) \neq 0$.

Proof.
$$\frac{F(x+h) - F(x)}{h} = \frac{1}{h}\left[\frac{1}{g(x+h)} - \frac{1}{g(x)}\right]$$
$$= \frac{1}{h}\left[\frac{g(x) - g(x+h)}{g(x)g(x+h)}\right]$$
$$= \frac{-1}{g(x)g(x+h)}\left[\frac{g(x+h) - g(x)}{h}\right].$$

From the theorems on limits and the continuity of g we obtain

$$F'(x) = \lim_{h \sim 0} \frac{F(x+h) - F(x)}{h} = \frac{-g'(x)}{[g(x)]^2}. \qquad \square$$

Example 1.

a. If $f(x) = \dfrac{1}{x+2}$, then $f'(x) = \dfrac{-1}{(x+2)^2}$.

b. If $g(x) = \dfrac{1}{x^3}$, then $g'(x) = \dfrac{-3x^2}{x^6} = \dfrac{-3}{x^4}$.

Corollary a. If f and g have derivatives at x and $g(x) \neq 0$, then the derivative of the quotient $G(x) = \dfrac{f(x)}{g(x)}$ is

$$G'(x) = \frac{g(x)f'(x) - f(x)g'(x)}{[g(x)]^2}.$$

The proof is left to Exercise 2.

Example 2.

a. If $G(x) = \dfrac{x-1}{x^2+3}$, then $G'(x) = \dfrac{(x^2+3)(1) - (x-1)(2x)}{(x^2+3)^2}$

$$= \frac{3 + 2x - x^2}{(x^2+3)^2}.$$

b. We can sometimes simplify the differentiation of a rational function by changing its algebraic expression. If

$$f(x) = \frac{x^3 + 3x^2 - 2}{x^2},$$

then $f(x) = x + 3 - \dfrac{2}{x^2}$ and $f'(x) = 1 + 4/x^3$.

This technique is particularly helpful when the division can be performed easily.

c. Sometimes addition helps to shorten the work. If

$$g(x) = \frac{x+1}{x-1} - \frac{x}{x+1} = \frac{3x+1}{x^2-1},$$

$$g'(x) = \frac{(x^2-1)(3) - (3x+1)(2x)}{(x^2-1)^2} = \frac{-3x^2 - 2x - 3}{(x^2-1)^2}.$$

Corollary b. If $f(x) = x^p$, then for any integer p, positive, negative, or zero, $f'(x) = px^{p-1}$.

The proof is left to Exercise 6.

Corollary c. Let R be a rational function. At every point where f' exists and Rf is defined, the derivative of Rf exists and is given by

$$D_x Rf(x) = D_u R(u) D_x u$$

where $u = f(x)$.

The proof is left to Exercise 6.

4.2c Exercises

1. Evaluate

   a. $D\left(\dfrac{x}{x-1}\right)$,

   b. $D\left(\dfrac{x^2}{1+x^2}\right)$,

   c. $D\left(1-\dfrac{1}{x}\right)^{-1}$,

   d. $D\left(\dfrac{3+2x^2}{2-x^2}\right)$,

   e. $D\left(\dfrac{1}{x}+\dfrac{1}{1-x}\right)$,

   f. $D\left(\dfrac{\sqrt{x}}{1+x^2}\right)$,

   g. $D\left(\dfrac{1}{1+\sqrt{x}}\right)$,

   h. $D\left(\dfrac{x^2-1}{x^2+1}\right)^{-1}$,

   i. $D\left(\dfrac{1}{[\![\sqrt{x}]\!]}\right)$,

   j. $D\left(\dfrac{1}{\sqrt{[\![x]\!]}}\right)$.

2. Prove Corollary 1a.

3. Evaluate

   a. $D\left(\dfrac{x^2+5}{x^2-5}\right)$,

   b. $D\left(\dfrac{x+1}{x}-\dfrac{x^2+1}{x^2}\right)$,

   c. $D\left(\dfrac{x-1}{x^2+x+1}\right)$,

   d. $D\left[\left(1+\dfrac{1}{x}\right)(x+1)\right]$,

   e. $D\left(\dfrac{1-x+x^2}{1+x+x^2}\right)$,

   f. $D\left[\dfrac{1-x}{x^2(1+x^2)}\right]$,

   g. $D\left(\dfrac{1+x^{-1}}{1-x^{-1}}\right)$,

   h. $D\left(\dfrac{ax^2+bx+c}{dx^2+ex+f}\right)$,

   i. $D\left(\dfrac{x^4+x^2+1}{x^2+x+1}\right)$,

   j. $D\left(\dfrac{x^5+x+1}{x^2+x+1}\right)$.

4. Determine both

$$D\left(\dfrac{ax+b}{cx+d}\right) \quad \text{and} \quad D\left(\dfrac{bc-ad}{c(cx+d)}\right).$$

   Explain why both are the same.

5. For each of the following functions find the derivative in as many ways as you can and describe its domain. (Do not overlook the definition of derivative.)

   a. $f: x \to \dfrac{|x|}{x}$.

   b. $f: x \to \dfrac{x}{[\![x]\!]}$.

   c. $f: x \to \dfrac{x-[\![x]\!]}{|x|}$.

   d. $f: x \to \dfrac{(x-[\![x]\!])^2}{|x|}$.

6. Prove Corollaries 1b and 1c.

7. Evaluate:

a. $D_x \left[\dfrac{(x^2 - x^3)^2 - (x^2 - x^3)^4}{(x^2 - x^3)^2 + 1} \right]^7$,

b. $D_x \left[\dfrac{5(1 - \sqrt{x}) + 3}{(1 - \sqrt{x})^2 - 3} \right]^2$,

c. $D_x \left[\dfrac{\left(\left(\sqrt{x} - \dfrac{1}{x} \right)^4 - 1 \right)}{\left(\sqrt{x} - \dfrac{1}{x} \right)^2 + 1} \right]^3$.

8. Consider the quotient $\phi(x) = \dfrac{f(x)}{g(x)}$ where f and g have derivatives at x and where $g(x) \neq 0$. Obtain the formula for the derivative of a quotient by applying the product rule (4.2b Theorem 1) to the equation $\phi(x)g(x) = f(x)$. Why does this not constitute a proof of the quotient rule, Corollary 1a?

4.3 INVERSE FUNCTIONS, FRACTIONAL POWERS

We need new methods to find the derivatives of such functions as

$$f : x \to \sqrt[n]{x}.$$

We recall (A2.5 Example 2) that the number $y = \sqrt[n]{x}$ is defined as the principal solution of the equation

$$y^n = x$$

(namely, as the only solution of the equation when n is odd, and as the only nonnegative solution when n is even and $x \geq 0$). A natural approach to a discussion of the function f is through the familiar and well-understood function

$$g : y \to y^n.$$

The function g is *inverse*† to f; thus, if f maps a onto b, that is,

$$f : a \to b,$$

then g maps b onto a, that is

$$g : b \to a.$$

In this section we shall show, in general, how to differentiate the inverse of a function whose derivative we know.

†The symbol f^{-1} is often used for the inverse of f.

It is easy to appreciate the graphical relation between inverse functions. If the point (a, b) is on the graph of f, then the point (b, a) is on the graph of g, and conversely; that is, $b = f(a)$ if, and only if,

$$a = g(b).$$

Since the points (a, b) and (b, a) are located symmetrically with respect to the line $y = x$, we observe that the graph $y = g(x)$ is the mirror image in the line $y = x$ of the graph $y = f(x)$, as shown in Figure 1. If the direction angle with respect to the horizontal of the graph $y = f(x)$ at (a, b) is given by θ, then θ also gives the direction angle with respect to the vertical of the graph $y = g(x)$ at (b, a). It follows that the slope of $y = g(x)$ at (b, a) is

$$\tan\left(\frac{\pi}{2} - \theta\right) = \cot\theta = \frac{1}{\tan\theta}.$$

(Of course, $\dfrac{1}{\tan\theta}$ is not defined if $\theta = 0$.) Intuitively, then, if f and g are differentiable functions and $f'(x) \neq 0$, we must have

$$(1) \qquad\qquad g'(b) = \frac{1}{f'(a)}.$$

From the figure it is intuitive that if f has a nonzero derivative at a, then g has a derivative at b given by (1).

Theorem 1. Let f be either increasing or decreasing in a neighborhood of a. Then, in that neighborhood, f has an inverse g. If f has a derivative at a and $f'(a) \neq 0$, then g has a derivative at $b = f(a)$ and

$$g'(b) = \frac{1}{f'(a)}.$$

Proof. In the neighborhood, f is one-to-one and hence has a one-to-one inverse g which, by 3.6d Theorem 1, is continuous at b. To investigate the existence and value of the derivative of g at b, we must consider the limit as y approaches b of

$$\frac{g(y) - g(b)}{y - b} = \frac{g(y) - a}{fg(y) - f(a)}$$

$$= \frac{1}{rg(y)},$$

where we have introduced the function r given by

$$r(x) = \begin{cases} \dfrac{f(x) - f(a)}{x - a}, & \text{for } x \neq a, \\[3mm] f'(a), & \text{for } x = a. \end{cases}$$

By 3.2 Definition 1, the function r is continuous at a. In succession we apply 3.6a Theorem 3 and 3.6c Theorem 1 on the continuity of quotients and compositions and obtain

$$g'(b) = \lim_{y \to b} \frac{g(y) - g(b)}{y - b} = \lim_{y \to b} \frac{1}{rg(y)}$$

$$= \frac{1}{rg(b)} = \frac{1}{r(a)} = \frac{1}{f'(a)}$$

as desired. □

Note that the theorem states that f' and g' are reciprocals at *different* points (see Figure 1), f' at a in the domain of f, and g' at b in the range of f.

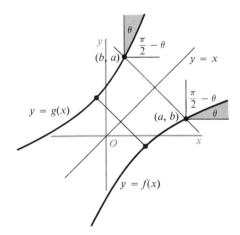

Figure 1

Example 1. Let $f : x \to x^2 + 1$ for $x > 0$. Then $g : x \to \sqrt{x - 1}$ for $x > 1$. Now, $f'(x) = 2x$, so that $f(3) = 10$ and $f'(3) = 6$; hence

$$g'(10) = \frac{1}{f'(3)} = \frac{1}{6};$$

but note that

$$g'(3) = \frac{1}{f'g(3)} = \frac{1}{f'(\sqrt{2})} = \frac{1}{2\sqrt{2}} \cdot$$

As a first and important application of Theorem 1, we compute the derivative of the *n*-th root function,

$$g : y \rightarrow \sqrt[n]{y} = y^{1/n} ,$$

which is defined as the inverse of the *n*-th power function

$$f : x \rightarrow x^n .$$

Here *n* is any natural number. We restrict the domain of *f* to non-negative numbers. (Why? See 4.3b Ex. 10.) With $b = a^n$, $a > 0$, we find that

$$g'(b) = \frac{1}{f'(a)} = \frac{1}{na^{n-1}} = \frac{1}{n} a^{1-n} = \frac{1}{n} (b^{1/n})^{1-n} = \frac{1}{n} b^{1/n-1} .$$

That is, the formula $Dx^r = rx^{r-1}$, previously established for integers, also holds for unit fractions $r = \frac{1}{n}$.

We can establish the same formula for any rational number $r = \frac{p}{q}$, where *p* and *q* are integers, $q \geq 1$. From 4.2c Corollaries 1b and 1c

$$Dx^r = D(x^{1/q})^p = p(x^{1/q})^{p-1} D(x^{1/q})$$

$$= p(x^{1/q})^{p-1} \frac{1}{q} x^{1/q-1} = \frac{p}{q} x^{p/q-1} = rx^{r-1} .$$

Thus we have:

Corollary a. For every rational number *r* ,

$$Dx^r = rx^{r-1} \qquad\qquad (x > 0) .$$

The extension of this corollary to general real powers (including irrational powers) is deferred until Chapter 8.

4.3 Exercises

1. Given $f : x \rightarrow mx + b$, let *g* be the inverse of *f*, and find f', *g*, and g'.

2. Given $g : x \rightarrow \sqrt{x - 1}$ for $x > 1$, let *f* be the inverse of *g*, and find $f(x)$, $g'(x)$, and $f'(x)$.

3. Given $f: x \to \dfrac{1-x}{1+x}$, where $x > -1$, let g be the inverse of f, and find $g(x)$, $f'(x)$, and $g'(x)$.

4. Verify that the inverse of $f: x \to x|x|$ exists and then find the derivative of the inverse.

5. Sketch the graph of $f: x \to x^3 - 3x$ and tell why f does not have an inverse. Indicate how you can divide the domain of f into three parts and define a restriction of f on each part so that each restriction has an inverse. Justify your result.

6. Consider the function

$$f: x \to \begin{cases} 2x, & \text{for } x > 0 \text{ and irrational,} \\ x^2 + 1, & \text{for } x \geq 0 \text{ and rational.} \end{cases}$$

   a. Show that f has a derivative at $x = 1$.
   b. Prove that f is one-to-one.
   c. Prove that the inverse of f is differentiable only at the point $y = 2$ of its domain.

7. Evaluate the following and express your answers using positive exponents only.
   a. $D x^{1/2}$.
   b. $D x^{2/3}$.
   c. $D x^{3/5}$.
   d. $D x^{-2/3}$.
   e. $D x^{-3/5}$.

8. Find $f'(2)$ if
   a. $f(x) = (2x)^{1/3}$,
   b. $f(x) = x^{-1/4}$,
   c. $f(x) = x^{-4/5}$.

9. Evaluate
   a. $D(x^{1/3} - 3x^{-1/3})$,

   b. $D\left(\dfrac{1 + x^{4/3}}{1 - x^{4/3}}\right)$,

   c. $D\left(\sqrt{x^3} - \sqrt{x} + \dfrac{1}{\sqrt{x}} - \dfrac{1}{\sqrt{x^3}}\right)$.

10. Let $f(x) = x^n$, where n is an integer. For what points a in the domain of f do the hypotheses of Theorem 1 hold?

11. Consider the function $f: x \to \sqrt[n]{x}$. We have $f(x)^n = x$. Applying 4.2b Theorem 2, obtain

$$D\sqrt[n]{x} = \frac{1}{n} x^{(1/n)-1}.$$

   Why is this not a proof of Corollary 1a?

12. Let $r = p/q$ under the hypothesis of Corollary 1a and let q be odd. Prove the corollary for $x < 0$. Why is the case $x = 0$ not included?

13. Under the conditions of the preceding exercise, show that for $g: x \to x^{p/q}$, where $p > q > 0$, the derivative of g at zero exists and $g'(0) = 0$.

4.4 CIRCULAR FUNCTIONS

In 2.3 Example 3 we ambitiously attacked the problem of evaluating $D \sin x$ at $x = 0$. We reduced the problem to the evaluation of

$$(1) \qquad\qquad \alpha = \lim_{h \sim 0} \frac{\sin h}{h}$$

under the assumption that the limit exists. As we shall now see, the evaluation of $D \sin x$ at any other point can also be reduced to the evaluation of this same limit. Using the formula for the sine of a sum, we have

$$\frac{\sin(x + h) - \sin x}{h} = \frac{\sin x \cos h + \cos x \sin h - \sin x}{h}$$

$$= \frac{\sin h}{h} \cos x + \frac{\cos h - 1}{h} \sin x \, .$$

From the theorems on limits,

$$D \sin x = \alpha \cos x + \beta \sin x$$

where $\beta = \lim\limits_{h \sim 0} \dfrac{\cos h - 1}{h}$. We shall assume for the present that α defined in (1) exists, and from this we shall prove that $\beta = 0$.

Since $\cos h - 1 = -2 \sin^2 \dfrac{h}{2}$, we obtain

$$\frac{\cos h - 1}{h} = -\frac{h}{2} \frac{\sin^2 \frac{1}{2}h}{(\frac{1}{2}h)^2} \, .$$

Since $\lim\limits_{h \sim 0} \dfrac{\sin \frac{1}{2}h}{\frac{1}{2}h} = \lim\limits_{k \sim 0} \dfrac{\sin k}{k} = \alpha$, and $\lim\limits_{h \sim 0} \frac{1}{2}h = 0$, it follows from 3.4a Theorem 4 on the limit of a product of functions that $\beta = 0$. Consequently,

$$(2) \qquad\qquad D \sin x = \alpha \cos x$$

where the constant of proportionality α has yet to be determined.

In reviewing the preceding argument we find several matters assumed without proof:

     a.   The formula for the sine of a sum:
            $\sin(u + v) = \sin u \cos v + \cos u \sin v$.

     b. $\sin 0 = 0$.

     c. $1 - \cos u = 2 \sin^2 \dfrac{u}{2}$.

d.   The existence of $\lim\limits_{h \to 0} \dfrac{\sin h}{h}$.

It may seem odd that the well-known properties (a)–(c) of the sine and cosine are listed as assumptions. The fundamental properties of circular functions given in A2.6 derive from an intuitively based idea of length for circular arcs. The concept of length for curves other than polygons is defined in a later chapter as a limit of approximations by polygonal arcs. Clearly, our knowledge of the circular functions does not rest upon such precise definition but upon geometrical intuition. Similarly, we derive property (d) not by analytical reasoning but by arguing plausibly from a picture. Later we shall see how the argument can be made analytically complete (Section 8.6), but the circular functions are too important for us to delay our account until all the logical gaps can be filled. In fact, we shall profit by gaining an intuitive understanding of the circular functions before attempting to be formally precise.

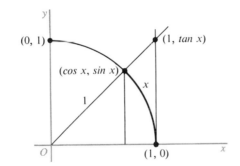

Figure 1

Consider a ray from the origin lying in the first quadrant, Figure 1. If, on the unit circle, x is the length of the arc between the ray and the positive horizontal axis, then the ray intersects the circle at the point with coordinates $(\cos x, \sin x)$. There are two similar triangles in the figure: the smaller has base $\cos x$ and altitude $\sin x$, the larger has base 1 and altitude $\tan x$. Since the circular sector determined by the arc contains one triangle and is contained in the other, its area, $\dfrac{x}{2}$, lies between their areas:

$$\tfrac{1}{2} \cos x \sin x < \frac{x}{2} < \frac{1}{2} \tan x .$$

Here we have used the intuitively evident fact that the area of a sector is proportional to the length of the corresponding arc. The factor of proportionality is $1/2$, since the complete unit circle has area π and circumference 2π. Later it will be easy to obtain the constant of proportionality analytically.

On multiplying by the positive value $\dfrac{2}{\sin x}$ in the preceding inequality, we obtain $\cos x < \dfrac{x}{\sin x} < \dfrac{1}{\cos x}$; whence,

$$(3) \qquad\qquad \frac{1}{\cos x} > \frac{\sin x}{x} > \cos x.$$

Since $\sin(-x) = -\sin x$ and $\cos(-x) = \cos x$, this inequality is also valid for x in the fourth quadrant, $-\dfrac{\pi}{2} < x < 0$. Since $\cos x$ is continuous at $x = 0$,†

$$\lim_{x \to 0} \cos x = \cos 0 = 1,$$

and $\lim\limits_{x \to 0} \dfrac{1}{\cos x} = 1$. By the Squeeze Theorem (3.4a Theorem 7) it follows immediately from (3) that

$$\alpha = \lim_{x \to 0} \frac{\sin x}{x} = 1.$$

Entering this result in Equation (2) we have, finally,

$$D \sin x = \cos x.$$

The proof of the analogous formula,

$$D \cos x = -\sin x,$$

is left as an exercise.

The derivatives of the other circular functions are now easily obtained. For instance, from the theorem on the differentiation of a quotient,

$$D \tan x = D \frac{\sin x}{\cos x} = \frac{\cos x \, D \sin x - \sin x \, D \cos x}{(\cos x)^2}$$

$$= \frac{\cos^2 x + \sin^2 x}{\cos^2 x} = \frac{1}{\cos^2 x} = \sec^2 x = 1 + \tan^2 x.$$

We leave the problem of differentiating the other circular functions as an exercise, but list some of the results for easy reference:

---

†Assumption (d) above implies the differentiability, hence the continuity of $\sin x$ at $x = 0$; the continuity of $\cos x$ at $x = 0$ then follows from (c).

(4) $$D \sin x = \cos x.$$

(5) $$D \cos x = -\sin x.$$

(6) $$D \tan x = 1 + \tan^2 x.$$

(7) $$D \cot x = -1 - \cot^2 x.$$

4.4 Exercises

1. Show that $D \cos x = -\sin x$.

2. Evaluate $\lim\limits_{h \sim 0} \dfrac{\tan h}{h}$.   (Hint: Express $\tan h$ in terms of $\sin h$ and $\cos h$.)

3. From the definition of the derivative as a limit and the result of Exercise 2 derive the formula

$$D \tan x = \sec^2 x.$$

$$\left[\text{Hint:} \quad \tan (x + h) = \frac{\tan x + \tan h}{1 - \tan x \tan h}. \right]$$

4. Evaluate the following and give your answers in several different equivalent forms.

   a. $D \cot x$.   b. $D \sec x$.

   c. $D \csc x$.   d. $D \sin^2 x$.

   e. $D \cos^2 x$.   f. $D (4 \cos^3 x - 3 \cos x)$.

   g. $D (3 \sin x - 4 \sin^3 x)$.

5. Evaluate the following limits.

   a. $\lim\limits_{h \sim 0} \dfrac{\sin 2h}{h}$.   b. $\lim\limits_{h \sim 0} \dfrac{1 - \cos h}{h^2}$.

6. a. Given that $\lim\limits_{x \sim 0} \sin x = \sin 0 = 0$, prove that

$$\lim_{x \sim 0} \frac{\sin x}{\cos x + 1} = 0.$$

   (Hint: Show that $\cos x$ is continuous at $x = 0$.)

   b. From the preceding result prove that $\sin x$ and $\cos x$ are continuous for all values of x .

   Make explicit just what is being assumed in the proofs of Parts a and b.

7. Given that $Df(x) = G(x)$, show that $Df(ax + b) = aG(ax + b)$, provided f is differentiable at $ax + b$.

8. Evaluate the following:

   a. $D \cos^2 x \sin 2x$,

   b. $D \sin^2 (ax + b)$,

   c. $D (\sin 7x) (\cos 2x)$.

9. Let $g(x) = |\cos x|$. Discuss the domain of the derivative for x in the interval $0 \le x \le \pi$.

10. Find a point on the graph of $y = \sin x$ at which the slope of the curve is equal to the slope of the line $x + 2y + 2 = 0$. Is there only one such point? Justify your answer.

11. Evaluate the following:

a. $D\dfrac{1 - \sin x}{1 + \cos^2 x}$,

b. $D\dfrac{1 - \tan^2 x}{2 \tan x}$,

c. $D\dfrac{\sin^4 x}{\cos^2 x}$,

d. $D\dfrac{3}{\cos^2 x}$,

e. $D\dfrac{1}{1 + \tan x}$,

f. $D\,(x \tan x)$,

g. $D\left(\dfrac{\sin x + \cos x}{\sin x - \cos x}\right)^2$.

12. Show that there are no points of the graph of $y = \sec x - \tan x$ at which the slope of the curve is zero.

13. Find all values of x for which the slope of the graph of $f : x \to \sin x \tan x$ is zero.

14. a. Sketch the graph of $f : x \to \dfrac{x}{\sin x}$ for $0 < x < \tfrac{1}{2}\pi$.

b. Determine $f'(x)$ and show that there is no value of x in the interval $0 < x < \tfrac{1}{2}\pi$ for which $f'(x) = 0$.

c. Explain how your results support the fact that f is increasing on the given interval.

15. a. Find the maximum and minimum values of the function

$$f : x \to a \cos x + b \sin x.$$

b. Sketch the graph of f.

16. Consider $f : x \to \sin\dfrac{1}{x}$ in the domain $0 < x \le 1$. Can f be extended to a continuous function on $[0, 1]$?

17. Consider $f : x \to x \sin\dfrac{1}{x}$ for $x \ne 0$.

a. Sketch the graph of f.

b. Is it possible to define f at $x = 0$ so that the extended function is continuous at $x = 0$?

18. Does the function

$$f : x \to \begin{cases} x^2 \sin\dfrac{\pi}{x}, & \text{for } x \ne 0, \\[2mm] 0, & \text{for } x = 0, \end{cases}$$

have a derivative at $x = 0$?

19. Given that the functions S and C satisfy the equations (differential equations)

$$D\,S = C \quad \text{and} \quad D\,C = -S.$$

Show that $D\,(S^2 + C^2) = 0$.

20. Given that the functions f, g, and h satisfy the equations $Df = g$, $Dg = h$, and $Dh = f$, show that $D(f^3 + g^3 + h^3 - 3fgh) = 0$.

4.5 INVERSE CIRCULAR FUNCTIONS

The most striking feature of the graphs of circular functions is their periodic or cyclic aspect, the regular iteration of the same geometric pattern. For the sine and cosine, this periodic property is expressed by the relations

$$\sin(x + 2\pi) = \sin x,$$
$$\cos(x + 2\pi) = \cos x,$$

where 2π is the fundamental period of these functions (see A2.6 Ex. 10). From the representation of the other circular functions in terms of the sine and cosine it follows that they, too, have 2π as a period. However, the tangent and cotangent have the fundamental period π.

From the periodicity of any circular function f, it follows at once that f cannot represent a one-to-one mapping on its entire domain: if $b = f(a)$, then $b = f(a + 2k\pi)$ for all integers k. Every point of the range of f is covered infinitely many times in the mapping. We cannot obtain an inverse for f over its entire domain, so we restrict ourselves to a special representative interval upon which f is strongly monotone. The names of the inverses of the sine, cosine, etc., on such restricted domains, are arcsine, arcosine, etc.† In terms of the geometrical definition of the circular functions, $\theta = \arcsin x$ means that θ is the (length of) arc which has the sine, x.

For the restriction of the sine function, we choose the representative interval $\left[-\frac{\pi}{2}, \frac{\pi}{2}\right]$ where the sine is increasing, see Figure 1. On the restricted domain $\left[-\frac{\pi}{2}, \frac{\pi}{2}\right]$, the range of the sine is the interval $[-1, 1]$. The arcsine, therefore, has the domain $[-1, 1]$ and the range $\left[-\frac{\pi}{2}, \frac{\pi}{2}\right]$. Consequently, we define the image of x in the mapping

$$\text{arcsin} : x \to y, \qquad \text{for} \quad -1 \le x \le 1,$$

as the one value $y = \arcsin x$ which satisfies $\sin y = x$ for

$$-\frac{\pi}{2} \le y \le \frac{\pi}{2}.$$

---

†A common alternative notation is $\sin^{-1}$ for arcsin. We do not use it in this text because it conflicts with the generally accepted convention of writing $\sin^n x$ for $(\sin x)^n$. The same convention applies to the other circular functions.

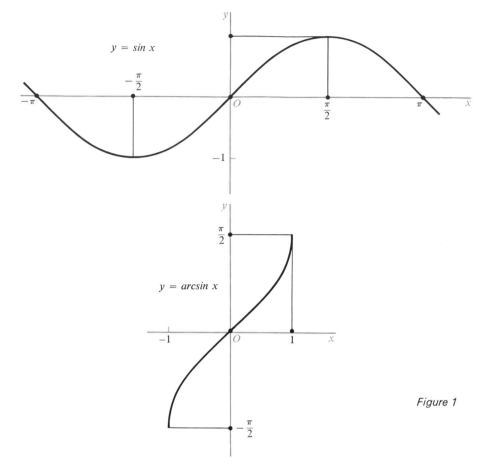

$y = \sin x$

$-\dfrac{\pi}{2}$

$y = arcsin\ x$

Figure 1

We could have used any other representative interval, $\left[k\pi - \dfrac{\pi}{2}, k\pi + \dfrac{\pi}{2}\right]$, for $k = 0, \pm 1, \pm 2, \cdots$, to define an inverse of the sine. For this reason the specific inverse, the arcsine, with range $\left[-\dfrac{\pi}{2}, \dfrac{\pi}{2}\right]$ is known as the principal inverse of the sine. Similarly, the particular inverse circular functions defined below are known as principal inverses of their respective circular functions.

For the restriction of the cosine, we choose the representative interval $[0, \pi]$ where the cosine is decreasing, see Figure 2. We define the value $y = \arccos x$ for $-1 \le x \le 1$ as the one value satisfying

$$0 \le y \le \pi$$

for which $\cos y = x$.

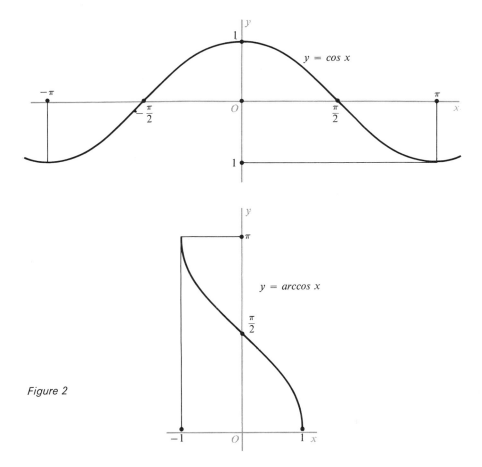

Figure 2

Finally, for the restriction of the tangent, we use the representative interval $\left(-\dfrac{\pi}{2}, \dfrac{\pi}{2}\right)$ and define $y = \arctan x$ for any x as the value in the interval $-\dfrac{\pi}{2} < y < \dfrac{\pi}{2}$ for which $\tan y = x$, see Figure 3.

We shall not be greatly concerned with inverse functions for the cotangent, secant, and cosecant; these can be treated in terms of the functions already at our disposal (see Ex. 4) and are used infrequently.

To find the derivatives of the inverse circular functions, we merely apply 4.3 Theorem 1. The function

$$g : y \to \arcsin y, \qquad \text{for} \quad -1 \le y \le 1,$$

is the inverse of

$$f : x \to \sin x, \qquad \text{for} \quad -\dfrac{\pi}{2} \le x \le \dfrac{\pi}{2},$$

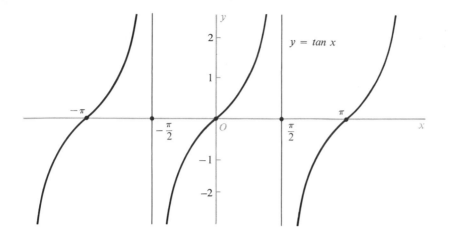

Figure 3

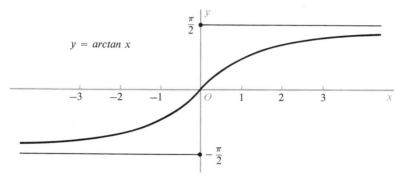

with derivative $f'(x) = \cos x$. Hence if $b = \sin a$, $-\dfrac{\pi}{2} < a < \dfrac{\pi}{2}$, then, for $-1 < b < 1$,

$$g'(b) = \frac{1}{f'(a)} = \frac{1}{\cos a} = \frac{1}{\sqrt{1 - \sin^2 a}} = \frac{1}{\sqrt{1 - b^2}}.$$

Therefore

$$D \arcsin x = \frac{1}{\sqrt{1 - x^2}}, \qquad \text{for } -1 < x < 1.$$

The same method yields the formulas

$$D \arccos x = \frac{-1}{\sqrt{1 - x^2}}, \qquad \text{for } -1 < x < 1,$$

$$D \arctan x = \frac{1}{1 + x^2}, \qquad \text{for all } x$$

(see Exs. 2, 3). It is noteworthy that the derivatives of all the inverse circular functions are algebraic functions.

4.5 Exercises

1. Determine the domain and range and draw the graph of each function.
   - a. $f : x \rightarrow \arcsin (\sin x)$.
   - b. $f : x \rightarrow \sin (\arcsin x)$.
   - c. $f : x \rightarrow \arcsin (\cos x$.
   - d. $f : x \rightarrow \cos (\arcsin x)$.
   - e. $f : x \rightarrow \arctan (\tan x)$.

2. Derive the formula

$$D \arccos x = - \frac{1}{\sqrt{1 - x^2}} :$$

   a. Without using the identity which relates $\arccos x$ to $\arcsin x$.
   b. Using the identity $\arccos x = \frac{1}{2}\pi - \arcsin x$.

3. Derive the formula

$$D \arctan x = \frac{1}{1 + x^2} .$$

4. Derive each of the following formulas.

   a. $\quad D \operatorname{arccot} x = - \dfrac{1}{1 + x^2} .$

   b. $\quad D \operatorname{arcsec} x = \dfrac{1}{|x| \sqrt{x^2 - 1}} .$

   c. $\quad D \operatorname{arccsc} x = - \dfrac{1}{|x| \sqrt{x^2 - 1}} .$

5. Evaluate

   a. $\quad D (\arcsin x + \arccos x) ,$
   b. $\quad D (x^2 \arcsin x) ,$

   c. $\quad D \dfrac{x^2}{\arctan x} ,$
   d. $\quad D (\arcsin x)^3 ,$

   e. $\quad D \dfrac{1}{1 + \arcsin x} .$

6. Find $\lim\limits_{h \sim 0} \dfrac{\arcsin h}{h} .$

7. Evaluate

   a. $\quad D \dfrac{\arcsin x}{1 + \arccos x} ,$
   b. $\quad D \dfrac{\operatorname{arcsec} x}{1 - \operatorname{arccsc} x} ,$
   c. $\quad D \dfrac{1 - \arctan x}{1 + \arctan x} .$

4.6 COMPOSITIONS, THE CHAIN RULE

We now set ourselves the problem of expressing the derivative of a composition in terms of the derivatives of its constituent functions. In 4.2b
Corollary 2c and in 4.2c Corollary 1c we gave a formula for the derivative
of a composition gf where g is a polynomial or a rational function,

namely

(1a) $$D_x gf(x) = D_u g(u) D_x u ,$$

where $u = f(x)$. In terms of operations on functions, (1a) can be written in the form

(1b) $$[gf]' = g'f \cdot f' .$$

We shall prove that (1a) holds for a composition of any two differentiable functions.

The formula (1b) enables us to obtain the derivative of a composition with any number of constituents; for example

$$[hgf]' = [h(gf)]' = h'gf \cdot (gf)'$$
$$= h'gf \cdot g'f \cdot f' .$$

The general formula for the derivative of a composition of any length is called the *Chain Rule;* given a composition $f_n f_{n-1} \cdots f_1$, we set $x = u_1$ and $u_2 = f_1(u_1)$, $u_3 = f_2(u_2)$, ... , $u_n = f_{n-1}(u_{n-1})$ to obtain the Chain Rule in the form

(2) $$D_x[f_n f_{n-1} \cdots f_1](x) = D_{u_n} f(u_n) \, D_{u_{n-1}} f_{n-1}(u_{n-1}) \cdots D_{u_1} f_1(u_1) .$$

Theorem 1. If f is differentiable at a, and g is differentiable at $b = f(a)$, then the composition $x \to gf(x)$ has the derivative at a given by

$$[gf]'(a) = g'f(a)f'(a) .$$

Proof. If $f(x) \neq f(a) = b$, then for $\phi = gf$,

$$\frac{\phi(x) - \phi(a)}{x - a} = \frac{gf(x) - gf(a)}{x - a} = \frac{gf(x) - g(b)}{f(x) - b} \cdot \frac{f(x) - f(a)}{x - a} .$$

If $f(x) = b$, it is true that for any number c

$$\frac{\phi(x) - \phi(a)}{x - a} = c \frac{f(x) - f(a)}{x - a}$$

since both sides are zero. In terms of the function r defined by

$$r(y) = \begin{cases} \dfrac{g(y) - g(b)}{y - b}, & \text{for } y \neq b , \\[2ex] c, & \text{for } y = b , \end{cases}$$

we then have

(3) $$\frac{\phi(x) - \phi(a)}{x - a} = rf(x)\frac{f(x) - f(a)}{x - a} .$$

We could apply 3.6c Theorem 1 which affirms the continuity of the composition of continuous functions if r were continuous at b. It is not continuous, however, unless we choose c judiciously. Choose $c = g'(b)$. Then $\lim\limits_{y \sim b} r(y) = \lim\limits_{y \sim b} \dfrac{g(y) - g(b)}{y - b} = g'(b) = r(b)$, that is, r is continuous at b. From (3) and the theorem on the continuity of compositions, we now obtain

$$\phi'(a) = \lim_{x \sim a} \frac{\phi(x) - \phi(a)}{x - a} = \lim_{x \sim a} rf(x) \lim_{x \sim a} \frac{f(x) - f(a)}{x - a}$$
$$= rf(a)f'(a) = g'f(a)f'(a).$$ □

Example 1. We differentiate $\sin x^2$. We use (1a) with

$$f(x) = x^2 \quad \text{and} \quad g(y) = \sin y,$$

where $y = f(x)$, so that $f'(x) = 2x$, $g'(y) = \cos y$, and therefore,

$$D \sin x^2 = 2x \cos x^2.$$

Example 2. We differentiate $\phi(x) = \arctan \dfrac{1}{x}$. We set $f(x) = \dfrac{1}{x}$ and

$$g(y) = \arctan y,$$

where $y = f(x)$, so that

$$f'(x) = \frac{-1}{x^2}, \quad g'(y) = \frac{1}{1 + y^2}, \quad \text{and}$$

$$\phi'(x) = D \arctan \frac{1}{x} = \frac{1}{1 + \left(\dfrac{1}{x}\right)^2} \left(\frac{-1}{x^2}\right) = \frac{-1}{x^2 + 1}.$$

Example 3. We evaluate $D \cos \left(\dfrac{1 - x}{1 + x}\right)^{2/3}$. We use (2), with

$$f(x) = \frac{1 - x}{1 + x}, \quad g(y) = y^{2/3}, \quad h(z) = \cos z,$$

where $y = f(x)$ and $z = g(y)$, so that

$$f'(x) = \frac{-2}{(1 + x)^2}, \quad g'(y) = \tfrac{2}{3} y^{-1/3}, \quad h'(z) = -\sin z.$$

The formula yields

$$D \cos \left(\frac{1 - x}{1 + x}\right)^{2/3} = -\sin \left(\frac{1 - x}{1 + x}\right)^{2/3} \cdot \frac{2}{3} \left(\frac{1 - x}{1 + x}\right)^{-1/3} \cdot \frac{-2}{(1 + x)^2}$$

$$= \tfrac{4}{3}(1 - x)^{-1/3}(1 + x)^{-5/3} \sin \left(\frac{1 - x}{1 + x}\right)^{2/3}.$$

4.6 Exercises

1. For each of the following, find $D\,fg(x)$, $D\,gf(x)$, $D\,ff(x)$, and $D\,gg(x)$.

   a. $f(x) = x^3 - 2x$, $g(x) = \sqrt{x}$.

   b. $f(x) = \sin x$, $g(x) = \cos x$.

   c. $f(x) = x^2$, $g(x) = \sin x$.

   d. $f(x) = \dfrac{x}{1 + x}$, $g(x) = \dfrac{x^2}{1 + x}$.

   e. $f(x) = \sin x^2$, $g(x) = \sqrt{1 - x^2}$.

2. Find $D\,ff(x)$ for

   a. $f(x) = \sin^2 x$,   b. $f(x) = \tan^2 x$.

3. Find $f'(x)$ if $f(x)$ is

   a. $(x^3 + 4)^{1/2}$,   b. $(2x^2 + 2)^{-1/2}$,

   c. $\dfrac{\sqrt{1 - 3x + 1}}{\sqrt{1 - 3x}}$,   d. $\sqrt{\sin^2 x + x^2}$.

4. Evaluate

   a. $D_x \sqrt{a^2 - x^2}$,

   b. $D_x \left((x^2 + 1)^{1/2} + (x^2 + 1)^{-1/2} \right)$,

   c. $D_x \dfrac{\sqrt{x^2 - a^2}}{\sqrt{x^2 + a^2}}$,

   d. $D_x \left(\dfrac{1 + \sqrt{1 - 2x}}{\sqrt{1 - 2x}} - \sqrt{1 - 2x} \right)$,

   e. $D_x \left(x\,(2x^2 - 2x + 1)^{-1/2} \right)$.

5. Evaluate

   a. $D_x \sqrt{1 + \cos x}$,   b. $D_x (x^2\sqrt{\sin x})$,

   c. $D_x \cos \cos \cos x$,   d. $D_x \arcsin (\cos x)$,

   e. $D_x \arctan (\arctan x)$,   f. $D_x (x^2 \sin x \cos x)$,

   g. $D_x \dfrac{\sin^2 x}{\sin x^2}$,   h. $D_x \tan \dfrac{1 + x}{1 - x}$.

6. Evaluate

   a. $D_x \arcsin (\sin x - \cos x)$,   b. $D_x \arcsin \dfrac{1 - x^2}{1 + x^2}$,

   c. $D_x \arctan (x + \sqrt{1 + x^2})$,   d. $D_x \arctan \dfrac{1 + x}{1 - x}$,

   e. $D_x \left((\arcsin x^2)^{-2} \right)$,   f. $D_x \arcsec \sqrt{1 + x^2}$,

   g. $D_x \left(\arctan \dfrac{x + 1}{x - 1} + \arctan x \right)$,

   h. $D_x \dfrac{\arcsin x}{\arctan x}$,   i. $D_x \arcsin (\arcsin x)$.

7. Evaluate

   a. $D_v \sin x$,   where $v = \cos x$,

   b. $D_u \sqrt{1 - x^2}$,   where $u = x^2$,

   c. $D_v(2 + 3 \cos^2 x)$,   where $v = \sin x$.

8. Compute the limits of each of the following ratios.

   a. $\displaystyle \lim_{x \sim a} \frac{\sqrt{x^2 - 1} - \sqrt{a^2 - 1}}{x - a}$.   b. $\displaystyle \lim_{x \sim a} \frac{(\arccos x)^2 - (\arccos a)^2}{x - a}$.

9. If $f(x) = (Ax + B)\sin x + (Cx + D)\cos x$,   determine the values of the constants A, B, C, D such that for all x, $f'(x) = x \sin x$.

10. If $g(x) = (Ax^2 + Bx + C)\sin x + (Dx^2 + Ex + F)\cos x$,   determine the values of the constants A, B, C, D, E, F such that for all x, $g'(x) = x^2 \cos x$.

11. Express g' in terms of f' if

   a. $g(x) = f(x^3) + f(x - 1/3)$,

   b. $g(x) = f(\sin^2 x) + f(\cos^2 x)$,

   c. $g(x) = f(\arcsin x) + f(\arctan x)$.

12. Prove that the derivative of an even function is odd and vice versa (it is assumed that the derivative exists).

13. Show that it is impossible to find polynomials p and q such that

   a. $D\, p(x) = \dfrac{1}{x}$,   b. $D\dfrac{1}{p(x)} = \dfrac{1}{x}$,   c. $D\dfrac{p(x)}{q(x)} = \dfrac{1}{x}$.

14. Why not apply the Chain Rule to $fg = I$,   where $I : x \to x$,   to obtain the derivative g' of the inverse to f?

4.7 NOTATION

There are several commonly used notations for the derivative. Each of these is valuable in an appropriate context. The notation of Leibniz,† in particular, will be convenient in the application of theorems on the differentiation of inverses and composite functions.

We have already used four notations for the derivative of a function at x. Consider, first, the three representations of the derivative,

$$(1) \qquad f'(x) = \lim_{z \sim x} \frac{f(z) - f(x)}{z - x} = \lim_{h \sim 0} \frac{f(x + h) - f(x)}{h}.$$

The notations (1) have the virtue of complete precision: independently of context we see immediately that a specific function f is being differentiated at a specific point x. This precision was desirable for logical clarity in our development of the foundations of our subject.

---

†Gottfried Wilhelm von Leibniz, 1646–1716. German mathematician and philosopher. Contemporaneously with Newton, he founded the calculus. A dabbler in politics, he helped create the Hanoverian dynasty of English kings — not his most significant work.

In more complicated situations a completely explicit notation may be a barrier to understanding rather than a help, simply because the complexity of the notation conceals our pattern of thought.

Before we examine other notations, let us review differences in usage for the notations we already have. The two limit notations place emphasis on the numerical value of the derivative at the point x, and they are used interchangeably. The other notation places emphasis on the function

$$f' : x \rightarrow \lim_{h \sim 0} \frac{f(x+h) - f(x)}{h}.$$

The prime is usually reserved for use with the abstract designation $f, g, ...,$ of a function as in $f', g', ...$. The symbol D_x is generally used when the function is given by an explicit name or formula, for example,

$$D_x \cot x, \ D_x(x^2 + ax + a^2).$$

(Here it is understood, unless the contrary is explicitly stated, that all symbols other than x appearing in the expression for the function are constants; thus,

$$D_x(x^2 + ax + a^2) = 2x + a.$$

If there is no possibility of confusion the subscript x is often omitted as in $D \cot x$.) This notation omits reference to the specific point where the derivative is being taken. The symbol D_x is an *operator* which, when applied to an expression giving the values of f for all x in a suitable domain, yields an expression giving the values of the derivative f'. Thus for

$$f : x \rightarrow x^2$$

we have

$$D_x f(x) = D_x x^2 = 2x.$$

This must be understood as the statement that, for all x, the derivative of $f : x \rightarrow x^2$ is $f' : x \rightarrow 2x$. The insertion of a specific value of x in this statement makes nonsense of the initial clause, "for all x". If we wish to refer to a point where the derivative is being evaluated we must make explicit mention of it in context or invent a special notation,† for example,

$$f'(a) = D_x f(x)|_{x=a}.$$

The further notations abbreviate the explicit notations by omitting the references to the function f and to the point at which the derivative is

---

†We cannot simply insert a value of x where x appears after the function symbol. For example, given $f : x \rightarrow x^2$ we have $D_x f(3) = D_x 9 = 0$, namely, the expression for the derivative of the constant function $x \rightarrow 9$. At the same time

$$D_x f(x)|_{x=3} = f'(3) = 6.$$

evaluated. The first of these notations parallels a common abbreviated mode of expression. We say, "y is a function of x" meaning that there exists a function

$$f : x \to y$$

which maps each number x in a certain domain onto a value y in a certain range. This expression is appropriate when we wish to call attention to the existence of such a relation but are not impelled to name the function or define it explicitly. It is suggestive in relation to the representation of the function by its graph, the set of points (x, y) where $y = f(x)$. We use a parallel notation for the derivative,

$$f' : x \to y'$$

and say that y' is the derivative of y, meaning that there exists a function f such that $y = f(x)$ and $y' = f'(x)$. Sometimes a dot is used to indicate a derivative; for example, $\dot{y}$ instead of y'. The dotted notation was introduced by Newton.† (It has been called "fly speck" notation by generations of irreverent teachers and students.) Clearly, to use such abbreviated notations and ways of expression, we must have a context in which they are intelligible and represent a genuine convenience. We shall find them so in the next section on implicitly defined functions and their derivatives, and later in the applications.

A slightly but significantly more explicit notation was introduced by Leibniz. We set $y_0 = f(x_0)$ and $y = f(x)$ and write the derivative in the form

$$f'(x_0) = \lim_{x \sim x_0} \frac{f(x) - f(x_0)}{x - x_0} = \lim_{x \sim x_0} \frac{y - y_0}{x - x_0}.$$

Leibniz introduced the "difference" notation

$$\Delta x = x - x_0,$$

$$\Delta y = y - y_0.$$

Here Δx is a single symbol with the same meaning as the symbol h used in (1), and Δy is a single symbol which represents the difference in the function values corresponding to the difference Δx between x and x_0. In this notation,

$$f'(x_0) = \lim_{\Delta x \sim 0} \frac{\Delta y}{\Delta x}.$$

---

†Isaac Newton, 1642–1727. English mathematician and physicist. Contemporaneously with Leibniz, he founded the calculus. He employed the calculus to develop his great theory of gravitation.

Further, in writing the derivative, Leibniz used a parallel notation

$$\frac{dy}{dx} = \lim_{\Delta x \sim 0} \frac{\Delta y}{\Delta x} .$$

Again, references to the function f and the point x_0 where the derivative is being taken are lacking and must be supplied from context. However, Leibnizian notation is slightly more explicit than Newtonian: there is not only a reference, y, to the range of f but also a reference, x, to the domain.

The symbol $\dfrac{dy}{dx}$ does not represent a ratio, but the limit of a ratio. The parallelism with the notation for fractions may be annoying at first, but it is singularly apt. Although the symbol $\dfrac{dy}{dx}$ represents a derivative and not a fraction, the rule for differentiating a composition (4.6 Theorem 1) permits us to handle quotients and products of these symbols formally as though they were fractions. For suitable functions

$$f : x \rightarrow y$$

and

$$g : y \rightarrow z ,$$

4.6 Theorem 1 states that

$$[gf]'(x) = g'f(x)f'(x) .$$

In Leibnizian notation this is written

$$\frac{dz}{dx} = \frac{dz}{dy} \frac{dy}{dx} .$$

We see, then, that the theorem has the formal appearance of a cancellation of fractions. More generally, if we put $z = f_n(u_n)$ in 4.6 (2), we obtain the Chain Rule in the form

$$\frac{dz}{du_1} = \frac{dz}{du_n} \frac{du_n}{du_{n-1}} \frac{du_{n-1}}{du_{n-2}} \dots \frac{du_2}{du_1} ,$$

which clearly reveals the sequence of mappings,

$$u_1 \rightarrow u_2 \rightarrow \dots \rightarrow u_n \rightarrow z$$

and at the same time exhibits the structure of the derivative of the composition as a product of derivatives. In the Leibnizian form we have omitted reference to the functions which define the mappings and to the points where the several derivatives are taken. This information has to be supplied from context. The completely explicit notation

$$[f_n f_{n-1} \cdots f_1]'(a) = [f_n' f_{n-1} \cdots f_1(a)] \cdot [f_{n-1}' f_{n-2} \cdots f_1(a)] \cdots [f_1'(a)]$$

is cumbersome and not particularly revealing at first glance; for large n, merely to write the derivative of a composition in this notation becomes a problem.   By sacrificing explicitness, Leibnizian notation resolves the problem.

As further evidence of the aptness of Leibnizian notation, we consider the inverse function f, g, where

$$f : x \rightarrow y$$

and

$$g : y \rightarrow x$$

that the relation

$$g'(y) = \frac{1}{f'(x)}$$

appears in Leibnizian notation as

$$\frac{dx}{dy} = 1 \bigg/ \frac{dy}{dx} .$$

It is sometimes convenient to supply the omissions of Leibnizian notation as follows. We consider $\dfrac{d}{dx}$ as an operator identical with D_x. We then write

$$\frac{dy}{dx} = \frac{d}{dx} f(x) = D_x f(x)$$

to supply the reference to f,   and write

$$\frac{dy}{dx}\bigg|_{x\,=\,x_0} = \frac{d}{dx} f(x)\bigg|_{x\,=\,x_0} = f'(x_0)$$

to supply the reference to the point at which the derivative is taken, for example,

$$\frac{d}{dx} x^2 \bigg|_{x\,=\,3} = 6 .$$

The successive higher derivatives are written $D^2 f = f''$, $D^3 f = f'''$, $D^4 f = f^{iv}$, $D^5 f = f^v$. The Roman superscript notation is inconvenient for high orders and we shall also use Hindu-Arabic numerals parenthetically, as $D^{13} f = f^{(13)}$. Thus, the n-th derivative of f is written $D^n f = f^{(n)}$. It is also useful to define the zero-order derivative of f as f itself, $f^{(0)} = f$.

In Leibnizian notation we write

$$D^n y = \left(\frac{d}{dx}\right)^n y = \frac{d^n y}{dx^n}.$$

4.7 Exercises

1. Find dy/dx if $y = mu + b$ and $u = \dfrac{1}{m} x - \dfrac{b}{m}$.

2. Let $y = \sin x$ and $x = t^2 + 1/t$. Find $\left.\dfrac{dy}{dt}\right|_{t=1}$ and $\left.\dfrac{dy}{dx}\right|_{x=1}$.

3. Let $y = f(x)$ and $x = h(t)$. Express $\left.\dfrac{dy}{dt}\right|_{t=t_0}$ in terms of t_0.

4. Let $y = f(x)$, $x = h(t)$, $x_0 = h(t_0)$. Using 4.6 Theorem 1 show that

$$\left.\frac{dy}{dx}\right|_{x=x_0} = \left.\frac{dy}{dt}\right|_{t=t_0} \bigg/ \left.\frac{dx}{dt}\right|_{t=t_0}.$$

5. Evaluate
   a. $D_x \sin x|_{x=0} + D_x \sin x|_{x=\pi/4}$,
   b. $D_x(x^2 + \sin a \sin x)|_{x=5\pi/3}$,
   c. $\left.\dfrac{d}{dx}(x^2 - a^2)\right|_{x=a}$,
   d. $D_x(f(a) \sin x + f(x) \sin a + f(x) \sin x)|_{x=a}$.

6. Let $y = f(t)$, $w = g(t)$, $t = h(x)$, $z = y/w$.
   a. Using Leibnizian notation, find dz/dx in terms of

   $$\frac{dy}{dt}, \frac{dw}{dt} \text{ and } \frac{dt}{dx}.$$

   b. Using Part (a) express $\left.\dfrac{dz}{dx}\right|_{x=x_0}$ in terms of f', g', and h'.

7. Consider the functions f and g such that $f(x) = f'(x)$ and

   $$fg(x) = x.$$

   Assume that $g'(x)$ exists and determine it.

8. a. Obtain an expression for the first and higher derivatives of x^n where n is a natural number.
   b. Do the same for $x^{p/q}$ where p and q are relatively prime integers. (If $\dfrac{p}{q}$ were an integer then Part (a) would apply.) What is the domain of f' when $f(x) = x^{1/2}$? For what values of $\dfrac{p}{q}$ is the domain of f' different from that of $f : x \to x^{p/q}$? Answer the same question for higher derivatives of $x^{p/q}$.

9. What is the twenty-ninth derivative of f if $f(x) =$

    a. $\sin x$?   b. $\cos x$?   c. $\sin 2x$?

    d. $17x^{23} + \sqrt{3}x^{15} - 78\pi x^5 - 462$?

10. Find the n-th derivatives of the following functions.

    a. $f : x \to (ax + b)^{-1}$.   b. $f : x \to \sin x$.

    c. $f : x \to \cos (ax + b)$.   d. $f : x \to \sin^2 x$.

    e. $f : x \to \cos^3 2x$.   f. $f : x \to x^n - [\![x]\!]^n$.

    g. $f : x \to \dfrac{1}{x^2 - a^2}$.   ⌁h. $f : x \to \dfrac{1}{x^2 + a^2}$.

4.8 IMPLICITLY DEFINED FUNCTIONS

A function constructed from known functions by means of rational operations, composition, and inversion, is said to be defined *explicitly*. No matter how complicated the construction, if a function is defined explicitly in terms of functions with known derivatives, we know how to differentiate the function. It often happens that a function is defined indirectly or *implicitly*. Thus the conditions

(1) $$x^2 + y^2 = 1, \quad y \geq 0,$$

determine y as a function of x.

A function defined implicitly can sometimes be given explicit expression; thus, the function defined by (1) is given by

(2) $$y = \sqrt{1 - x^2}.$$

Often there is no equivalent explicit definition of a function defined implicitly, or it may be very difficult to find one. For example, the equation

(3) $$x^2 \arctan z + z = \sin x$$

determines a unique value z for every number x; thus, the equation defines a function $x \to z$, but we are not able to get an explicit expression for z.

It is easy to see that (3) defines z as a function of x. For any given number x, the function $\phi : z \to x^2 \arctan z + z$ is continuous and has arbitrarily large values, both positive and negative. Hence, by the Intermediate Value Theorem, there is some value z for which (3) is satisfied; since ϕ is an increasing function, that value must be unique, and the function $x \to z$ is defined implicitly by relation (3).

For the function defined by (2), we can differentiate directly and obtain

$$(4) \qquad y' = \frac{-x}{\sqrt{1-x^2}}.$$

A second method is to employ (1) and use the Chain Rule to obtain

$$2x + 2yy' = 0 \,;$$

whence,

$$(5) \qquad y' = \frac{-x}{y}.$$

The formula (5) is not explicit, since it expresses y' in terms of y as well as x, whereas the formula (4) gives y' explicitly in terms of x alone. From (5), we could still get a formula involving x alone if we want it, by using (2) to eliminate y, but it may be more convenient to write y instead of the expression it represents. For most purposes, we do not need the completely explicit formula for the derivative. If we wish to find the value y' for a specified value of x, for instance, we can first compute the corresponding value y (explicitly from (2) in this case, but by numerical approximation in most practical problems), and then compute y' from the shorter formula.

For (3), the choice of an explicit representation is not open to us. We obtain no explicit formula for z in the first place, but we can still obtain a formula for $\dfrac{dz}{dx}$ by implicit differentiation. Thus, if z is a differentiable function of x, we may apply the rules of differentiation and obtain

$$2x \arctan z + x^2 \frac{1}{1+z^2} \frac{dz}{dx} + \frac{dz}{dx} = \cos x$$

or

$$(6) \qquad \frac{dz}{dx} = \frac{\cos x - 2x \arctan z}{\dfrac{x^2}{1+z^2} + 1}.$$

If we wish to evaluate dz/dx for a specific value of x, we will first have to find z from (3), probably by some approximate numerical technique.

We emphasize that we have not shown that (6) holds, merely that if $\dfrac{dz}{dx}$ exists it must have the value given by (6). There is, in fact, a theorem which applies under rather general conditions (which covers the present case and most of those that arise in practice). This theorem states that if an equation defining a function implicitly can be formally differentiated and if the resultant equation can be solved for the derivative of the function, then the derivative of the function exists and has the value found. To prove, or even precisely state, this theorem would take us too far afield, and the proof will be postponed to the theory of functions of several variables. Hereafter, we shall use implicit differentiation freely to solve problems, without each time reiterating the warning that the derivative has not been proved to exist.

Even though the implicitly defined function may exist, we cannot always solve for the derivative at every point, as the following example illustrates.

Example 1. The equation

(7)
$$u^5 + x^2 u = x$$

defines u unambiguously for each x. Implicit differentiation yields

$$(5u^4 + x^2)\frac{du}{dx} + 2xu = 1,$$

which can be solved for $\dfrac{du}{dx}$ everywhere except where $5u^4 + x^2$ vanishes. From (7) we have $u = 0$ when $x = 0$; therefore, we cannot solve for $\dfrac{du}{dx}$ at $x = 0$. In fact, u is not differentiable at $x = 0$.

Example 2. Even if a function is differentiable at a given point, the method may fail. For instance, consider the equation which explicitly defines v as a function of x,

(8)
$$v^5 + v^3 = x^3.$$

As before, at $x = 0$, we have $v = 0$ and there is no solution for $\dfrac{dv}{dx}$ from the implicitly differentiated result

$$(5v^4 + 3v^2)\frac{dv}{dx} = 3x^2.$$

In this case, however, there is a derivative at $x = 0$, and we can find it by writing (8) in the equivalent form

$$v(v^2 + 1)^{1/3} = x$$

and then differentiating:

$$[(v^2 + 1)^{1/3} + \tfrac{2}{3}v^2(v^2 + 1)^{-2/3}]\frac{dv}{dx} = 1.$$

This gives $\dfrac{dv}{dx} = 1$ at $x = 0$.

In general, a function will be defined implicitly by an equation

(9) $$g(x, y) = 0$$

where g is a function of two variables. Several points remain to be clarified: if a relation between two variables does not express one variable explicitly in terms of another, under what circumstances may it describe a function implicitly? Is the implicitly defined function differentiable? If it is differentiable, how may the derivative be found? We consider an example which exhibits most of the difficulties.

Example 3. We consider the equation

$$g(x, y) = (x^2 + y^2) - c^2(x^2 - y^2) = 0$$

whose graph is the lemniscate of Bernoulli, see Figure 1.

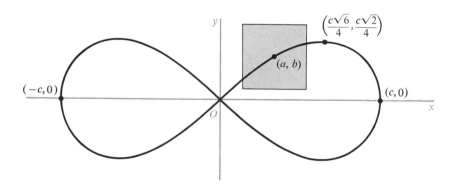

Figure 1

For each point (a, b) on the graph other than $(0, 0)$, $(c, 0)$, and $(-c, 0)$ there is a neighborhood† of (a, b) wherein no vertical line

---

†The idea of neighborhood of a point of the plane is a natural extension of the idea of neighborhood of a point on the number line. The δ-neighborhood of (a, b) is the square

$$\{(x, y) : |x - a| < \delta \text{ and } |y - b| < \delta\}.$$

A δ-neighborhood of a point is to be understood as a linear neighborhood of the point if it is described by one coordinate (point on the number line), as a planar neighborhood of the point if it is described by two coordinates (point of the plane).

meets the graph more than once (Figure 1). Within such a neighborhood, then, the graph can be represented by a function $f : x \rightarrow y$ where

$$g(x, f(x)) = (x^2 + [f(x)]^2)^2 - c^2(x^2 - [f(x)]^2) = 0.$$

We cannot do the same thing at $(0, 0)$ or at the points $(\pm c, 0)$; at none of these points can the entire graph in a neighborhood be represented by a function.

It is easy to see analytically why the relation $g(x, y) = 0$ must describe a function in the vicinity of some points of its graph. For example, let us restrict x to the open interval $(0, c)$ and y to be nonnegative. Along a vertical line $x = a$ we introduce the function ϕ_a given by

$$\phi_a(y) = g(a, y) = (a^2 + y^2)^2 - c^2(a^2 - y^2).$$

Now, we observe that ϕ_a can have both positive and negative values; namely,

$$\phi_a(a) = g(a, a) = 4a^4 > 0$$

and, since $a < c$,

$$\phi_a(0) = g(a, 0) = a^4 - c^2a^2 = a^2(a^2 - c^2) < 0.$$

Since ϕ_a is a polynomial function, hence continuous, we now know by the Intermediate Value Theorem that there is a zero of ϕ_a in the interval $(0, a)$; that is, the vertical line $x = a$, for $0 < a < c$, must meet the graph $g(x, y) = 0$ in at least one point above the x-axis. In order that the portion of the graph $g(x, y) = 0$ in the given region may describe a function, each line $x = a$ must meet that part of the graph in no more than one point. This will be the case if ϕ_a has no more than one zero, for which it is sufficient that ϕ_a be strongly monotone. Since, for $y > 0$ and $0 < a < c$,

$$\phi_a'(y) = 2y[2(a^2 + y^2) + c^2] > 0,$$

we infer that ϕ_a is increasing. Consequently, there is exactly one value $y = b$ for which $\phi_a(b) = g(a, b) = 0$.

In this way we have proved that to each number $x = a$ in $(0, c)$ there corresponds a unique value $b > 0$ such that $g(a, b) = 0$. Thus, the equation $g(x, y) = 0$, subject to the conditions $x \in (0, c)$ and $y \geq 0$, defines a unique function f such that $g(x, f(x)) = 0$. This same approach to implicitly defined functions leads to a general proof of existence known as the Implicit Function Theorem.

The expression $g(x, y)$ in (9) may be differentiated with respect to x with y treated as a constant, or differentiated with respect to y with x treated as a constant; these derivatives, written $D_x g(x, y)$ and

$$D_y g(x, y),$$

respectively, are called the *partial derivatives* of g. If there is a differentiable function $f : x \rightarrow y$ which satisfies

$$g(x, f(x)) = 0,$$

then the derivative $y' = f'(x)$ satisfies

(10) $$D_x g(x, y) + D_y g(x, y) y' = 0$$

where y satisfies (9). Thus we must satisfy the following conditions to calculate the derivative of f at x implicitly: for the given value of x, the value $y = f(x)$ must satisfy $g(x, y) = 0$ and $D_y g(x, y) \neq 0$. In that case, $y' = -\dfrac{D_x g(x, y)}{D_y g(x, y)}$. If $D_y g(x, y) = 0$ and $D_x g(x, y) \neq 0$ then (10) cannot be satisfied and the derivative certainly does not exist; if $D_y g(x, y) = 0$ and $D_x g(x, y) = 0$, the case is in doubt. The proof of these results is not difficult, but is reserved to the time when we shall be discussing such questions systematically.

Finally, we observe that the problem of obtaining the derivative of an inverse function, solved in 4.3, is a special case of the problem of differentiating an implicitly defined function. If g is the inverse of f, then $y = g(x)$ satisfies the equation

$$f(y) - x = 0.$$

Differentiating implicitly with respect to x, we obtain

$$f'(y) y' - 1 = 0,$$

or

$$y' = \frac{1}{f'(y)},$$

in agreement with the result of 4.3 Theorem 1. However, when we prove the Implicit Function Theorem we shall impose somewhat more restrictive conditions on f than were necessary in 4.3.

4.8 Exercises

1. For positive x, if $y = x^r$ and r is a rational number, $r = p/q$ where p and q are integers, $y^q = x^p$. Assuming the existence of the derivative $D_x y$, obtain the formula $D_x y = rx^{r-1}$ using implicit differentiation and the differentiation formula $D_x x^n = nx^{n-1}$, for integral n.

2. For each of the following, find $D_x y$ without solving for y as a function of x.

   a. $5x^2 + y^2 = 12$.

   b. $2x^2 - y^2 + x - 4 = 0$.

   c. $y^2 - 3x^2 + 6y = 12$.

   d. $x^3 + y^3 - 2xy = 0$.

3. a. Sketch the graph of $x^2 - 2xy + y^2 = 1$.
   b. Find dy/dx if $x^2 - 2xy + y^2 = 1$.
   c. Sketch the graph of $|x - y| = 1$.
   d. If $|x - y| = 1$, find $D_x y$.

4. For each of the following use implicit differentiation to find $D_x y$.

   a. $x^2 = \dfrac{y - x}{y + x}$.

   b. $x^2 y + xy^2 = x^3$.

   c. $x^m y^n = 10$ (m, n integers).

   d. $\sqrt{xy} + x = y^{-1}$.

5. Use implicit differentiation to find $D_y x$.

   a. $x\sqrt{y} + y\sqrt{x} = a\sqrt{a}$, where a is constant.
   b. $2x^2 + 3xy + y^2 + x - 2y + 1 = 0$.
   c. $(x + y)^{1/2} + (x - y)^{1/2} = 4$.
   d. $3x^2 + x^2 y^2 = y^4 + 5$.
   e. $4x^2 + 3xy - 7y^2 = 0$.

6. For each equation, find the slope of the given curve at the stated point.

   a. $2x^2 + 3xy + y^2 + x - 2y + 1 = 0$ at the point $(-2, 1)$.
   b. $x^3 + y^2 x^2 + y^3 - 1 = 0$ at the point $(1, -1)$.
   c. $x^2 - x\sqrt{xy} - 6y^2 = 2$ at the point $(4, 1)$.
   d. $x \cos y = 3x^2 - 5$ at the point $(\sqrt{2}, \tfrac{1}{4}\pi)$.

7. Prove that the following equations uniquely define y as an implicit function of x near the points indicated.

   a. $3x^2 + xy + 3y^2 = 7$ $(\sqrt{\tfrac{7}{3}}, 0)$.
   b. $F(x, y) = x^3 - 3xy + y^3 = 0$ $(\tfrac{3}{2}, \tfrac{3}{2})$.
   c. $F(x, y) = x \cos xy = 0$ $(1, \tfrac{1}{2}\pi)$.

8. Show that there is no unique solution for y in Exercise 7b in any neighborhood of the point $(2^{2/3}, 2^{1/3})$.

9. Find $D_x y$ by implicit differentiation.

   a. $a \sin y + b \cos x = 0$ $(a, b$ constant$)$.
   b. $x \cos y + y \sin x = 0$.
   c. $\sin xy = \sin x + \sin y$.

   d. $\csc(x + y) = y$.

   e. $x \tan y - y \tan x = 1$.

   f. $\tan xy - x^2 = 0$.

   g. $y \sin x = x \tan y$.

   h. $xy + \sin y = 5$.

10. If $0 < x < a$, then the equation $\sqrt{x} + \sqrt{y} = \sqrt{a}$ defines y as a function of x. Assuming the existence of the derivative show without solving for y that $f'(x)$ is always negative.

11. Assuming that $D_x y = D_y x = 0$ (i.e., x and y are independent), find the following:

a. $D_x (x^2 + xy + \cos y)$, b. $D_x y^2 + D_y x^2$,
c. $D_x x^2 + D_y y^2$, d. $D_x f(xy) + D_y f(x)$,
e. $D_x(xy)^2$.

12. Find the slopes (if any exist) of the following curves at points for which $x = y$.

a. $x + y = A$. b. $x + xy + y = 3A$.
c. $xy = A^2$. d. $|x + y| + |x - y| = 2A$.
e. Check your answers by sketching each of the above curves.
f. Generalize the results of Parts (a)—(d).

13. For each equation, find the slope of the represented curve at the point or points where $x = y$. Give a geometric explanation for these results.

a. $x^3 - 3axy + y^3 = 0$. b. $x^m + y^m = 2$.
c. $x^2 + y^2 = 2axy + a^2$ $(a \neq 0)$.

14. Let C_1 and C_2 be two curves which intersect at the point (x_0, y_0) and let the slopes of C_1 and C_2 at (x_0, y_0) be m_1 and m_2, respectively. If the product $m_1 m_2$ equals -1, we say that the curves C_1 and C_2 are *orthogonal*.

a. Show that the lines with equations $4y - 3x - 40 = 0$ and $3y + 4x + 15 = 0$ are orthogonal.

b. Show that the circle $x^2 + y^2 = r^2$, r constant, is orthogonal to the line $y = mx$, m constant.

15. Find the points of intersection of the ellipse $x^2 + 10y^2 = 10$ and the hyperbola $x^2 - 8y^2 = 8$, and the slopes of the curves at these points of intersection. Show that the curves are orthogonal.

16. Show that the family of curves $y^2 = 4a(x + a)$ is self-orthogonal; i.e., any two members of the family that intersect, necessarily intersect at right angles.

17. For what values of k will there be exactly one line passing through the point $(0, k)$ and orthogonal to the parabola $y = x^2$? For what values of k will there be exactly three orthogonal lines?

18. A ball dropped out of a window falls $16t^2$ feet in t seconds. An observer is watching from another window at the same height 48 feet away. At what rate is the distance of the ball from the observer increasing two seconds after the ball is dropped?

a. Write an equation which implicitly defines the distance $y = \phi(t)$ between the observer and the ball at time t.

b. Use implicit differentiation to answer the question of the problem.

4M MISCELLANEOUS EXERCISES

1. a. Given that simple harmonic motion is described by the function

$$\rho : t \rightarrow \sin (\omega t + c)$$

where ω and c are constants. Find the velocity at time $t = t_0$.

   b. Simple harmonic motion may also be described by the function

$$\rho : t \rightarrow \cos (\omega t + c)$$

where ω and c are constants. Find the velocity at time $t = t_0$.

   c. In what sense are the motions in Parts (a) and (b) the same?

2. If a simple harmonic motion is described by the function

$$\rho : t \rightarrow A \sin \omega t + B \cos \omega t$$

where A, B, and ω are constants, determine the maximum speed.

3. Evaluate

   a. $D \left(x + \dfrac{1}{x} \right)^{1/2}$,   b. $D (\arcsin \sqrt{x})^2$,   c. $D \sqrt{3x^2 - 1}\,|_{x=3/2}$,

   d. $D_u \sqrt{x - x^2}$ (where $u = x^2$ and $0 < x < 1$),

   e. $D \sqrt{x + \sqrt{x}}$,   f. $D (x^3 - 2)^6$,   g. $D \sqrt[3]{x^2 - 3}$,

   h. $D_u (x^2 - x^{-1/2} + x^{-2})$ (where $u = \sqrt{x}$),

   i. $D \dfrac{x}{x + \sqrt{a^2 - x^2}}$,   j. $D \sqrt{x + 1}$,

   k. $D_v (\sin x \cot x)$ (where $v = \cos x$),

   l. $D (\sin x^{-1/2} - \cos x^{1/2})$,

   m. $D_v \dfrac{1 - \sin x}{1 + \cos x}$ $\left(\text{where } v = \cos \dfrac{x}{2} \right)$,

   n. $D \dfrac{2 + t}{3t^2 - 1}$,   o. $D \dfrac{(2x - 3)^2}{x^3 - 1}$,   p. $D (2x^3 + 5x^2 - x + 2)^{10}$,

   q. $D_v \dfrac{1 - x}{x^2}$ (where $v = \arcsin x$),   r. $D \cos \sqrt{1 - x^2}$,

   s. $D [\arcsin x^2 + \arccos (\tfrac{1}{2}\pi - x^2)]$,   t. $D \tan (x^{-1} - x)$.

4. Let f be a function defined for all values of x with the property,

$$f(a + b) = f(a)f(b), \quad \text{for all } a \text{ and } b.$$

   a. Show that either $f(0) = 1$ or $f(x) = 0$ for all x.

   b. If $f(0) = 1$, show that $f(x) \neq 0$ for all x.

   c. If, additionally, $f(0) = 1$ and f has a derivative at $x = 0$, show that f' exists for all x and that $f'(x) = f'(0) \cdot f(x)$.

∧5. If $F(x + y) = F(x) + F(y)$, where F is continuous at one point and defined for all x, show that $F(x)$ is everywhere differentiable.

6. Given that the function F is defined for all x, is differentiable for

$$0 \leq x < a,$$

and satisfies $F(x + a) = kF(x)$ for all x (a, k constants). Show that F is everywhere differentiable and sketch some possible graphs of F assuming:

a. $F(0) = 0$, $F'(0) = 0$,
b. $F(0) = 0$, $F'(0) = 1$.
c.   If $F(0) = 0$, if F is differentiable for $0 < x < a$ and if the graph of F is tangent to the y-axis, show that F is differentiable for $x \neq na$, n an integer, and sketch some possible graphs of F.

5

Applications of the Derivative

5.1 INTRODUCTION

Thus far, we have been concerned more with the idea of derivative at a point, a number, rather than with the idea of derivative, a function. The derivative $f'(a)$ of the function f at a is defined as

$$f'(a) = \lim_{h \sim 0} \frac{f(a + h) - f(a)}{h};$$

thus, the derivative at a is defined by the values of f in any neighborhood of a, no matter how small. The derivative at the point a is a *local* property of the function f; it is determined by the values of f in any sufficiently small neighborhood of a. We shall refer to such a local property as a property of the function f *at* the point a. However, we are often more interested in the properties of a function defined in terms of its values at *all* points of its domain; such a synoptic property is called *global*. That f is monotone, and that it has an upper bound, these are global properties of f. We refer to a global property as a property of f *on* its domain.

In order to apply the concept of derivative, we shall have to relate global properties of a function f to a local property. For example, we shall prove the assertion made in the Introduction (page 8) that a function f defined on an interval is increasing if f' is positive at each point of that interval.

In this chapter, we explore the properties of functions differentiable on an interval. We focus attention upon the function f' rather than upon the values $f'(x)$ of the derivative at individual points. We also consider the functions obtained by repeating the operation of differentiation; in particular, we shall investigate properties related to the second derivative,

$$D(Df) = D^2f = f'',$$

and shall also have occasional use for derivatives of higher order.

Our major aim is to see how the derivative f' gives us information about the function f and its graph. We already have obtained one such item of information in 3.6a Theorem 1: because f must be defined and continuous where it is differentiable, each point x on the domain of f' is also a point of continuity of f. Consequently, upon any closed interval in the domain of the derivative f', we obtain the global properties of f given by the extreme and intermediate value theorems of 3.7. Further, in 5.2 we shall see how knowledge of f' on an interval enables us to locate the extreme values of f in that interval. In 5.5 we shall see how information about the second derivative f'', the derivative of f', gives information about f' and about the function f itself.

5.1 Exercises

1. For $f : x \rightarrow 44 + 4x - 13x^2 + 18x^3 - 9x^4$ we tabulate certain of the function values and give a graph on which points are plotted from the table. Sketch a graph connecting the points. Where do you think the maximum value of f is?

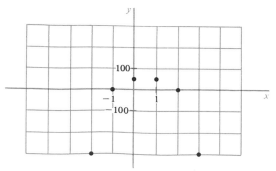

x	-2	-1	0	1	2	3
$f(x)$	-304	0	44	44	0	-304

2. Given the following table, estimate the value or values of x for which the function $f : x \to 39 - 640x^2 - 1280x^3 - 640x^4$ has a maximum.

x	-2	-1	0	1
$f(x)$	-2520	39	39	-2520

5.2 THE DERIVATIVE AT AN EXTREMUM

In 1.1 we considered the problem of maximizing the total writing time of a committee by an appropriate choice of the number of members. We reduced the problem to one of finding the maximum value of a differentiable function on a given interval. Other problems may lead to a search for a minimum value; for example, the reflection problem, to be treated in the chapter on geometrical optics, yields the problem of determining the path of minimum length which connects two given points and meets a given curve somewhere between them. We have defined the maximum of f as an upper bound for the values of f that is reached at some point of the domain. Similarly, the minimum of f is a value of f that is a lower bound for the values of f. We combine the two and define an *extremum* of f as a value of f that is either an upper or lower bound of the range.†

5.2a Location of an extremum on a closed interval

We consider a function f differentiable on the open interval

$$a < x < b$$

and continuous on the closed interval $a \le x \le b$. Since f is continuous on the closed interval it has a maximum M there (3.7 Theorem 2). That is, for all values x such that $a \le x \le b$ we have $f(x) \le M$ and for at least one value a we have $f(a) = M$. The possibility that a is an endpoint of the interval must always be considered. If a is an interior point of the interval then, as we indicated in 1.1, for $f(a)$ to be a maximum, $f'(a)$ must be 0. Now, we shall prove that fact.

Theorem 1. Let $f(a)$ be an extremum of f for some value a in the interior of the domain of f. If $f'(a)$ exists, then $f'(a) = 0$.

†Maximum, minimum, and extremum are words of Latin origin meaning greatest, smallest, and outermost, respectively.

Proof. Suppose $f'(a) \neq 0$. Then, either $f'(a) > 0$, or $f'(a) < 0$. Suppose $f'(a) > 0$; then, by 3.4a Lemma 1, since

$$f'(a) = \lim_{x \sim a} \frac{f(x) - f(a)}{x - a},$$

there is a deleted neighborhood I of a where

$$r(x) = \frac{f(x) - f(a)}{x - a} > 0, \qquad\qquad \text{for } x \text{ in } I.$$

Since a is an interior point of the domain of f, there will be points α, β in the domain and in I for which $\alpha < a < \beta$ and where both $r(\alpha)$ and $r(\beta)$ are positive. Consequently,

$$f(\alpha) < f(a) < f(\beta),$$

and $f(a)$ cannot be an extremum.

There is a parallel proof for the case $f'(a) < 0$.   ⬜

Corollary a. If f is differentiable on the open interval (a, b) and continuous on the closed interval $[a, b]$, then the extreme values of f are taken on at endpoints of the interval or at interior points where the derivative is zero.

A constant function is singular: the value of the function at every point is both a maximum and a minimum. Conversely, if the value of a function at any one point is both a maximum and a minimum, the function is constant.

Example 1. In 1.1 we approached the problem of maximizing the total writing time of a committee by locating the maximum of the function

$$f: x \rightarrow 40x\left[1 - \left(\frac{x-1}{20}\right)^2\right]$$

on the interval $[0, 21]$. The derivative

$$f': x \rightarrow \tfrac{1}{10}[399 + 4x - 3x^2]$$

has zeros $x = \tfrac{1}{3}(2 \pm \sqrt{1201})$. Only the positive zero of f' is relevant. At the endpoints of the interval, we have $f(0) = f(21) = 0$. Since

$$\tfrac{1}{3}(2 + \sqrt{1201}) \approx 12.22 > 0,$$

it follows from Corollary 1a that this zero yields the maximum of f.

Example 2. To determine the extrema of

$$f : x \rightarrow 18x^2 - 2x^3$$

on the interval $[0, 8]$, we obtain

$$f'(x) = 36x - 6x^2 .$$

The derivative is zero at $x = 0$ and $x = 6$. We have $f(0) = 0$,
$f(6) = 216$, $f(8) = 128$. The maximum occurs at $x = 6$, the minimum at $x = 0$; that the derivative happens to be zero at the minimum
is irrelevant since the minimum occurs at an endpoint.

Example 3. Consider the function $f : x \rightarrow |x|$ on the interval $[-1, 1]$.
We know that $|x| \geq 0$ and that $|0| = 0$. It follows that the minimum
of $|x|$ on $[-1, 1]$ is zero and appears at $x = 0$. Here is a case
where an extreme value occurs at an interior point, but the conditions of
the corollary do not apply; $|x|$ does not have a derivative at $x = 0$.
We have had to appeal to other evidence to locate the minimum. However,
$|x|$ is differentiable for $x \neq 0$. Since the derivative of $|x|$ is nowhere
zero, we conclude that any extreme value of $|x|$ on $[-1, 1]$ must
be located among the points $x = -1$, $x = 0$, $x = 1$.

We have developed the solid theoretical foundation called for by the
inquiry of 1.1. We now have an effective method for solving a broad class
of extreme value problems. In summary, for a function f that is continuous on a closed interval, we know that the extrema exist, and we know that
if an extremum exists at an interior point u of an interval where f is
differentiable, then $f'(u) = 0$. To locate the extrema of f on the interval, then, we need only try the endpoints of the interval, points where f
has no derivative and points where the derivative is zero. (Most of the
functions considered here are differentiable everywhere, although in some
cases there may be exceptional points where the derivative does not exist.)
To determine which of these points yield extrema, we may calculate the
values of the function at each point of this restricted class; the largest such
value is the maximum value of the function on the interval, the smallest is
the minimum.

5.2a Exercises

1. Determine the extreme values of the function

$$f : x \rightarrow 44 + 4x - 13x^2 + 18x^3 - 9x^4 .$$

Compare your results with your answer to 5.1 Exercise 1.

2. Determine the values of x for which the function

$$f : x \to 39 - 640x^2 - 1280x^3 - 640x^4$$

has a maximum. (Compare 5.1 Exercise 2.)

3. Make a careful sketch on the closed interval $[0, 8]$ of the graph of

$$f : x \to 18x^2 - 2x^3$$

given in Example 2. Does your graph confirm the conclusion of the text?

4. Locate and characterize the extreme values of each of the following functions on the interval $[-1, 1]$.
   a. $f : x \to x^{2/3}$.
   b. $f : x \to |x|^{3/2}$.

5. Complete the proof of Theorem 1 by proving if $f'(u) < 0$ that $f(u)$ cannot be an extremum.

6. A stone wall 100 yards long stands on a ranch. Part or all of it is to be used in forming a rectangular corral, with an additional 260 yards of fencing for the other three sides. Find the area of the largest region which can be so enclosed.

7. A metal can with a square base and open top is required to contain a gallon (231 cubic inches) of oil. Neglecting the thickness of the metal and the waste material in construction, find the dimensions of the can that require the least material.

8. A right triangle with hypotenuse k is rotated about one of its legs. Find the maximum volume of the right circular cone produced.

9. Determine the lengths of the sides of a triangle of maximum area with base b and perimeter p. (Hint: use Heron's formula for the area of a triangle: $A = \sqrt{s(s - a)(s - b)(s - c)}$, where a, b, c are the lengths of the sides, and $s = \frac{1}{2}(a + b + c) = \frac{1}{2}p$.

10. a. Three men live in different houses on the same straight road. Where on the road should they agree to meet so that the sum of the distances they travel along the road from their homes to their meeting place is to be a minimum?
    b. What is the answer if the number of men is four?
    c. Answer the question for n men where n is any positive integer.

5.2b Local extrema

In 5.2a, Examples 1 through 3, we showed how to locate the global extrema on a closed interval of a differentiable function f. Clearly, an extremum of the function at an interior point of a given interval may fail to be an extremum in the interior of a larger interval. However, if $f(u)$ is an extreme value of f in some neighborhood of u, then it is an ex-

tremum in any smaller neighborhood; in this case, we call $f(u)$ a *local*
extremum of f (some texts use the term *relative* extremum). From 5.2a
Theorem 1, if $f(a)$ is a local extremum, then $f'(a) = 0$, provided
$f'(a)$ exists. In seeking the global extrema by the method described in
5.2a Examples 1–3, we shall also find the local extrema of f.

Example 1. Consider the function

$$f(x) = 3x^4 + 4x^3 - 12x^2 + 5.$$

We have

$$f'(x) = 12x^3 + 12x^2 - 24x = 12x(x-1)(x+2),$$

whence

$$f'(0) = f'(1) = f'(-2) = 0.$$

We tabulate the values of f at the zeros of the derivative and at the endpoints of an interval that contains the zeros.

x	-3	-2	0	1	2
$f(x)$	32	-27	5	0	37

From the table, we conclude that $f(-2)$ is the minimum of $f(x)$ on
the interval $[-3, 2]$, $f(0)$ a maximum on $[-2, 1]$, and $f(1)$ a minimum on $[0, 2]$. Since there are no other local maxima or minima, we
expect the graph of f to have the appearance of Figure 1. Thus, we

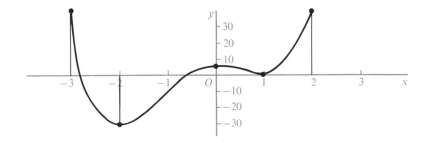

Figure 1

expect f to be a decreasing function for $x \leq -2$; $f(-2)$ is a local
minimum. For $-2 \leq x \leq 0$, the function should be increasing and
$f(0)$ is a local maximum. Over the interval $0 \leq x \leq 1$, the function
should decrease again to the local minimum $f(1)$; for $x > 1$, the function should be increasing.

We shall prove that the inferences concerning the function of the example are correct. By determining the positions of the local extrema of the function, we have been able to say a great deal about the general character of the function. We have intuitively utilized the idea that throughout the interval, between successive extrema, the function must be strongly monotone. In the proof of this theorem, we shall use a result which, together with 5.2a Theorem 1, is basic to the logical development of the rest of this chapter.

Lemma 1. Let f be a continuous function on the closed interval $[a, b]$. If $f(a) = f(b)$, then there is an extremum of f on the open interval (a, b).

Proof. Assume no extremum exists on the interior of the interval. By the Extreme Value Theorem, extrema exist on the closed interval. The extrema of f can then only occur at the endpoints. Since $f(a) = f(b)$, the maximum and minimum of f must then be the same. It follows that f is constant on $[a, b]$. Hence, $f(x)$ is an extreme value for all x satisfying $a \leq x \leq b$. This contradicts the assumption that f has no extremum on (a, b). □

We shall also use the following simple consequence of the Intermediate Value Theorem.

Lemma 2. If α, β, and γ are three points in $[a, b]$ such that

$$\alpha < \beta < \gamma$$

and

(1) $$f(\beta) > f(\alpha), \quad f(\beta) > f(\gamma),$$

then there exist distinct points c_1 and c_2 such that $f(c_1) = f(c_2)$, where $\alpha \leq c_1 < \beta < c_2 \leq \gamma$; see Figure 2.

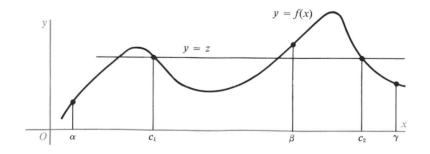

Figure 2

Proof. Let z be any value less than $f(\beta)$ but greater than both $f(\alpha)$ and $f(\gamma)$, for example,

$$z = \tfrac{1}{2}[f(\beta) + \max\ \{f(\alpha), f(\gamma)\}]\,.$$

Then $f(\alpha) < z < f(\beta)$, and, by the Intermediate Value Theorem, there exists a $c_1 \in [\alpha, \beta]$ such that $f(c_1) = z$; likewise, since

$$f(\gamma) < z < f(\beta)\,,$$

there exists a $c_2 \in [\beta, \gamma]$ such that $f(c_2) = z$. Finally, $c_1 \neq \beta$, $c_2 \neq \beta$, since $f(c_1) = f(c_2) = z \neq f(\beta)$.

A similar argument produces the same result in the case when the inequalities in (1) are reversed.   ☐

Theorem 1. If f is continuous on the closed interval $[a, b]$, and has no local extrema on the open interval (a, b), then f is strongly monotone on $[a, b]$.

Proof. By Lemma 1, we have $f(a) \neq f(b)$, hence either $f(a) < f(b)$ or $f(a) > f(b)$. If $f(a) < f(b)$, we shall prove f is increasing on $[a, b]$. (A parallel argument would prove f is decreasing if $f(a) > f(b)$.)

Let u, v be any two points of $[a, b]$ with $u < v$. We want to show that $f(u) < f(v)$. The case $f(u) = f(v)$ is impossible in view of Lemma 1 and thus it will be sufficient to show that the assumption $f(u) > f(v)$ results in a contradiction.

Assuming that $f(u) > f(v)$, we shall use Lemma 2 to exhibit two points c_1 and c_2 in $[a, b]$ such that $f(c_1) = f(c_2)$. It then follows, by Lemma 1, that f has a local extremum on (a, b), in contradiction to the hypothesis of the theorem.

Either $f(u) \leq f(a)$ or $f(u) > f(a)$. Suppose, first, that $f(u) > f(a)$. Then, $u \neq a$ so that $a < u < v$, while $f(u) > f(a)$ and

$$f(u) > f(v)\,.$$

We apply Lemma 2 with $\alpha = a$, $\beta = u$, and $\gamma = v$ to exhibit the desired points c_1 and c_2. Finally, suppose that $f(u) \leq f(a)$; thus,

$$f(v) < f(u) \leq f(a) < f(b)\,.$$

We conclude then that $a < v < b$, while

$$f(v) < f(a) \quad \text{and} \quad f(v) < f(b)\,.$$

We can now apply Lemma 2, with $\alpha = a$, $\beta = v$, and $\gamma = b$ and with inequalities in (1) reversed, to exhibit the desired points c_1 and c_2. ☐

Our method for finding the global extrema of a differentiable function has a useful by-product: the local extrema also are determined. Theorem 1 justifies the description of the gross properties of the function given in Example 1.

We know that on an open interval all the local extrema of a differentiable function f satisfy the condition $f'(x) = 0$. There may be points other than local extrema of f for which $f'(x) = 0$.

Example 2. Consider $f: x \to x^3$ on the interval $[-1, 1]$. We have $f'(x) = 3x^2$, hence $f'(0) = 0$ and the derivative vanishes nowhere else. We have $f(-1) = -1$, $f(0) = 0$, and $f(1) = 1$. It is easy to prove that x^3 is an increasing function, hence that $f(0)$ is not an extremum. We conclude only that the graph of f is horizontal at $x = 0$, but this information is also useful in sketching the graph; see Figure 3.

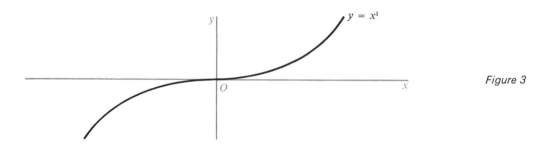

Figure 3

The result of the preceding example is a particular instance of the following corollary of Theorem 2.

Corollary a. Let $[a, b]$ be a closed interval in the domain of f where f is continuous. If f is differentiable on the open interval (a, b) and there exists only one point u in (a, b) where $f'(u) = 0$, and if $f(u)$ lies between $f(a)$ and $f(b)$ (that is, either $f(a) < f(u) < f(b)$ or $f(a) > f(u) > f(b)$), then $f(u)$ is not a local extremum.

The proof of this corollary is left to Exercise 1.

We say that f is *stationary* at a if a lies in an interval within the domain of f', and $f'(a) = 0$. Thus, a stationary point is any point where the graph of f is directed horizontally. Corollary 1a yields a necessary condition that an isolated stationary point be a local extremum. We now give a sufficient condition.

Corollary b. Let $[a, b]$ be a closed interval in the domain of f where f is continuous. Let f be differentiable on the open interval (a, b) and let there be only one point u in the open interval where

$$f'(u) = 0.$$

If $f(u) > f(a)$ and $f(u) > f(b)$, then $f(u)$ is the maximum of f on $[a, b]$. If $f(u) < f(a)$ and $f(u) < f(b)$, then $f(u)$ is the minimum of f on $[a, b]$.

The proof of this corollary is left to Exercise 1.

Example 3. We apply the knowledge we have gained to find the local and global extrema of the function

$$f: x \rightarrow 4x^5 - 5x^4 - 40x^3 + 100$$

on the interval $-3 \le x \le 4$. We differentiate and obtain

$$f'(x) = 20x^4 - 20x^3 - 120x^2 = 20x^2(x + 2)(x - 3).$$

Computing the values of f at the zeros of f' and at the endpoints of the interval, we obtain the following table.

x	-3	-2	0	3	4
$f(x)$	-197	212	100	-413	356

We consider triples of consecutive values of f in this table in the light of Corollaries 1a and 1b and find that the function f increases from a local minimum at $x = -3$ to a local maximum at $x = -2$, then decreases to its global minimum at $x = 3$ and increases to its global maximum at $x = 4$. (If we were to consider the entire real axis as the domain of f then, since f' has no zeros outside the open interval $(-3, 4)$, we

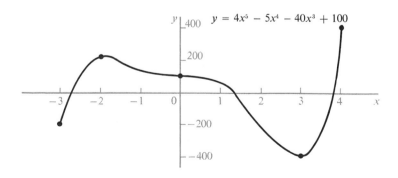

$y = 4x^5 - 5x^4 - 40x^3 + 100$

Figure 4

would conclude that f is increasing for $x < -3$ and also for $x > 4$.)
We can utilize the information of the table and plot a few additional points
to obtain an excellent idea of the behavior of f on the given interval;
see Figure 4.

In summary, in the light of the preceding discussion, to locate the extrema
of a continuous function on a closed interval, we restrict our search to the
endpoints of the interval, to interior points where the derivative does not
exist, and to interior points where the derivative is zero.

5.2b Exercises

1. Prove Corollaries 1a and 1b.

2. For each of the following functions locate and characterize all extrema. On
   what intervals is the function increasing? decreasing?

   a. $f : x \to 4x^4 - 8x^2 + 1$.   b. $f : x \to x^4 - 4x^3$.

   c. $f : x \to \dfrac{x^3}{1 + x^2}$.   d. $f : x \to \dfrac{x}{x^2 - 1}$.

   e. $f : x \to \dfrac{x}{1 + x^2}$.

3. A rectangle is inscribed in a circle of radius R . Find the rectangle of maximum area, the rectangle of maximum perimeter.

4. The area of the printed text on a page is A square centimeters. The left
   and right margins are each c centimeters wide, and both the upper and
   lower margins, d centimeters. What are the most economical dimensions
   of the pages if only the amount of paper matters?

5. A rectangle has two of its vertices on the x-axis and the other two above the
   axis on the parabola $y = 6 - x^2$. What are the dimensions of such a
   rectangle if its area is to be a maximum?

6. A rectangular sheet of galvanized metal is bent to form the sides and bottom
   of a trough so that the cross section has this shape: ⌊___⌋. If the metal is 14
   inches wide, how deep must the trough be to carry the most water?

7. Find the right circular cylinder of greatest volume that can be inscribed in a
   right circular cone of radius r and height h .

8. The lower right corner of a page is
   folded over so as to reach the left edge
   in such a way that one endpoint of the
   crease is on the right edge of the page
   and the other endpoint is on the bottom edge of the page, as in the figure.
   If the width of the page is c inches,
   find the minimum length of the crease.
   (Assume that the width is no more
   than $\frac{2}{3}$ the length.)

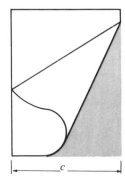

9. What is the smallest positive value of t such that the slope of

$$y = 2 \sin \left(\frac{t}{2} - \frac{\pi}{3} \right)$$

is zero?

10. A wall h feet high stands d feet away from a tall building. A ladder L feet long reaches from the ground outside the wall to the building. Let ϕ be the angle between the ladder and the building.

   a. Show that if the ladder touches the top of the wall, $L = d \csc \phi + h \sec \phi$.

   b. Find the shortest ladder that will reach the building if

$$h = 8 \quad \text{and} \quad d = 24.$$

11. A set of n experimental trials yields the numbers $a_1, a_2, \ldots, a_n$ for a certain physical quantity x. What value should we take for x in order to:

   a. minimize the sum of the squares of the deviations,

$$(x - a_1)^2 + (x - a_2)^2 + \cdots + (x - a_n)^2 \, ?$$

   b. minimize the sum of the absolute values of the deviations,

$$|x - a_1| + |x - a_2| + \cdots + |x - a_n| \, ?$$

12. Find the maximum of $x^p y^q$ (p, q rational and positive) if $x + y = c$ (c constant) and $x \geq 0$, $y \geq 0$.

13. Find the minimum value of $x + y$ if $x^p y^q = k$ (k constant, p and q rational and positive).

14. Prove that if f is continuous and has an inverse on an interval, then f is strongly monotone on the interval.

5.3 THE LAW OF THE MEAN

So far, we have used the derivative only to locate the extrema of a function. In 5.4, we shall prove that the derivative f' almost completely determines the function f. To argue from the properties of the derivative to the properties of the function, we use a basic theorem, the *Law of the Mean*.

In geometrical terms, the Law of the Mean states that on the arc between any two points of the graph of a differentiable function there exists a point where the curve has the same slope as the chord joining the points.† Thus, if $(p, f(q))$ and $(q, f(q))$ are any two points on the graph of a dif-

---

†The word "mean" here signifies "average." The slope of the chord is interpreted as the average rate of change (see 2.1 p. 24) of $f(x)$ with respect to x. The Law of the Mean states that this average is equal to a value of the derivative at some point of the interval.

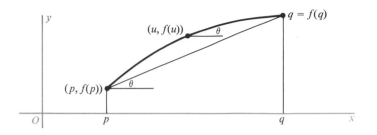

Figure 1

ferentiable function f with $p < q$ (see Figure 1), then, according to the Law of the Mean, there exists a point u between p and q where

$$f'(u) = \frac{f(q) - f(p)}{q - p}.$$

We can make the Law of the Mean plausible by an argument similar to that used in 1.1 where we first found that the slope of a graph at an interior extremum is zero. Let $(u, f(u))$ be a point that lies on the arc at maximal distance from the chord; we take a parallel to the chord through this point. Since no point of the arc lies at a greater distance from the chord, the arc cannot cross the parallel. The arc cannot meet the parallel at a positive angle for then it would cross; therefore, the two must have the same direction at $(u, f(u))$; see Figure 2.

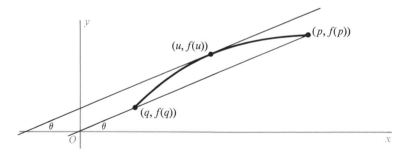

Figure 2

We first derive the Law of the Mean for the special case in which the chord is horizontal. We then use the special result as a lemma to help us prove the general result.

Lemma 1. (Rolle's Theorem) If f is continuous on the closed interval $[p , q]$ and differentiable on the open interval (p , q), and if $f(p) = f(q)$, then there is at least one point u in the open interval where $f'(u) = 0$.

Proof. From the assumption of continuity alone we have already shown that f has an extremum on the open interval (5.2b Lemma 1). If u is a point of (p, q) for which $f(u)$ is an extremum, then since f is differentiable on the open interval, we know by 5.2a Theorem 1 that $f'(u) = 0$.   □

Before proving the Law of the Mean, let us examine some of the other consequences of Rolle's Theorem (Lemma 1).

Corollary a. Let f be differentiable on an interval. Any zeros of f within the interval are separated by zeros of the derivative.

Proof. If $x_1 < x_2$ and $f(x_1) = f(x_2) = 0$, the conditions of Lemma 1 are satisfied and there exists a value u such that $x_1 < u < x_2$ and $f'(u) = 0$.   □

As a consequence of this result, we observe further that, in a given interval, a function may have at most one more zero than its derivative. From this fact there follows a familiar result.

Corollary b. A polynomial of degree n can have no more than n distinct real zeros.

The proof is left to Exercise 1.

Example 1. a. We apply Corollary a to the zeros of

$$f(x) = x^3 - 3x + 1.$$

We know that $f'(x) = 3x^2 - 3$ has zeros at $x = 1$ and $x = -1$. It follows that f may have as many as three zeros. We observe that $f(-1) = 3$ and $f(1) = -1$. By the Intermediate Value Theorem, we conclude that there is a zero of f between -1 and 1. Clearly, we can make $f(x)$ negative for sufficiently large negative values and positive for sufficiently large positive values. It follows that f has a zero for $x < -1$ and another for $x > 1$. Specifically, we have $f(-2) = -1$ and $f(2) = 3$, so that there is one zero between -2 and -1 and another between 1 and 2.

b. The function

$$f(x) = x^3 + 3x + 1$$

has the derivative $f'(x) = 3x^2 + 3$ which is always positive. Since the derivative is always positive, f can have at most one zero. Observing that $f(-1) = -3$ and $f(0) = 1$, we see that a zero exists and lies between $x = -1$ and $x = 0$.

c. The function

$$f(x) = x^4 - 4x^3 - 8x^2 + 64$$

has the derivative $f'(x) = 4x^3 - 12x^2 - 16x$ which has zeros at $x = -1$, $x = 0$, and $x = 4$. Thus, f may have as many as four zeros. We have $f(-1) = 61$, $f(0) = 64$, and $f(4) = -64$. It follows that f has a local maximum at $x = 0$ and, from 5.2b Theorem 1, that f is increasing on the interval $(-1, 0)$; consequently, there is no zero between -1 and 0. Further, from $f(-2) = 80$, we see that f has a local minimum at $x = -1$, hence that f is decreasing for $x < -1$, and there is no zero to the left of -1. Finally, we observe that $f(6) = 208$ so that $f(x)$ has precisely two zeros, one between 0 and 4, another between 4 and 6.

The information obtained in these examples is useful in sketching the graphs of the functions (see Exercise 2).

Theorem 1. The Law of the Mean. If f is continuous on the closed interval $[p, q]$ and differentiable on the open interval (p, q), then there is at least one point u in the open interval where

(1)
$$f'(u) = \frac{f(q) - f(p)}{q - p}.$$

Proof. If $d(x)$ is the perpendicular distance from the point $(x, f(x))$ to the line joining the points $(p, f(p))$ and $(q, f(q))$ and θ is the inclination of the line, then the vertical distance $h(x)$ from the point $(x, f(x))$ to the line is given by

$$h(x) = d(x) \sec \theta \, ;$$

see Figure 3. Since the quantities $h(x)$ and $d(x)$ are proportional, an extremum of one corresponds to an extremum of the other at the same value of x. For convenience, we work with the vertical distance $h(x)$. The line joining the points $(p, f(p))$ and $(q, f(q))$ is given by

(2)
$$g(x) = f(p) + (x - p)\frac{f(q) - f(p)}{q - p},$$

and the vertical distance $h(x)$ by

(3) $\quad h(x) = f(x) - g(x) = f(x) - f(p) - (x - p)\dfrac{f(q) - f(p)}{q - p}.$

From this equation it follows straightforwardly that $h(x)$ satisfies the conditions of Rolle's Theorem on $[p, q]$. First, as we may verify directly,

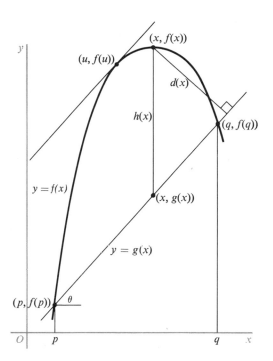

Figure 3

$h(p) = h(q) = 0$. Next, we observe that since f and g are both differentiable on the open interval (p, q) and continuous on the closed interval $[p, q]$, it follows from the theorems on the derivative of a linear combination and on the sums of continuous functions (4.2a Theorem 1 and 3.6a Theorem 1) that $h = f - g$ is also differentiable on the open interval and continuous on the closed interval. From Rolle's Theorem, we conclude that for some value u in (p, q)

$$h'(u) = f'(u) - g'(u) = 0,$$

whence, from Equation (3) for $h(x)$ that

$$f'(u) - \frac{f(q) - f(p)}{q - p} = 0. \qquad\qquad \Box$$

5.3 Exercises

1. Prove Corollary b to Lemma 1.
   Corollary b. A polynomial of degree n can have no more than n distinct real roots.

2. Sketch the graphs of the functions in Example 1.

3. Is the following converse of Rolle's Theorem true? If f is continuous on the closed interval $[p, q]$ and differentiable on the open interval (p, q), and if there is at least one point u in the open interval where $f'(u) = 0$, then there are two points m and n where $p \leq m < u < n \leq q$ such that $f(m) = f(n)$.

4. Does Rolle's Theorem justify the conclusion that $\dfrac{dy}{dx} = 0$ for some value of x in the interval $-1 \leq x \leq 1$ for $(y + 1)^3 = x^2$?

5. Given that $f(x) = x(x - 1)(x - 2)(x - 3)(x - 4)$. Determine the number of zeros of f' and find intervals including each of these without calculating $f'(x)$.

6. Test whether the hypothesis of Rolle's Theorem holds for the given function in the given interval. If it does not, is the conclusion of the theorem valid anyway?

a. $f : x \to x^3 + 4x^2 - 7x - 10$, on $[-1, 2]$.

b. $f : x \to \dfrac{2 - x^2}{x^4}$, on $[-1, 1]$.

7. Prove that the equation $f(x) = x^n + px + q = 0$ cannot have more than two real solutions for an even integer n nor more than three real solutions for an odd n.

8. A function g has a continuous second derivative on the closed interval $[a, b]$. The equation $g(x) = 0$ has three different solutions in the open interval (a, b). Show that the equation $g''(x) = 0$ has at least one solution in the open interval (a, b).

9. Show that the conclusion of the Law of the Mean does not follow for $f(x) = \tan x$ in the interval $1.5 < x < 1.6$ and explain why.

10. For each of the following functions show that the Law of the Mean fails to hold on the interval $[-a, a]$ if $a > 0$. Explain why the theorem fails.

a. $f : x \to |x|$.   b. $f : x \to \dfrac{1}{x}$.

11. Show that the equation $x^5 + x^3 - x - 2 = 0$ has exactly one solution in the open interval $(1, 2)$.

12. Show that $x^2 = x \sin x + \cos x$ for exactly two real values of x.

13. Find a number that can be chosen as the number u in the Law of the Mean for the given function and interval.

a. $f : x \to \cos x$, $0 \leq x \leq \frac{1}{2}\pi$.
b. $f : x \to x^3$, $-1 \leq x \leq 1$.
c. $f : x \to x^3 - 2x^2 + 1$, $-1 \leq x \leq 0$.
d. $f : x \to \cos x + \sin x$, $0 \leq x \leq 2\pi$.

14. Derive each of the following inequalities by applying the Law of the Mean.

a. $|\sin x - \sin y| \leq |x - y|$.

b. $\dfrac{x}{1 + x^2} < \arctan x < x$ if $x > 0$.

15. a. Show that a straight line can intersect the graph of a polynomial function of n-th degree at most n times for $n > 1$.
    b. Obtain the corresponding result for rational functions.
    c. Could $x \to \sin x$ or $x \to \cos x$ be rational functions? Justify your answer.

16. Prove the intermediate value property for derivatives; namely, if f is differentiable on the closed interval $[p, q]$ then $f'(x)$ takes on every value between $f'(p)$ and $f'(q)$ in the open interval (p, q).

5.4 APPLICATIONS OF THE LAW OF THE MEAN

In this section we apply the Law of the Mean in a variety of ways. In 5.4a we estimate the error of linear interpolation; in 5.4b we describe the characteristics of a monotone function in terms of the sign of the derivative; in 5.4c we determine the nature of an extremum by applying the results of 5.4b.

5.4a Linear interpolation

Linear interpolation is a useful method of approximating the values of a function in an interval when the endpoint values are known. If bounds on the range of the derivative can be obtained, the Law of the Mean gives a way of estimating the error of approximation.

Geometrically, linear interpolation consists of replacing the arc of the graph of f on the interval (p, q) by the chord joining the endpoints. Thus, on (p, q) we approximate $f(x)$ by the linear function $g(x)$ given by 5.3 (2). The error of the approximation $g(x) - f(x) = -h(x)$ is given by 5.3 (3). We wish to find an upper bound for the error

$$|g(x) - f(x)| \, .$$

For our purposes it is convenient to recast 5.3 (3) in the form

$$g(x) - f(x) = (x - p) \left(\frac{f(p) - f(q)}{p - q} - \frac{f(x) - f(p)}{x - p} \right) .$$

Now, by the Law of the Mean

(1) $$g(x) - f(x) = (x - p)[f'(u_2) - f'(u_1)]$$

where $p < u_1 < x < q$, $p < u_2 < q$. If the derivative is bounded on (p, q), then from (1)

$$|g(x) - f(x)| \le |x - p| \, (|f'(u_2)| + |f'(u_1)|) \, ;$$

whence

(2) $$|g(x) - f(x)| \leq 2M_1|x - p|,$$

where $|f'(z)| \leq M_1$ for all z in (p, q).

Example 1. Let us estimate $\sqrt{10}$ by linear interpolation applied to the function $f : x \to \sqrt{x}$. Since $3 < \sqrt{10} < 4$ we take $p = 9$ and $q = 16$ in 5.3 (2) and obtain $g(10) = \frac{22}{7}$ as our estimate for $\sqrt{10}$. On the interval $(9, 16)$, since $f'(x)$ is positive and decreasing,

$$|f'(x)| = \frac{1}{2\sqrt{x}} < \frac{1}{2\sqrt{9}} \leq \tfrac{1}{6}.$$

Entering this bound in (2) we obtain

$$|\tfrac{22}{7} - \sqrt{10}| \leq \tfrac{1}{3}.$$

We observe, however, that

$$(\tfrac{22}{7})^2 = \tfrac{484}{49} = 10 - \tfrac{6}{49}$$

and we suspect that our estimate of error is rather crude.

If f' has a derivative f'' (the second derivative of f) on the interval (p, q), we may again apply the Law of the Mean, now to the difference $f'(u_2) - f'(u_1)$ in Equation (1), to obtain

$$g(x) - f(x) = (x - p)(u_2 - u_1)f''(v)$$

where v is somewhere between u_2 and u_1. Since u_2 and u_1 are both points of (p, q) we know that the distance between the two points is less than the length of the interval:

$$|u_2 - u_1| < q - p.$$

Suppose, in addition, that we have a bound on the second derivative. Then we obtain an upper estimate for the error in terms of the second derivative:

(3) $$|g(x) - f(x)| \leq (x - p)(q - p)M_2,$$

where $|f''(x)| \leq M_2$ for all x in (p, q).

Example 2. Now let us use (3) to obtain an estimate for the error of approximation to $\sqrt{10}$ by the linear interpolation scheme of Example 1. Since $|f''(x)| = 1/4x^{3/2}$ is decreasing for $x \geq 0$,

$$|f''(x)| = \frac{1}{4x^{3/2}} < \frac{1}{4 \cdot 9^{3/2}} \leq \frac{1}{108}$$

for x in $(9, 16)$. Consequently, from (3),

$$|\tfrac{22}{7} - \sqrt{10}| \leq \tfrac{7}{108} < 0.065.$$

It follows that

$$3.07 < \sqrt{10} < 3.21.$$

We have obtained sharper estimates for $\sqrt{10}$ and now we can repeat the process to obtain still sharper estimates using $p = (3.07)^2$ and $q = (3.21)^2$.

5.4a Exercises

1. Use the Law of the Mean to approximate $\sqrt[3]{1.008}$.

2. Use the Law of the Mean to approximate $\cos 61°$.

3. Show that

$$a\left(1 + \frac{\epsilon}{n(a^n + \epsilon)}\right) < \sqrt[n]{a^n + \epsilon} < a\left(1 + \frac{\epsilon}{na^n}\right)$$

   for $\epsilon > 0$, $a > 1$, $n > 1$, and n rational.

4. Using Exercise 3, obtain the following approximations:

   a. $3 + \tfrac{1}{10} < \sqrt[3]{30} < 3 + \tfrac{1}{9}$.

   b. $3 + \dfrac{3}{5(244)} < \sqrt[5]{244} < 3 + \dfrac{1}{405}$.

   c.   Show that the approximation $\dfrac{1}{2}\left[\left(3 + \dfrac{3}{5(244)}\right) + \left(3 + \dfrac{1}{405}\right)\right]$ to $\sqrt[5]{244}$ is correct to at least five decimal places.

5.4b Monotone functions

In 5.2 we related the zeros of the derivative f' to the extrema of a function f. We now consider the properties of f' on those intervals where there are no interior extrema of f. As we know from 5.2b Theorem 1, the function f on such an interval, must be strongly monotone. The monotone nature of f is directly connected with the sign of the derivative f'. If f is increasing, we do not expect the slope of the graph to be negative, although, as the function $f : x \to x^3$ illustrates (5.2b Example 2), there may be values of x where $f'(x) = 0$. Since we cannot exclude the possibility that $f'(x) = 0$ at some point in the domain of a strongly monotone function, we use weak inequalities and prove a result for weakly monotone functions.

Theorem 1. Let f be differentiable on (a, b). Then f is weakly increasing on (a, b) if and only if $f'(x) \geq 0$ for all x in (a, b).

Proof. If f is weakly increasing on (a, b), then, for x in (a, b) and h so small that $x + h$ lies in (a, b),

$$\frac{f(x + h) - f(x)}{h} \geq 0$$

whether $h > 0$ or $h < 0$. It follows from 3.4a Theorem 6 that

$$f'(x) = \lim_{h \sim 0} \frac{f(x + h) - f(x)}{h} \geq \lim_{h \sim 0} 0 \geq 0.$$

Conversely, suppose $f'(x) \geq 0$ on (a, b). For any two values x_1, x_2 in the interval satisfying $x_1 < x_2$ we have, by the Law of the Mean,

$$f(x_2) - f(x_1) = f'(u)(x_2 - x_1),$$

where $x_1 < u < x_2$. Since $f'(u) \geq 0$ and $(x_2 - x_1) > 0$ we conclude that $f(x_2) - f(x_1) \geq 0$. Since $f(x_2) \geq f(x_1)$ for any pair satisfying $x_2 > x_1$, the monotone property of f is established. ⬜

Corollary a. Let f be differentiable on (a, b). Then f is weakly decreasing on (a, b) if and only if $f'(x) \leq 0$ for all x in (a, b).

The proof of this corollary is left to 5.4b, c Exercise 3.

Corollary b. If $f'(x) = 0$ for all points x in the interval (a, b) then f is constant on (a, b).

Proof. From Theorem 1, f must be both weakly increasing and weakly decreasing, hence constant; see A2.5 Exercise 4. ⬜

From Corollary 1b we can see to what extent the derivative of a function determines the function. If two functions g and f have the same derivative then $D(g - f) = Dg - Df = 0$. It follows from the corollary that

$$g - f = c$$

where c is a constant function. Thus

$$g = f + c.$$

In words, the derivative of a function determines the function to within an additive constant. Geometrically, the graph of a function is determined by the derivative except for a possible vertical translation. This result is summarized as follows.

Corollary c. If two differentiable functions have the same derivative on an interval they differ by a constant. Conversely, if two functions differ by a constant they have the same derivative.

Proof. The proof of the first proposition is given above. The converse is a direct consequence of the differentiation theorems of 4.2. ☐

Finally, we observe that the proof of the converse proposition in Theorem 1 remains valid if all weak inequalities are replaced by strong ones:

Theorem 2. If $f'(x) > 0$ for all x in (a, b) then f is increasing on (a, b). If $f'(x) < 0$, then f is decreasing.

The converse of Theorem 2 is not true. (Why not?) See if you can find a condition on the derivative of f which is equivalent to requiring that f is strongly monotone (5.4b, c Exercise 15).

Consider a curve given in the parametric form A3.5 (1a),

$$(1) \qquad \begin{cases} x = \varphi(t), \\ y = \psi(t), \end{cases} \qquad a < t < b,$$

where φ and ψ are defined and have continuous derivatives on the parameter interval (a, b). We can obtain a formula for the slope of the curve (1) at any point (x_0, y_0) where $x_0 = \varphi(t_0)$, $y_0 = \psi(t_0)$, and t_0 is any point of the parameter interval where $\varphi'(t_0) \neq 0$. In order to apply the definition of the slope of a curve, we must express y as a function of x. Since $\varphi'(t_0) \neq 0$ and φ' is continuous at t_0, it follows from 3.4 Lemma 1 that φ' has constant nonzero sign on some neighborhood of t_0. From Theorem 2, we conclude that φ is strongly monotone on the neighborhood of t_0 and, hence, has an inverse $\omega : \varphi(t) \to t$. Thus

$$y = \psi(t) = \psi\omega(x).$$

From the theorems on the derivative of a composition, 4.6 Theorem 1, and the derivative of an inverse, 4.3 Theorem 1, we obtain

$$y'(x_0) = \psi'\omega(x_0)\, \omega'(x_0) = \psi'(t_0)/\varphi'(t_0).$$

In Leibnizian notation, this takes the easily remembered form

$$(2) \qquad \frac{dy}{dx} = \frac{dy}{dt} \bigg/ \frac{dx}{dt}.$$

Example 1. We determine the slope at points of the circle

$$x = r \cos t,$$
$$y = r \sin t, \qquad\qquad 0 < t < 2\pi.$$

On the open interval $(0, 2\pi)$,

$$\frac{dx}{dt} = -r \sin t, \qquad \frac{dy}{dt} = r \cos t,$$

whence,

$$\frac{dy}{dx} = -\frac{1}{\tan t}.$$

Note that this result can be put in the form

$$\frac{dy}{dx} = -\frac{x}{y}$$

in agreement with the result of 4.8 Example 1.

Observe that $\dfrac{dx}{dt}$ vanishes for $t = 0$ and $t = \pi$, so that (2) does not apply. These values of t correspond to the points $(1, 0)$ and $(-1, 0)$ where the inclination of the curve is vertical; therefore the slope of the curve at these points could not be defined meaningfully.

5.4c The reversal of sign test for an extremum

In the examples of 5.2b we determined the local behavior of f near a point a where $f'(a) = 0$, namely, whether $f(a)$ is a local maximum, minimum, or neither. For this purpose, we compared $f(a)$ with $f(p)$ and $f(q)$, where $p < a < q$ and p, q are chosen as next adjacent zeros of f' or as endpoints of the interval. Since the values of f in any neighborhood of a are sufficient to establish a local property, we are led to seek a criterion that does not depend upon the values of f at distant points, such as other zeros of f'.

Theorem 1. Reversal of sign test Let f be differentiable on a neighborhood of a point a where $f'(a) = 0$. If $f'(x)$ reverses sign at a then $f(a)$ is an extremum on the neighborhood. Specifically, if $f'(a) < 0$ when $x < a$ and $f'(x) > 0$ when $x > a$ then $f(a)$ is a minimum; if $f'(x) > 0$ when $x < a$ and $f'(x) < 0$ when $x > a$ then $f(a)$ is a maximum; see Figure 1.

Proof. Here we prove the criterion for a maximum. Let x be a point of the neighborhood other than a. By the Law of the Mean,

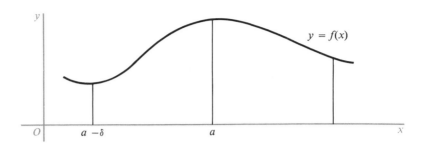

Figure 1

$$f(a) - f(x) = f'(u)(a - x)$$

where u lies between a and x. Whether $x > a$ or $x < a$, it follows from the conditions of the theorem that $f'(u)(a - x) > 0$. We conclude that $f(a) > f(x)$ for all x in the deleted neighborhood. ▯

The conclusion of the theorem remains valid if the inequalities governing the sign of the derivative are weak, but we seldom need the theorem in that form (5.4b, c Ex. 12). The proof parallels that of Theorem 1. With strong inequalities we have a sharper result:

Corollary a. Under the conditions of Theorem 1, the extremum of f at a is *isolated;* that is, in the deleted neighborhood of a, we have

$$f(x) \neq f(a).$$

Proof. For the given neighborhood of Theorem 1, when $f(a)$ is a maximum, we have already proved that there is a strong inequality $f(x) < f(a)$ for $x \neq a$. A similar argument establishes the result $f(x) > f(a)$ for $x \neq a$ when $f(a)$ is a minimum. ▯

To complement the preceding theorem, we need to know when $f(a)$ is not a local extremum.

Theorem 2. Let f be differentiable on a neighborhood of a point a for which $f'(a) = 0$. If $f'(x)$ has constant nonzero sign on a deleted neighborhood of a, then $f(a)$ is not a local extremum.

Proof. Suppose that $f'(x)$ is positive on a deleted neighborhood of a. Let $h > 0$ be any value smaller than the radius of the neighborhood. From 5.4b Theorem 2 and 5.2b Theorem 1 it follows that f is increasing on both closed intervals $[a - h, a]$ and $[a, a + h]$. Consequently,

$$f(a - h) < f(a) < f(a + h).$$

It follows that a can be neither a local minimum nor a local maximum. ∎

Example 1. If $f(x) = 3x^7 - 5x^4 + \sqrt{2}\, x^2 + 93$ then

$$f'(x) = 21x^6 - 20x^3 + 2\sqrt{2}\, x.$$

Observing that $f'(0) = 0$, we ask whether $f(0)$ is a local minimum or maximum. To find the other zeros of $f'(x)$, we would have to solve the fifth degree equation $21x^5 - 20x^2 + 2\sqrt{2} = 0$. It seems preferable to test for reversal of sign. Writing

$$f'(x) = x(2\sqrt{2} - 20x^2 + 21x^5)$$

we observe that for x near zero the factor in parentheses is close to $2\sqrt{2}$, hence positive. It follows that for sufficiently small x, $f'(x)$ changes sign with x; if $x < 0$ then $f'(x) < 0$ and if $x > 0$ then $f'(x) > 0$. We conclude that $f(0) = 93$ is a local minimum.

Example 2. If $f(x) = x^8 - 7x^5 + \pi x^3 - 1024$ then

$$f'(x) = 8x^7 - 35x^4 + 3\pi x^2 \quad \text{and} \quad f'(0) = 0.$$

We test for reversal of sign. Writing

$$f'(x) = x^2(3\pi - 35x^2 + 8x^5)$$

we see that the factor in parentheses is positive when x is sufficiently small. It follows that $f'(x)$ is positive whether $x > 0$ or $x < 0$. We conclude, by Theorem 2, that $f(0)$ is neither a local maximum nor a local minimum, but that f is an increasing function in the neighborhood of $x = 0$.

The reversal-of-sign test is especially valuable when there is only one zero of the derivative in an interval. The criterion is then sufficient to confirm an interior global extremum. (See 5.4b, c Exercise 13.)

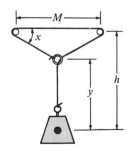

Example 3. A cord of length L has a small ring attached to one end; the other end is first passed through the ring so as to form a loop, then fastened to a weight. If the loop is passed over two horizontal pegs a distance M apart, jutting out of a wall at the same level (Figure 2), at what height h below the level of the pegs will the weight come to rest?

(It is assumed that L is considerably longer than $2M$, that the height of the pegs above the ground is greater than L, and that friction plays no role.)

We denote the distance between the level of the weight and the level of the pegs by h, and the distance between the levels of the weight and ring by y. If x denotes the angle formed by the cord at either peg,

$$h = y + \left(\frac{M}{2}\right) \tan x, \qquad L = y + M + 2\left(\frac{M}{2}\right) \sec x,$$

where we may assume $0 \leq x < \frac{\pi}{2}$. We eliminate y between these two relations, and obtain a function f given by the equation

$$f(x) = h = \left(\frac{M}{2}\right) \tan x + L - M - M \sec x,$$

whose maximum we seek. The derivative

$$f'(x) = \left(\frac{M}{2}\right) \sec^2 x - M \sec x \tan x$$

$$= \left(\frac{M}{2}\right) \sec x (\sec x - 2 \tan x)$$

is zero only when $\sec x = 2 \tan x$, or $\sin x = \frac{1}{2}$, that is, when $x = \frac{1}{6}\pi$. From the rearranged form

$$f'(x) = \left(\frac{M}{2}\right) \sec^2 x (1 - 2 \sin x)$$

we see that $f'(x) > 0$ for $0 < x < \frac{1}{6}\pi$ and $f'(x) < 0$ for

$$\frac{\pi}{6} < x < \frac{\pi}{3},$$

so that $f(\frac{1}{6}\pi)$ is a local maximum value of f. Thus, the weight comes to rest when

$$h = f\left(\frac{\pi}{6}\right) = \left(\frac{M}{2}\right) \tan \frac{\pi}{6} + L - M - M \sec \frac{\pi}{6}$$

$$= L - \left(\frac{M}{2}\right)(2 + \sqrt{3}).$$

It would take little effort to show that no greater value of f is attained at the endpoints of the interval of physically possible values of the angle x, namely, when the ring is at the level of the pegs or when the ring is at the level of the weight. We observe, however, that there is no other zero of f' in the extended domain $0 \leq x < \dfrac{\pi}{2}$. Thus, without further test we know that $f\left(\dfrac{\pi}{6}\right)$ is the over-all maximum and describes the equilibrium position.

5.4b, c Exercises

1. On what intervals is the function $f : x \to \dfrac{x^2 - 3}{x - 2}$ strongly monotone? Use 5.4c Theorem 1 to characterize all extrema. Sketch the graph of f.

2. Locate all intervals on which the function $f : x \to 44 + 4x - 13x^2 + 18x^3 - 9x^4$ is increasing; decreasing. Compare with 5.1 Exercise 1, and 5.2a Exercise 1.

3. Prove 5.4b Corollary 1a.

4. For each of the following functions find all points a for which $f'(a) = 0$, determine those intervals on which f is strongly monotone and sketch the graph of each function.

   a. $f(x) = \dfrac{x}{1 + x^4}$.

   b. $f(x) = (1 - x)^4$.

   c. $f(x) = (1 - x)^5$.

   d. $f(x) = \dfrac{x^2 + 10}{x^2 - 5}$.

5. If p and q are integers and
$$f(x) = (x - 1)^p (x + 1)^q, \qquad (p \geq 2, \ q \geq 2)$$
   find the extrema of f for the following cases.

   a. p and q are both even.   b. p is odd and q is even.
   c. p is even and q is odd.   d. p and q are both odd.

6. If p, q and r are positive integers, and $a < b < c$, discuss the graph of the function
$$f : x \to (x - a)^p (x - b)^q (x - c)^r.$$
   Discuss some special cases as in Exercise 5.

7. A tank is to have a given volume V and is to be made in the form of a right circular cylinder capped by hemispheres. The material for the caps costs twice as much per square foot as that for the cylindrical part. Find the most economical dimensions.

8. Find the length of the longest rod which can be carried horizontally around a corner from a corridor 10 ft. wide into one 5 ft. wide.

9. Find a point P on the arc AB of a circle such that the sum of the lengths of the chords $[AP]$ and $[BP]$ is a maximum. Assume that AB is no greater than a semicircle.

10. If possible, determine a line which passes through the point $(5, 8)$ such that the area of the triangle formed in the first quadrant with the coordinate axes is a positive number a. For what values of a is it impossible to construct such a triangle?

11. Find a point on the altitude of an isosceles triangle such that the sum of its distances from the vertices is the smallest possible.

12. Let f be differentiable on a neighborhood of a point a for which

$$f'(a) = 0.$$

If $f'(x) \le 0$ when $x < a$ and $f'(x) \ge 0$ when $x > a$ then $f(a)$ is a minimum. If $f'(x) \ge 0$ when $x < a$ and $f'(x) \le 0$ when $x > a$ then $f(a)$ is a maximum. Give a proof.

13. Let f be continuous on the closed interval $[a, b]$ and differentiable on the open interval (a, b). Suppose u is the one point in (a, b) where $f'(u) = 0$. Prove that if $f'(x)$ reverses sign at u then $f(u)$ is the global extremum of f on the interval $[a, b]$ appropriate to the sense of reversal.

14. Given a function f such that $f(1) = f(2) = 4$, and such that $f''(x)$ exists and is positive throughout the interval $1 \le x \le 3$. What can you conclude about $f'(2.5)$? about $f(2.5)$? Prove your statements, stating whatever theorems you use in your proof.

15. Let f be a differentiable function on (a, b). Prove that the requirement that f be increasing is equivalent to the condition that $f'(x) \ge 0$ everywhere but that every interval contains points where $f'(x) > 0$.

16. Given that f is everywhere differentiable. If $f(x) \le f(0)$ whenever $f'(x) \ge 0$ prove that $f(x) \le f(0)$ for all positive x.

17. If g'' is continuous and positive on the interval (p, q), what is the maximum number of roots of each of the equations $g(x) = 0$ and $g'(x) = 0$ in (p, q)? Prove your results and give some illustrative examples.

18. a. If $f'(a) > 0$ show for values of x in a neighborhood of a that if $x > a$ then $f(x) > f(a)$, and if $x < a$ then $f(x) < f(a)$.
b. Give an example of a function f for which $f'(a) > 0$ but which is not increasing on any neighborhood of a, no matter how small.

5.5 THE TANGENT APPROXIMATION

In 5.4a we approximated a differentiable function f on an interval by the linear function g which has the same values as f at the endpoints of the interval. Estimates of the error were obtained with the help of the

Law of the Mean. Here, we generalize the idea of tangent line introduced for the circle in A3.5b and the ellipse in A3.5c Ex. 12. We shall treat the equation of the tangent line to the graph of f at a as a linear approximation to f in a neighborhood of a.

The tangent line to a circle or ellipse at a given point on the curve was defined as the unique line through the point which meets no other point of the curve. This definition will not do for other curves because there may be more than one line which meets a curve at a given point and no other point. For example, the two lines $x = 0$ and $y = 0$ meet the parabola $y = x^2$ at the one point $(0, 0)$; see Figure 1. We want to use the concept of tangent line as a line that "touches" the curve.† In Figure 1, the line

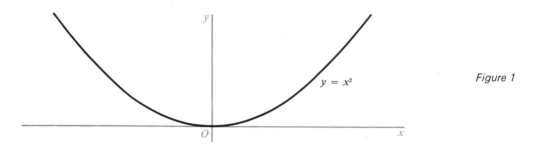

Figure 1

$y = 0$ should be considered a tangent line, the line $x = 0$ should not. In general, we define a tangent line to the graph of f at a as the line which passes through the point $(a, f(a))$ and has the direction of the graph at the given point; see Figure 2.

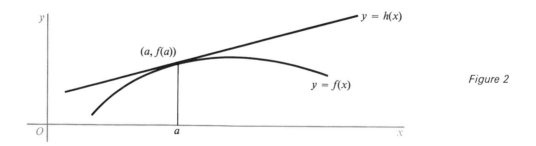

Figure 2

Definition 1. The *tangent line* to the graph of a differentiable function f at a is the line

(1) $$y = f(a) + f'(a)(x - a).$$

†The word "tangent" derives from Latin, *tangentis*, touching.

If f is not differentiable at a, but has an inverse with derivative 0 at $f(a)$, the tangent line to the graph of f at a is the vertical line $x = a$.

Example 1. The parabola $y = \frac{1}{2}x^2 + x + \frac{5}{2}$ goes through the point $(1, 4)$ with slope $m = 2$. The tangent line through $(1, 4)$ has the equation

$$y = 4 + 2(x - 1).$$

Elimination of y from this equation and the equation of the parabola yields $\frac{1}{2}x^2 + x + \frac{5}{2} - (2x + 2) = \frac{1}{2}(x^2 - 2x + 1) = \frac{1}{2}(x - 1)^2 = 0$. It follows that the parabola and its tangent line meet only at $(1, 4)$.

Example 2. We show that Definition 1 is equivalent to the original definition of tangent line for the circle. We choose the coordinate axes so that the equation of the circle has the form $x^2 + y^2 = r^2$, where r is the radius. For a point (a, b) on the circle, implicit differentiation yields the slope $m = -\dfrac{a}{b}$. The tangent line through (a, b) has the equation

$y = b - \dfrac{a}{b}(x - a)$. Using $a^2 + b^2 = r^2$, we obtain the symmetrical form of the equation,

$$ax + by = r^2.$$

In the vicinity of the point of tangency, the line tangent to a graph $y = f(x)$ usually does have the property that the curve lies on one side of the tangent line. However, at special points the curve may cross its tangent line. Thus, the curve $y = x^3$ crosses its tangent line at $x = 0$.

For a point x in a neighborhood of a, the tangent approximation to $f(x)$ is the number y given by (1). The error of this approximation can easily be estimated if f has a bounded second derivative on the neighborhood of a.

Using the Law of the Mean, we find for the absolute error e

$$e = |f(x) - y| = |f(x) - f(a) - f'(a)(x - a)|$$
$$= |f'(z)(x - a) - f'(a)(x - a)|$$

where z is some value between x and a. Thus,

$$e = |f'(z) - f'(a)| \, |x - a|.$$

In this result, we now apply the Law of the Mean to f' and obtain

$$e = |f''(u)| \, |z - a| \, |x - a| \le |f''(u)| \, (x - a)^2,$$

where u lies between z and a. If the bound for f'' on the neighborhood of a is given by $|f''(\xi)| \leq M_2$, we obtain the error estimate

$$(2) \qquad\qquad e \leq M_2(x - a)^2 .$$

This estimate for the error is to be compared with the estimate 5.4a (3) for the error of linear interpolation.

Example 3. We obtain an estimate of the error in approximating $f(x) = x^3$ by the equation of the tangent line at $x = a$ on the neighborhood $a - \delta \leq x \leq a + \delta$.

We have $f''(x) = 6x$ for all x, so that

$$\begin{aligned}
|f''(x)| = 6|x| &= 6|(x - a) + a| \\
&\leq 6(|x - a| + |a|) \\
&\leq 6(\delta + |a|) .
\end{aligned}$$

Consequently,

$$\begin{aligned}
e &\leq 6(|a| + \delta)(x - a)^2 \\
&\leq 6(|a| + \delta)\delta^2 .
\end{aligned}$$

If, for example, we take $a = 5$, $\delta = 0.1$ we see that the error in estimating $f(x)$ is less than 0.31 in the approximation of a function value near $f(5) = 125$.

The tangent line at a is the "best" linear approximation to the graph of f on the neighborhood of $x = a$ in a sense which is easily understood. If we take any other line passing through $(a, f(a))$, say

$$y = f(a) + m(x - a),$$

where $m \neq f'(a)$, then, from the Law of the Mean we obtain for the absolute error of approximation

$$\begin{aligned}
\bar{e} &= |f(x) - f(a) - m(x - a)| \\
&= |f'(\bar{z}) - m|\,|x - a|
\end{aligned}$$

where $\bar{z}$ lies between x and a. Since f' is differentiable it is continuous, and by taking x sufficiently close to a we can make $f'(\bar{z})$ as close to $f'(a)$ as we wish. Since $m \neq f'(a)$ we can guarantee that $|f'(\bar{z}) - m|$ is greater than some fixed positive quantity k (say, $k = \frac{1}{2}|f'(a) - m|$) by taking $|x - a|$ small enough. We then have

$$(3) \qquad\qquad \bar{e} > k|x - a| \qquad\qquad (x \neq a).$$

It follows from (2) and (3) that

$$e < \frac{M_2}{k} |x - a|\bar{e} ;$$

that is, by taking x sufficiently close to a, we can make the ratio $e/\bar{e}$ as small as desired. Thus, for x sufficiently close to a, the tangent approximation is better than any other arbitrarily given linear approximation to f.

5.5 Exercises

1. The normal line to a curve at a given point is the perpendicular to the tangent line at the same point. Show that the normal line to the graph of f at a is given by the equation

   (i) $$x - a = -f'(a) [y - f(a)] .$$

2. Find equations for the tangent and normal lines to the graphs of the following functions at the given points.

   a. $f : x \to x \sin x$, at $x = 0$, $x = \dfrac{\pi}{2}$.

   b. $f : x \to \arcsin \dfrac{1}{x}$, at $x = 2$.

   c. $f : x \to \dfrac{x^3}{1 + x^2}$, at $x = -1$, $x = 0$.

   d. $f : x \to \dfrac{x}{x^2 - 1}$, at $x = x_0$ where $|x_0| \neq 1$.

3. Show that the graphs of the functions $f : x \to 6x^2$ and $g : x \to 4x^3 + 2$ have a common tangent line at the point $(1, 6)$. Sketch the graphs.

4. Prove that the line tangent to the circle of Example 2 at (a, b) meets the circle at no other point.

5. a. For the ellipse

   $$\frac{x^2}{p^2} + \frac{y^2}{q^2} = 1$$

   and for the hyperbola

   $$\frac{x^2}{p^2} - \frac{y^2}{q^2} = 1 ,$$

   obtain an equation of the line tangent to the curve at (a, b) in a symmetrical form like that of Example 2 for the circle.
   b. For each of the curves, obtain an equation for the normal line to the curve at (a, b) in an analogous form.
   c. Show for the ellipse that the definition of tangent line (1) agrees with the definition of A3.5c Exercise 12.

6. Show that the number of tangent lines that can be drawn from the point (h, k) to the curve $y = x^2$ is two, one, or zero, according to whether k is less than, equal to, or greater than h^2, respectively.

7. If $f : x \to ax^2 + bx + c$ $(a \neq 0)$, show that the tangent line to the graph of f at the point $(p, f(p))$ is parallel to the chord joining the two points $(u, f(u))$ and $(v, f(v))$ only if $p = \frac{1}{2}(u + v)$.

8. Given the ellipse $b^2x^2 + a^2y^2 = a^2b^2$ and an arbitrary point P on the curve but not on either axis, prove that if the normal at P to the ellipse passes through the origin, the ellipse is a circle.

9. Find an equation of the tangent line to the graph of the equation

$$x^2 - x\sqrt{xy} - 2y^2 = 6$$

at the point $(4, 1)$.

10. Find an equation of the tangent line to the folium of Descartes

(i) $$x^3 + y^3 - 3axy = 0$$

at the point (x_0, y_0). Note particularly the situation at $(0, 0)$.

11. The angle between two curves at a point of intersection is defined as the angle between their tangent lines at the given point. Determine the angles at which the line $y = x$ meets the parabola $y = x^2$ at their points of intersection.

12. a. Estimate the error of approximation to $y = \sin x$ by the tangent at $x = 0$.
    b. Show that the error is at least third order in $|x|$, namely, that

$$|x - \sin x| \leq c |x|^3,$$

where c is constant.

13. Show how to approximate $\sqrt[n]{2^n + 1}$, where n is a positive integer, and estimate the error of approximation.

14. Comment on the footnote in 1.1, p. 6.

15. Compare the linear approximation method of this section with those of 5.4a.

5.6 FURTHER APPLICATIONS OF THE SECOND DERIVATIVE

In this section we explore the significance of the second derivative f'' of a function f. In 5.6a we are concerned with a local property, the nature of an extremum as determined by the sign of the second derivative. In 5.6b and 5.6c we consider the global properties of the function f on an interval where the second derivative f'' has no reversals of sign.

5.6a The second derivative test for an extremum

In 5.4c Theorem 1 we showed that a reversal of sign of the first derivative is a sufficient condition for an extremum. For example, if $f'(x)$ is negative for $x < a$, if $f'(a) = 0$, and if $f'(x)$ is positive for $x > a$, we know that $f(a)$ is a local minimum. To guarantee a minimum at a, it would be sufficient to demonstrate that $f'(a) = 0$ and that f' is increasing on a neighborhood of a. To establish the increasing character of f' and hence that $f(a)$ is a minimum it is sufficient to show by 5.4b Theorem 2 that f'', the derivative of f', is positive on a neighborhood of a. Actually, it is enough to know only that $f''(a) > 0$ as we now prove.

Theorem 1. If $f'(a) = 0$ and $f''(a) > 0$ then $f(a)$ is a local minimum of f.

Proof. Since $f''(a) > 0$ and

$$f''(a) = \lim_{x \sim a} \frac{f'(x) - f'(a)}{x - a}$$

we know from 3.4 Lemma 1 that for a sufficiently small deleted neighborhood of a

$$\frac{f'(x) - f'(a)}{x - a} > 0 .$$

This inequality implies for $x > a$ that $f'(x) - f'(a) > 0$ and for $x < a$ that $f'(x) - f'(a) < 0$. But, by 5.4c Theorem 1, this condition assures a minimum on the neighborhood. □

Corollary a. If $f'(a) = 0$ and $f''(a) < 0$ then $f(a)$ is a local maximum of f.

The proof of this corollary is left as an exercise.

Example 1. In 5.4c Example 4 of the weight suspended from a string looped over pegs we found for the derivative of the height function

$$f'(x) = \left(\frac{M}{2}\right) \sec^2 x \, (1 - 2 \sin x)$$

and thus showed that $x = \dfrac{\pi}{6}$ was the only zero of h' in the relevant domain. We use Theorem 1 to test for an extremum and obtain

$$f''\left(\frac{\pi}{6}\right) = -M \sec \frac{\pi}{6} = -\frac{2M}{\sqrt{3}} .$$

Since $f''\left(\dfrac{\pi}{6}\right) < 0$ we conclude that $f\left(\dfrac{\pi}{6}\right)$ is a local maximum, and

since $\dfrac{\pi}{6}$ is the only zero of f' we conclude that the maximum is global.

Example 2. Let us find the extrema of

$$f(x) = 4x^5 + 5x^4 - 20x^3 - 50x^2 - 40x .$$

We obtain the first and second derivatives:

$$f'(x) = 20x^4 + 20x^3 - 60x - 100x - 40$$
$$= 20(x + 1)^3(x - 2)$$

and

$$f''(x) = 20[(x + 1)^3 + 3(x + 1)^2(x - 2)]$$
$$= 20(x + 1)^2(4x - 5) .$$

The zeros of f' occur at $x = -1$ and $x = 2$. We attempt to apply the second derivative test and obtain $f''(-1) = 0$, $f''(2) = 540$. It follows that $f(2)$ is a local minimum. The criterion of Theorem 1 gives us no information about $f(-1)$, but we observe that there is a reversal of sign of f' from positive to negative so that $f(-1)$ is a local maximum.

5.6b Convexity

Let us suppose that the second derivative has constant nonzero sign on an interval, say $f''(x) > 0$. Then, by 5.4b Theorem 2, f' is increasing on the interval. Thus as x increases, the inclination of the graph of f increases; we say the curve is flexed or bent upward; see Figure 1. A motion

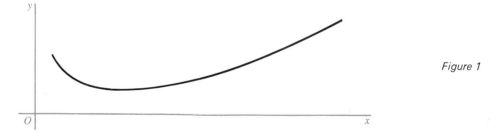

Figure 1

in either direction along an upwardly flexed curve always turns toward the upward vertical.

For the purposes of geometry it is convenient to adopt a definition of flexure which does not involve the idea of derivative.

Definition 1. The graph of the function f is said to be *flexed upward* on an interval of the domain if no point on any chord to the graph lies below the corresponding arc of the graph. The graph of f is said to be *flexed downward* if the graph of $-f$ is flexed upward. In both cases, we say the function f is *convex* on the interval.

Under this definition, note, in particular, that a straight line is considered to be flexed both upward and downward. Thus, a linear function is convex. Figure 2 illustrates the graph of a function with a downwardly flexed

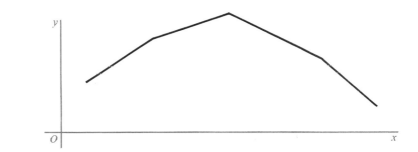

Figure 2

graph and no derivatives at isolated points. As the figure illustrates, the idea of flexure in Definition 1 does not imply a continuous bending or turning, but allows for abrupt changes of direction. If the second derivative exists, then the first derivative is continuous and abrupt changes of direction are not possible. In any case, if f'' exists and has no reversals of sign on a given interval, the function f must be convex.

Theorem 1. Let f have a second derivative on the open interval (a, b). The graph of f is flexed upward on (a, b) if and only if $f''(x) \geq 0$ on the interval.

The proof of Theorem 1 is given in 5.6c, where we investigate the properties of convex functions more deeply.

It is geometrically intuitive that if a curve is convex in a neighborhood of $x = a$ then it does not cross the tangent at $x = a$; see 5.6c Ex. 3a. The curve $y = x^3$ does cross its tangent at $x = 0$, but as x increases there is a transition at $x = 0$ from downward flexure for $x < 0$ to upward flexure when $x > 0$; see 5.6c Ex. 3b. At such a point of transition we must have $f''(a) = 0$ if the second derivative exists. These considerations suggest that such special points be singled out for consideration in a description of the gross properties of a function. In particular, we introduce the concept of point of inflection:

Definition 2. If f'' is strongly monotone in the neighborhood of a, and $f''(a) = 0$ then $(a, f(a))$ is defined to be an *inflection* point of f.

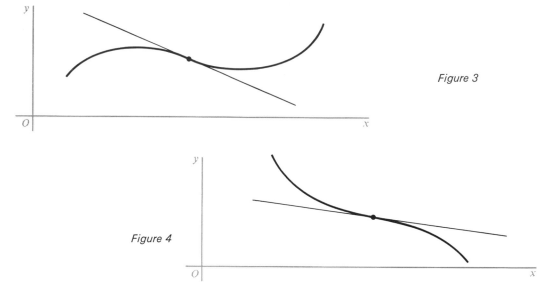

Figure 3

Figure 4

The two possible cases are illustrated in Figures 3 and 4. Usually the zeros of the second derivative will be isolated and the graph will consist of convex arcs separated by points of inflection where the flexure reverses sense.

Example 1. The function

$$f(x) = 4x^5 + 5x^4 - 20x^3 - 50x^2 - 40x$$

of 5.6a Example 2 has the second derivative given by

$$f''(x) = 20(x + 1)^2(4x - 5).$$

The graph of f is flexed downward for $x < -1$, and at $x = -1$, the second derivative is zero but the curve remains flexed downward as may be seen from the fact that $f(-1)$ is a local maximum. At $x = \frac{5}{4}$, $f''(x)$ is again zero, and now it changes sign. There is an inflection point at $(\frac{5}{4}, -142\frac{99}{128})$, and the flexure changes from downward to upward, remaining upward on the portion $x > \frac{5}{4}$ of the domain.

5.6a, b Exercises

1. Let A, B, C, D, E, and F be points on the graph of a function f such that

$$f(x) < 0, \quad f'(x) < 0, \quad \text{and} \quad f''(x) < 0 \quad \text{at} \quad A,$$

$$f(x) < 0, \quad f'(x) > 0, \quad \text{and} \quad f''(x) < 0 \quad \text{at} \quad B,$$
$$f(x) > 0, \quad f'(x) < 0, \quad \text{and} \quad f''(x) = 0 \quad \text{at} \quad C,$$
$$f(x) < 0, \quad f'(x) > 0, \quad \text{and} \quad f''(x) = 0 \quad \text{at} \quad D,$$
$$f(x) > 0, \quad f'(x) = 0, \quad \text{and} \quad f''(x) = 0 \quad \text{at} \quad E,$$
$$f(x) > 0, \quad f'(x) = 0, \quad \text{and} \quad f''(x) < 0 \quad \text{at} \quad F.$$

Discuss the behavior of the graph of a function f satisfying these conditions. (You may use sketches to indicate the behavior in neighborhoods of the points.)

2. Sketch the graphs of f, f', and f'' using the same coordinate axes.

   a. $f: x \to x^4 + 2x^3 - 12x^2 + 14x$.

   b. $f: x \to \dfrac{3x - 5}{x - 1}$.

3. For each of the following functions, locate and characterize all extrema and give the intervals on which the function is strongly monotone (state whether increasing or decreasing). On what intervals is the graph flexed upward? downward? Sketch the graph of f.

   a. $f: x \to x^2 + x^{-2}$.   b. $f: x \to \dfrac{2}{x^2} + \dfrac{1}{x}$.

   c. $f: x \to x^{1/2} + x^{-1/2}$.   d. $f: x \to x^3 + ax^2 + bx + c$.

4. Show that the graph of the function

   $$f: x \to 3 \sin 2x + 5 \cos 2x$$

   is flexed upward when $f(x) < 0$ and flexed downward when $f(x) > 0$.

5. Discuss the function $f: x \to x\sqrt{x + 1}$ and sketch its graph.

6. Find and characterize the extrema of the function

   $$f: x \to x \sin x + \cos x$$

   on the closed interval $[0, \pi]$. On what intervals is the graph of the function flexed downward? upward? Sketch the graph of f.

7. Use 5.6a Theorem 1 and Corollary 1a to locate and classify all extrema of the function

   $$f: x \to \sin x (1 + \cos x)$$

   on the closed interval $[-\pi, \pi]$. On what intervals is the graph of the function flexed downward? upward? Sketch the graph of f.

8. Assume that the function f has a local maximum (or minimum) at a, where $f'(a) = 0$, and $f''(a) \neq 0$. Obtain sufficient conditions on the function g, assumed twice differentiable, such that gf also has a local maximum (or minimum) at a.

9. Locate the point of inflection on the graph of $f: x \to (x + 1) \arctan x$.

10. Prove that the inflection points of the graph of $y = x \sin x$ lie on the curve $y^2(4 + x^2) = 4x^2$.

11. Consider the points $P = (0, 3)$ and $Q = (4, 7)$. At what point X on the positive x-axis is $\angle PXQ$ greatest?

12. Suppose that $f'(a) = f''(a) = \cdots = f^{(n-1)}(a) = 0$ but that $f^{(n)}(a) \neq 0$. Determine whether $f(a)$ is a local extremum and if it is, which kind. (Hint: consider separately the cases n even and n odd.)

13. The graph of a function f is flexed downward and $f(x)$ is positive for all x. Show that f is a constant function. Do not assume f' exists.

14. If the graph of f is flexed upward and $f(a) = f(b) = f(c)$, where $a < b < c$, show that $f(x)$ is constant on (a, c).

15. Under what circumstances will the graph of a function f and its inverse both be flexed downward? One flexed downward and the other upward? Answer this question both with and without calculus.

16. Given twice differentiable functions f and g whose graphs have upward flexure, with f increasing, show that the graph of fg also has upward flexure.

E5.6c Properties of convex functions

The idea of convex function is closely linked to the geometrical concept of *convex set*. A set of points is *convex* if, for each pair of points in the set, the set contains the entire line segment joining them. This idea can be expressed analytically as follows. If a and b are two points of the number line, then x is a point of the closed segment joining them if and only if

$$x = \theta a + (1 - \theta)b$$

for some number θ satisfying $0 \leq \theta \leq 1$. Similarly, if (a, b) and (α, β) are two points of the plane, the point (x, y) is on the closed segment joining them if and only if

$$\begin{cases} x = \theta a + (1 - \theta)\alpha, \\ y = \theta b + (1 - \theta)\beta, \end{cases}$$

for some θ satisfying $0 \leq \theta \leq 1$. (The verification of these assertions is left to Ex. 2a.)

Figure 1 makes the connection between convex sets and convex functions evident: if the graph of f is flexed upward, then the set of points $\mathfrak{D}$ above the graph is a convex set. Here, the set $\mathfrak{D}$ of points above the graph for an interval I in the domain of the function is defined by

$$\mathfrak{D} = \{(x, y) : x \in I \text{ and } y \geq f(x)\}.$$

The definition of convex function, 5.6b Definition 1, can be expressed in analytic terms as follows. Let f be flexed upward on the interval I.

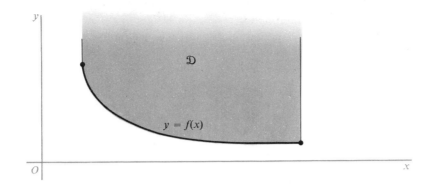

Figure 1

Let a and b be points of I. We represent a point (x, y) of the chord joining $(a, f(a))$ to $(b, f(b))$ by

$$(\theta a + (1 - \theta)b, \theta f(a) + (1 - \theta)f(b))$$

where $0 \leq \theta \leq 1$. The statement that the graph $y = f(x)$ is flexed upward on I is equivalent to

$$f(\theta a + (1 - \theta)b) \leq \theta f(a) + (1 - \theta)f(b)$$

for all numbers a and b in I and all θ satisfying $0 \leq \theta \leq 1$.

Example 1. The graph of $y = |x|$ is easily shown to be flexed upward: from A1.3 (2)

$$|\theta a + (1 - \theta)b| \leq |\theta a| + |(1 - \theta)b|$$
$$\leq \theta |a| + (1 - \theta)|b|$$

where $0 \leq \theta \leq 1$.

The theory of convex functions and convex sets is an elegant and useful subject but to prove many of its significant results would lead us too far astray from our main theme. Here, we confine ourselves to ideas connected with the proof of 5.6b Theorem 1. We leave to the exercises the derivation of a few other preliminary results of the theory. The exercises require a subtle interweaving of geometry and analysis. After exploring the problems of this section, you may wish to extend your knowledge by collateral readings.†

†For the theory of convex sets, see Yaglom, I. M. and Boltyanskii, V. G. *Convex Figures*. Holt, Rinehart, and Winston, 1961. For some applications see Glicksman, A. M. *An Introduction to Linear Programming and the Theory of Games*. Wiley, New York, 1963. For the theory of convex functions at a more advanced level, see Hardy, Littlewood and Polya. *Inequalities*. University Press, Cambridge, England, 1953.

We shall proceed to the proof of 5.6b Theorem 1 by increasing the restrictions on the function f. First we assume that f is continuous, then that it is differentiable, finally that it is twice differentiable.

Theorem 1. It is necessary and sufficient for f to be flexed upward on I that, for each $a \in I$, the slope of the chord joining a point $(x, f(x))$ to the fixed point $(a, f(a))$ is a weakly increasing function of x on I; see Figure 2.

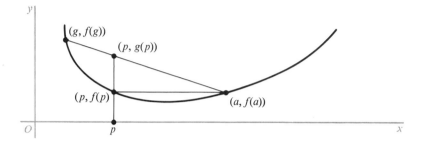

Figure 2

Proof. Let a be any fixed point in I. The equation of the chord through $(a, f(a))$ and $(q, f(q))$, for any other point $q \neq a$ in I is

$$y = g(x) = f(a) + (x - a)\frac{f(q) - f(a)}{q - a}.$$

By 5.6b Definition 1, the graph of f is flexed upward only if $f(p) \leq g(p)$ for all p between a and q, i.e., for all p such that $a < p < q$ or $q < p < a$; see Figure 2. In either case, we have

$$f(p) \leq g(p) \leq f(a) + (p - a)\frac{f(q) - f(a)}{q - a}.$$

If $a < p < q$, this becomes

$$\frac{f(p) - f(a)}{p - a} \leq \frac{f(q) - f(a)}{q - a}.$$

If $q < p < a$, we have

$$\frac{f(p) - f(a)}{p - a} \geq \frac{f(q) - f(a)}{q - a}.$$

In both cases, we have shown the slope function

$$x \to \frac{f(x) - f(a)}{x - a}$$

to be weakly increasing.

Now we prove the converse. By 5.6b Definition 1, we need to show that if the slope function for chords through any point $(a, f(a))$, with a in I, is weakly increasing, and if $y = g(x)$ is the linear equation of an arbitrary chord whose endpoints are $(a, f(a))$ and $(b, f(b))$, with a and b in I, then $f(p) \leq g(p)$ for any p between a and b.

Let $a < p < b$. Then by hypothesis,

$$\frac{f(p) - f(a)}{p - a} \leq \frac{f(b) - f(a)}{b - a}.$$

The equation of the chord through $(a, f(a))$ and $(b, f(b))$ is

$$y = g(x) = f(a) + (x - a)\frac{f(b) - f(a)}{b - a}.$$

By the definition of g,

$$\frac{g(x) - f(a)}{x - a} = \frac{f(b) - f(a)}{b - a},$$

so that

$$\frac{g(x) - f(a)}{x - a} \geq \frac{f(p) - f(a)}{p - a},$$

for all x in I. In particular, taking $x = p$, we obtain $g(p) \geq f(p)$, as we sought to prove.   □

Corollary a. Let f be differentiable and its graph be flexed upward on an interval I. For each $a \in I$, the function ϕ given by

$$\phi(x) = \begin{cases} \dfrac{f(x) - f(a)}{x - a}, & x \neq a, \\ f'(a), & x = a, \end{cases}$$

is weakly increasing.

Proof. We have already shown that ϕ is weakly increasing on I with the point a deleted. We now show that ϕ is weakly increasing on the entire interval.

Let t be any point of I with $t < a$. If a point x of I, other than a satisfies $x \geq t$, then $\phi(x) \geq \phi(t)$. From 3.4 Theorem 6,

$$\lim_{x \sim a} \phi(x) \geq \lim_{x \sim a} \phi(t).$$

In this inequality, $\phi(t)$ is constant and $\phi(x)$ is continuous at a; consequently, $\phi(a) \geq \phi(t)$.

A similar argument yields $\phi(t) \geq \phi(a)$ for $t > a$ and completes the proof.   □

From Corollary 1a we obtain:

Theorem 2. If f is differentiable, a necessary and sufficient condition that the graph of f is flexed upward on I if and only if f' is weakly increasing.

Proof. We first prove that if the graph of f is flexed upward on I, that f' is weakly increasing on I.

Let a, b be points of I such that $a < b$. From Corollary 1a, the function ϕ defined by

$$\phi(x) = \begin{cases} \dfrac{f(x) - f(a)}{x - a}, & x \neq a, \\ f'(a), & x = a, \end{cases}$$

and the function ψ defined by

$$\psi(x) = \begin{cases} \dfrac{f(x) - f(b)}{x - b}, & x \neq b, \\ f'(b), & x = b, \end{cases}$$

are both weakly increasing on I. Since $\phi(b) = \psi(a)$, $\phi(a) \leq \phi(b)$, and $\psi(a) \leq \psi(b)$, it follows that

$$f'(a) = \phi(a) \leq \phi(b) \leq \psi(a) \leq \psi(b) = f'(b).$$

Thus, f' is weakly increasing on I.   □

We show, conversely, that if f' is weakly increasing on I, the graph of f is flexed upward on I.

For any points p, q, r of I with $p < q < r$ we have, by the Law of the Mean,

$$\frac{f(q) - f(p)}{q - p} = f'(u), \text{ where } p < u < q$$

and

$$\frac{f(r) - f(q)}{r - q} = f'(v), \text{ where } q < v < r.$$

Since $u < v$, and since, by hypothesis, f' is weakly increasing we have $f'(u) \leq f'(v)$. It follows that

$$\frac{f(q) - f(p)}{q - p} \leq \frac{f(r) - f(q)}{r - q}.$$

This inequality can be interpreted geometrically as a statement that the slope of the chord joining the fixed point $(q, f(q))$ to any point $(x, f(x))$, $x \in I$, is an increasing function of x on I. It follows by Theorem 1 that the graph of f is flexed upward. □

We now restate and prove 5.6b Theorem 1.

Convexity Theorem. Let f have a second derivative on the open interval (a, b). The graph of f is flexed upward on (a, b) if and only if $f''(x) \geq 0$ on the interval.

Proof. If $f''(x) \geq 0$ on (a, b), then, by 5.4b Theorem 1, f' is weakly increasing on (a, b). From Theorem 2, we conclude at once that the graph of f is flexed upward on (a, b).

Conversely, if the graph of f is flexed upward, then by Theorem 2, f' is weakly increasing on (a, b). Since f has a second derivative f'' on (a, b) which is the first derivative of f', we conclude from 5.4b Theorem 1 that $f''(x) \geq 0$ on (a, b). □

5.6c Exercises

1. Prove if the graph of f is flexed downward on an interval I, that the set $\mathfrak{D}$ of points under the graph is a convex set.

2. a. Let x and y be two points in an interval I in the domain of a function f. Show that a point is on the chord joining the points $(x, f(x))$ and $(y, f(y))$ on the graph of f if and only if its coordinates are

$$(\theta x + (1 - \theta)y, \; \theta f(x) + (1 - \theta)f(y))$$

for some θ such that $0 \leq \theta \leq 1$.

b. Show that 5.6b Definition 1 asserts that f is flexed upward on I if and only if for all x and y in I and all θ such that $0 \leq \theta \leq 1$,

$$f(\theta x + (1 - \theta)y) \leq \theta f(x) + (1 - \theta)f(y).$$

c. Use Part b to show that the graphs of the following functions are flexed upward.
   (i) $f : x \rightarrow ax + b$.
   (ii) $f : x \rightarrow x^2$.
   (iii) $f : x \rightarrow -\sqrt{x}$.

⋏3. a. Prove that if a curve is differentiable and flexed downward on an interval, the curve lies wholly under its tangent lines in this interval.

b. Show that the graph of f crosses its tangent at $x = a$ if a is a point of inflection.

c. Let $f(x) = x^n$ where n is a natural number. For what values of n, if any, does the graph have inflection points? Give sketches comparing the graphs for different values of n.

4. a. Derive the following property of convex functions. If the graph of f is flexed downward on an interval I, then, for all points a, b in I and any positive numbers p, q,

$$f\left(\frac{pa + qb}{p + q}\right) \geq \frac{pf(a) + qf(b)}{p + q}.$$

In words, the function value of a weighted average is less than the weighted average of the function values.

b. Prove that this property is sufficient for downward flexure.

⋏ 5. a. Prove if the graph of f is flexed downward that for x_1, x_2, ..., x_n in the domain of f,

$$f\left(\frac{x_1 + x_2 + \cdots + x_n}{n}\right) \geq \frac{f(x_1) + f(x_2) + \cdots + f(x_n)}{n}.$$

b. Prove that if f is continuous, then a necessary and sufficient condition for its graph to be flexed downward on an interval I is that

$$f\left(\frac{a + b}{2}\right) \geq \frac{f(a) + f(b)}{2},$$

for all points (a, b) in I.

6. Define f and g by $f : x \to xF(x)$ and $g : x \to F\left(\frac{1}{x}\right)$. If either of $f''(x)$ or $g''(x)$ is of one sign for $x > 0$, show that the other one has the same sign. Interpret geometrically and illustrate by several examples.

7. a. Let a, b, c be three points in I such that $a < b < c$, and suppose that the graph of f is flexed upward on I. Show that

$$f(b) \leq \frac{c - b}{c - a} f(a) + \frac{b - a}{c - a} f(c),$$

$$f(a) \geq \frac{c - a}{c - b} f(b) - \frac{b - a}{c - b} f(c),$$

$$f(c) \geq \frac{c - a}{b - a} f(b) - \frac{c - b}{b - a} f(a).$$

(Hint: use the result of Exercise 2).

⋏ b. If the graph of f is flexed upward on a closed interval, show that f is bounded on the interval.

c. Show by a counterexample that the result in Part b is not valid for an open interval.

8. a. If the graph of f is flexed upward on an open interval, show that f is continuous on the interval.

b. Show by a counterexample that the result of Part a is not valid for a closed interval.

9. If the graph of f is flexed upward on an interval, then f possesses left and right derivatives at each interior point of the interval. (See 4.2a Exercise 8.)

5.7 CONSTRAINED EXTREME VALUE PROBLEMS

In this section, we treat the problem of finding the extreme value of a function of more than one variable. Such problems can be solved by the methods at our disposal provided side conditions or constraints are imposed.

Example 1. Problem: to find the point or points nearest to the origin on the parabola

$$4y^2 - 16y - 12x - 75 = 0 .$$

We wish to minimize the distance of (x, y) from $(0, 0)$, namely

$$d(x, y) = \sqrt{x^2 + y^2} ,$$

subject to the constraint,

$$g(x, y) = 4y^2 - 16y - 12x - 75 = 0 .$$

However, to avoid dealing with square roots, we may minimize

$$f(x, y) = x^2 + y^2 = [d(x, y)]^2 .$$

Let us assume that x is implicitly defined by the constraint as a differentiable function of y, that is, $x = \phi(y)$ where

$$g(\phi(y), y) = 0 .$$

Now, set $u = f(\phi(y), y)$, $v = g(\phi(y), y)$. Differentiation with respect to y yields

(1)
$$\frac{dv}{dy} = 8y - 16 - 12\frac{dx}{dy} = 0 ,$$

because $g(x, y)$ is constrained to be a constant, and also

(2)
$$\frac{du}{dy} = 2x\frac{dx}{dy} + 2y .$$

We obtain $\dfrac{dx}{dy}$ from (1), and use the result in (2) to find

$$\frac{du}{dy} = \frac{2}{3}(2xy - 4x + 3y) .$$

For an extremum, we must have $\dfrac{du}{dy} = 0$. In the two equations $\dfrac{du}{dy} = 0$ and $g(x, y) = 0$, namely, in

$$x = \frac{3y}{4 - 2y}, \quad 4y^2 - 16y - 12x = 75 ,$$

we eliminate x and find that the y-coordinate of each extreme point must satisfy

$$8y^3 - 48y^2 - 50y + 300 = 0.$$

Factoring, we write this equation in the form

$$0 = 8y^2(y - 6) - 50(y - 6) = 8(y^2 - \tfrac{25}{4})(y - 6).$$

The roots $y = -\tfrac{5}{2}, \tfrac{5}{2}, 6$ correspond to the x-coordinates $x = -\tfrac{5}{6}$, $-\tfrac{15}{2}, -\tfrac{9}{4}$, respectively. Computing the distances from the origin for the three possible extrema, we find that $(-\tfrac{5}{6}, -\tfrac{5}{2})$ is the nearest point, at a distance of $\tfrac{5}{6}\sqrt{10}$; see Figure 1.

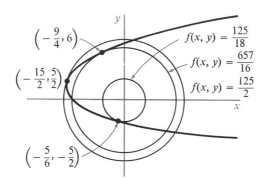

Figure 1

The general idea of a constrained extreme value problem of this type is easily visualized geometrically. We wish to find the extrema of $f(x, y)$ subject to the constraint $g(x, y) = 0$. We may think of $f(x, y)$ in a three-dimensional frame of reference as the height above the x,y-plane of a point on the surface $z = f(x, y)$. The equation $g(x, y) = 0$ may be thought of as the equation of a cylinder, with generators parallel to the z-axis, which meets the surface along a curve. The extreme value problem is to determine the high and low points of this curve. The general situation is depicted in Figure 2. In Figure 3 we show the picture for Example 1.

A natural approach to the constrained extreme value problem, i.e., to find the extrema of $f(x, y)$ subject to $g(x, y) = 0$, is to solve the equation $g(x, y) = 0$ to express one variable in terms of the other and to substitute this expression in $f(x, y)$. The problem is then reduced to the ordinary one of extremizing a function of a single variable. As we have indicated in 4.8, however, such explicit representations are often difficult or impossible to obtain; furthermore, if obtained they may not be particularly useful.

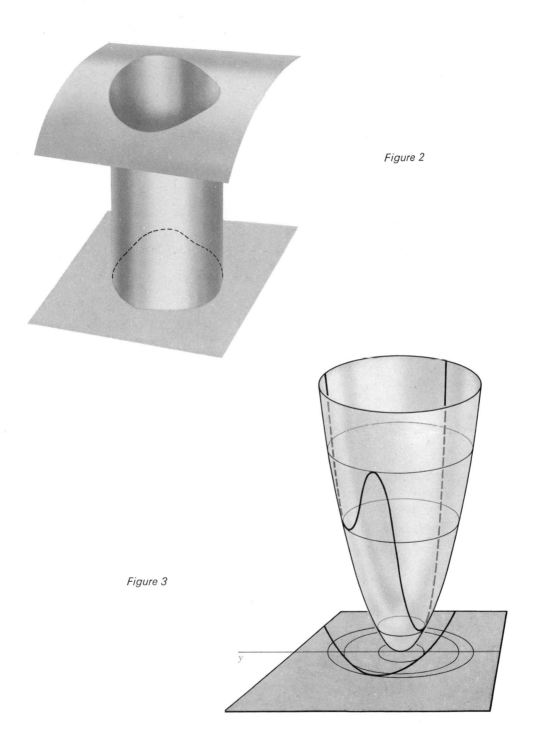

Figure 2

Figure 3

We consider the problem of maximizing a function of three variables subject to two constraints in order to show how the techniques can be extended to more complicated cases.

Example 2. In 5.4c Example 3 we might have introduced the quantity z which represents the difference in level between the ring and the pegs (see 5.4c Figure 2, p. 180) and reformulated the problem as the problem of finding the maximum of

$$h = f(y, z) = y + z$$

where y and z are subject to the constraints

$$g_1(x, z) = 2z \cot x - M = 0,$$
$$g_2(x, z) = y + 2z \csc x + M - L = 0.$$

Of course, we could eliminate z and y and obtain the same problem as before but we need not do so. This time, we treat x and y as functions of z and obtain

$$h' = y' + 1,$$

where the primes indicate differentiation with respect to z. From the constraining conditions we obtain

(3) $$2 \cot x - 2zx' \csc^2 x = 0,$$

(4) $$y' + 2 \csc x - 2x'z \csc x \cot x = 0,$$

since L, M are constants. From (3) we obtain

$$zx' = \cos x \sin x,$$

and substituting for zx' in (4) we obtain

$$y' + 2 \csc x(1 - \cos^2 x) = y' + 2 \sin x = 0.$$

The condition for a maximum then becomes

$$h' = 1 - 2 \sin x = 0$$

which yields the same condition as before.

There is no special merit in the present treatment of this problem over the earlier one. Our only purpose is to show that elimination of variables is not necessary should it be inconvenient or difficult.

The next example is cautionary.

Example 3. Given 15 yards of fencing, I decide to plant one square and one circular flower bed, and to surround them with the fencing. What should be the dimensions of the two fences so as to contain flower beds of greatest total area?

We express the total perimeter in terms of the side s of the square bed and the radius r of the circle, leaving the variables in the implicit functional relationship

$$4s + 2\pi r = 15 .$$

Subject to this constraint, s and r are to be chosen so as to maximize

$$A = s^2 + \pi r^2 .$$

Denoting derivatives with respect to s by primes, we obtain

$$4 + 2\pi r' = 0 \quad \text{and} \quad A' = 2s + 2\pi r r' .$$

Using $A' = 0$, we eliminate r' to get the condition $s = 2r$ for the extremum. Because of the constraint, this occurs when $8r + 2\pi r = 15$, or

$$r = \frac{15}{(8 + 2\pi)}, \qquad s = \frac{30}{(8 + 2\pi)} .$$

The sum of the corresponding areas is 7.68 sq. yds. (to two places after the decimal point).

We take the usual precaution of checking the endpoints of the intervals of physically possible values of r and s. If $r = 0$, then $s = \frac{15}{4}$, and we have a single square bed of area 14.06 sq. yds.; if $s = 0$, then $r = \frac{15}{2\pi}$, and we have a single round bed of area 17.90 sq yds. Both exceed the sum of areas found by the method of implicit differentiation, which, in fact, is a local minimum. It appears that the problem has no solution in the terms posed; a square and a round flower bed together will never encompass as great an area as a single round bed whose perimeter equals the total length available.

This example reveals one of the weaknesses of the method: if there should be an endpoint extremum it may be concealed by the formulation of the problem.

In the next example, we use the method to find an extremum when too few constraints are imposed by the problem. In that case, we introduce an artificial constraint.

Example 4. The U. S. Post Office Department restricts the size of parcels it will accept. The regulation at the time this was written stated "Parcels mailed at a first-class post office in the United States for delivery ... at ... any ... first-class post office ... must not exceed 72 inches in length and girth combined." For a rectangular carton, the length is the length of the longest edge and the girth is the perimeter of the cross-section perpendicular to that edge. We seek the dimensions of the rectangular carton of largest volume which meets the post office regulations. In analytical terms, we wish to find the linear dimensions z, x, y which maximize the volume

$$(5) \qquad\qquad V = zxy$$

subject to the constraint

$$(6) \qquad\qquad 2x + 2y + z = 72 \qquad (z \geq x \text{ and } z \geq y)$$

(i.e., the length z of the longest side plus the "girth" or perimeter of the cross-section perpendicular to the longest side is fixed).

We take as an unproved assumption that there exist dimensions z_0, x_0, y_0 which maximize V. If we knew z_0 we could then take $z = z_0$ as a constraint and solve the problem as an ordinary constrained extreme value problem in x and y. We do not know z_0 but we can impose the artificial constraint

$$(7) \qquad\qquad z = k, \qquad k \text{ constant},$$

and solve the extreme value problem subject to this extra constraint. For each choice of k, we obtain the largest possible value V; this association will ordinarily be expressible as a function of k;

$$f : k \rightarrow V.$$

Finally, we determine k so that $V = f(k)$ is a maximum.

In the foregoing problem, then, we begin with the constrained extreme value problem, to maximize V as given by (5), subject to the constraints (6) and (7). We assume that y is a function of x. Differentiating with respect to x, we obtain the condition for an extremum

$$(8) \qquad\qquad \frac{dV}{dx} = z\left(x\frac{dy}{dx} + y\right) = 0$$

subject to

$$(9) \qquad\qquad 2\frac{dy}{dx} + 2 = 0,$$

where we have employed condition (7) to set $\dfrac{dz}{dx} = 0$. From (8) and (9) and the observation that $z = 0$ certainly does not maximize V, we obtain

$$y = x.$$

Thus, the box must have square ends. From this point on, the solution is conventional.

The second derivative can also be computed by implicit differentiation, but this usually entails further complication. Moreover, the most we can do with the second derivative is to infer the nature of a local extremum. Even if only one extremum is found by this method, we cannot conclude, as we could in 5.4b, c Exercise 13, that it is global. As we already remarked in 4.8, the problem may define not one but several implicit functions and it is possible that a global extremum does not exist, or is an endpoint maximum for an implicit function other than the one for which a local extremum was found. An example is given by the equation

$$x^3 - x^2 y - x^2 - xy + y^2 + y = (y - x^2)(y - x + 1) = 0,$$

which has as its graph the parabola $y = x^2$ and the line $y = x - 1$ (Figure 4). Our technique locates a local minimum of y at $x = 0$ on

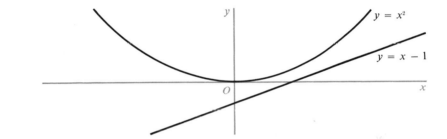

Figure 4

the branch $y = x^2$ but misses the fact that the graph, considered as a whole, does not have a lowest point. In general, before hard and fast conclusions can be drawn for any given problem of this type, a deeper investigation is necessary.

5.7 Exercises

1. a. For a given volume V find the dimensions of a cylindrical tin can with smallest surface area.
   b. If the cost of the sides, top, and bottom of the can is a cents per square inch, and if the cost of the bead joining the top and bottom to the side is b cents per linear inch, find the most economical dimensions of the can for a given volume V.

2. a. A cylindrical sheet-iron tank without top is to have volume V. Let h be the height of the tank, and r, the radius of the base. The side of the tank is to be constructed from stock costing a dollars per square foot

and the base from stock costing b dollars per square foot. Find the radius and height of the tank for which the cost of material in the tank is minimized.

b. More realistically, suppose that the base has to be cut from a square of side $2r$. Find the dimensions yielding minimum cost including the cost of material trimmed away.

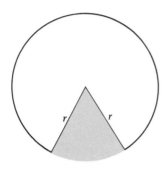

3. Find the radius and height of the cone of greatest volume that can be made from a circular sheet of radius r by cutting a wedge from the center and bending the remaining portion to form a cone. (See adjacent figure.)

4. A point P is at a distance h above the center C of a sphere of radius r, where $h > r$. A cone is constructed having P for vertex, and for base the circle formed by cutting the sphere with a plane perpendicular to PC. In order to have the volume of the cone as great as possible, should this plane be above or below C? How far?

5. A paper tape 8 inches wide is cut off square at one end. A corner A of this end is then folded over to the opposite side at A', thus forming triangle $[ABC]$. Find the area of the smallest triangle that can be formed in this way.

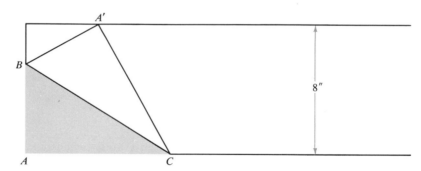

6. a. Let the general equation of a straight line L be given in the form

$$ax + by = c.$$

Find the point Q on L for which the distance to a given point P not on L is a minimum. Prove that the line joining P to Q is perpendicular to L.

b. On the curve C given by $f(x, y) = 0$ let Q be the point nearest to a point P not on the curve. If Q is not an endpoint of C, and all necessary derivatives exist, prove that the line joining P to Q is perpendicular to C. (Compare 5M Exercise 10.)

7. Find the extrema of $x^2 + y^2$ if x and y are subject to the constraint $x^2 - 12x + y^2 - 8y + 51 = 0$. Give a geometric interpretation.

8. If $x_i \geq 0$, $i = 1, 2, \ldots, n$, and $x_1 + x_2 + \cdots + x_n = c$, where c is constant, find the maximum value of the product

$$x_1 x_2 \cdots x_n$$

(assuming the maximum exists).

5.8 SKETCHING OF GRAPHS

We seek a sketch of the graph of a function f, a picture which reveals the important general features of the graph but which need not be a precise point-by-point representation.

Some aspects of the graph are found without calculus. The x-intercepts (the solutions of $f(x) = 0$ or zeros of f) and the y-intercept $f(0)$, yield easily plotted reference points $(a, 0)$ and $(0, f(0))$ on the graph of f. Moreover, we have tests for symmetry with respect to the y-axis and the origin (see A3.6), and observe that we can construct the entire graph of a symmetric function from the portion lying in a halfplane. The entire graph of a periodic function (p. 260) with period p can be constructed from the portion of the graph over any interval of length p.

From the calculus we obtain more information. Most of the functions we deal with here are differentiable to all orders on an interval. Such a function must be continuous and we know that its graph has no gaps. Furthermore, since the first derivative is continuous the graph is smooth; thus, such a function has no corners like that of the graph $y = |x|$ at the origin. Almost always, the zeros of the derivative are *isolated;* that is, each zero has a neighborhood in which no other zero of the derivative appears. From 5.2a Theorem 1 and 5.2b Theorem 1 we then know that the graph of f is strongly monotone between successive zeros of the derivative. Furthermore, by observing the rise and fall of the values of the function at successive zeros of the derivative we can determine which zeros yield extrema.

Almost always, the zeros of the second derivative are isolated and the second derivative has opposite signs on either side of a zero. Such zeros of the second derivative are inflection points which separate the curve into arcs of upward and downward flexure. With this information we can obtain an excellent idea of the appearance of the graph.

The concept of *asymptote*, a line approached by the graph for large values of x or y, was introduced in the study of the hyperbola (see p. 349). We give simple criteria which help to locate horizontal and vertical asymptotes like thsoe of the rectangular hyperbolas $xy = k$.

In rough terms, an asymptote may be defined as a line which approximates a given curve at large distances from the origin. The simplest case is that of a horizontal asymptote, $y = c$ where c is constant. The line $y = c$ may occur as an asymptote to the graph of f in two ways: for large positive values of x or for large negative values of x. In precise terms, $y = c$ is an asymptote of f for large positive values of x if

$$\lim_{x \sim \infty} f(x) = c,$$

and for large negative x if

$$\lim_{x \sim -\infty} f(x) = c$$

(see 3.4b).

Example 1. Let us consider a typical rational function,

$$f: x \rightarrow 4 + \frac{x}{(x+3)(x-1)}.$$

We find the horizontal asymptotes, if any, by comparing the leading terms of the numerator and denominator (see 3.4 Ex. 4 and 5.8 Ex. 4). In the fraction above, the degree of the denominator is greater than that of the numerator and we conclude that the fraction approximates zero for large positive or negative x. It follows that f has the asymptote $y = 4$ for both large positive and negative x.

A vertical asymptote $x = a$ can occur only at a point, a, where f is discontinuous because $|f(x)|$ exceeds any given positive real value for all x in some sufficiently small deleted neighborhood of a. For a vertical asymptote, it is sufficient to show that $\dfrac{1}{f(x)}$ approximates zero when x is near a.

Example 2. For the function f of the previous example we have

$$\frac{1}{f(x)} = \frac{(x+3)(x-1)}{(4x^2 + 9x - 12)},$$

and $\dfrac{1}{f(x)}$ approximates 0 for x near -3 and for x near 1. The lines $x = -3$, $x = 1$ are vertical asymptotes; see Figure 1.

Oblique asymptotes are also easily defined; the appropriate condition that the line $y = mx + b$ be an asymptote to the graph of f for large

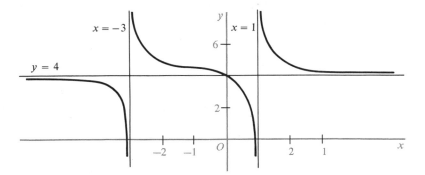

Figure 1

positive x is

$$\lim_{x \to \infty} |f(x) - (mx + b)| = 0.$$

If the graph of $y = f(x)$ has a slant asymptote, it is easy to verify that the slope of the asymptote is given by

$$m = \lim_{x \to \infty} \frac{f(x)}{x}$$

(5.8 Ex. 7a). On the other hand, the limit may exist although the curve may not be an asymptote (5.8 Ex. 7b).

With the wealth of auxiliary information obtained by the methods described, the plotting of relatively few points is sufficient to obtain an adequate sketch of the graphs of most functions met in applications. Here we give a checklist of the information.

A. $f(x)$ determines:
1. The domain of definition;
2. The x-intercepts, the zeros of f; the y-intercept, $f(0)$. (For a curve in implicit form $g(x, y) = 0$, the x-intercepts are the solutions of $g(x, 0) = 0$, and the y-intercepts are the solutions of $g(0, y) = 0$. For a curve given in parametric representation, $x = \varphi(t)$, $y = \psi(t)$, the x-intercepts are the values of φ at the zeros of ψ, and the y-intercepts are the values of ψ at the zeros of φ.)
3. Symmetry with respect to the y-axis if $f(x) = f(-x)$, with respect to the origin if $f(x) = -f(-x)$. (For a curve in implicit form $g(x, y) = 0$ there is symmetry with respect to the x-axis if $g(x, y) = g(x, -y)$; with respect to the y-axis if $g(x, y) = g(-x, y)$; with respect to the origin if $g(x, y) = g(-x, -y)$; with respect to the line $y = x$ if $g(x, y) = g(y, x)$.)
4. Periodicity.

B. $f(x)$ also determines:
1. A horizontal asymptote $y = p$ to the right if
$$\lim_{x \sim \infty} f(x) = p.$$
2. A horizontal asymptote $y = q$ to the left if
$$\lim_{x \sim -\infty} f(x) = q.$$
3. A vertical asymptote $x = a$ if $\dfrac{1}{f(x)}$ approximates 0 in a deleted neighborhood of a.
4. A slant asymptote $y = mx + b$ to the right, if both limits
$$m = \lim_{x \sim \infty} \frac{f(x)}{x} \quad \text{and} \quad b = \lim_{x \sim \infty} [f(x) - mx]$$
exist.

C. $f'(x)$ determines:
1. An interval on which f is increasing if $f'(x) > 0$ (weakly increasing if $f'(x) \geq 0$) on the interval.
2. An interval on which f is decreasing if $f'(x) < 0$ (weakly decreasing if $f'(x) \leq 0$) on the interval.
3. A maximum value $f(a)$ if $f'(a) = 0$ and $f'(x)$ changes from positive to negative as x increases through the value a.
4. A minimum value $f(a)$ if $f'(a) = 0$ and $f'(x)$ changes from negative to positive as x increases through the value a.

D. $f'(x)$ and $f''(x)$ determine:
1. A maximum value $f(a)$ if $f'(a) = 0$ and $f''(a) < 0$.
2. A minimum value $f(a)$ if $f'(a) = 0$ and $f''(a) > 0$.

E. $f''(x)$ determines:
1. An interval on which the graph of f is flexed downward if
$$f''(x) < 0$$
on the interval.
2. An interval on which the graph of f is flexed upward if $f''(x) > 0$ on the interval.
3. An inflection point $(a, f(a))$ if $f''(a) = 0$ and $f''(x)$ changes sign as x increases through the value a.

It is good procedure to prepare for the sketch of a graph by making a table in which pertinent items from the check list are presented. Do all calculations separately from the table so that only those data are shown which go directly into the sketch.

Example 3. We give a complete checklist for the function

$$f : x \to 4 + \frac{x}{(x+3)(x-1)}$$

of Examples 1 and 2.

x-intercepts: $x = -3.19$, 0.94 (approximately).
y-intercept: $y = 4$.
Horizontal asymptote: $y = 4$ to both left and right.
Vertical asymptotes: $x = -3$ and $x = 1$.
Intervals of decreasing f: $x < -3$, $-3 < x < 1$, $1 < x$.
Downward flexure: $x < -3$, $x_1 < x < 1$, where x_1 is the ab-
    scissa of the inflection point.
Upward flexure: $-3 < x < x_1$, $1 < x$.
Inflection point: $(x_1, f(x_1))$, where $x_1{}^3 + 9x_1 + 6 = 0$; to one place
    after the decimal point, $-0.7 < x_1 < -0.6$.

The sketch, Figure 1, makes use of all this information.

Note that intercepts, extrema, or inflection points may be only approximately determinable, with an accuracy dependent on one's skill in approximately solving the appropriate equations $f(x) = 0$, $f'(x) = 0$, and
$f''(x) = 0$.

Example 4. We sketch the graph of $f : x \to \cos x - 2 \sin x$, for

$$0 \le x \le 2\pi .$$

Here,

$$f'(x) = -\sin x - 2 \cos x , \quad f''(x) = -\cos x + 2 \sin x = -f(x) .$$

The zeros of $f(x)$ (and simultaneously of $f''(x)$) are values of x for
which $\tan x = \frac{1}{2}$; the zeros of $f'(x)$ are values of x for which

$$\tan x = -2 .$$

Numerical values have been taken from a trigonometric table, rounded off
to two places after the decimal point:

x-intercepts: $x = 0.46$, $x = 3.60$.
y-intercept: $y = 1$.
Minimum: $x = 2.03$, $f(x) = -2.24$.
Maximum: $x = 5.17$, $f(x) = 2.24$.
Intervals of decreasing f: $0 < x < 2.03$, $5.17 < x < 2\pi$.

Intervals of increasing f: $2.03 < x < 5.17$.

Inflection points: same as x-intercepts.

Intervals of downward flexure: $0 < x < 0.46$, $3.60 < x < 2\pi$.

Intervals of upward flexure: $0.46 < x < 3.60$.

The values $f(x)$ for x a multiple of $\dfrac{\pi}{2}$ are also easily plotted, and were used in the construction of Figure 2.

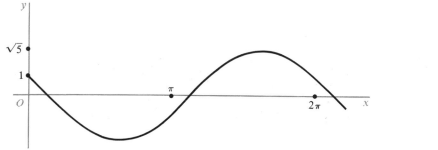

Figure 2

The graph of $f: x \rightarrow \cos x - 2 \sin x$ could have been obtained more easily by noting that

$$\cos x - 2 \sin x = \sqrt{5}\left(\frac{\cos x}{\sqrt{5}} - \frac{2}{\sqrt{5}} \sin x\right) = \sqrt{5} \cos (x + \alpha),$$

where $\cos \alpha = \dfrac{1}{\sqrt{5}}$, but for the sake of illustration we have proceeded in a more complicated way.

Example 5. We sketch the curve with equation $\sqrt{x} + \sqrt{y} = 1$. Only points in the square $0 \le x \le 1, 0 \le y \le 1$ can lie on the graph. Implicit differentiation gives

$$\frac{1}{2\sqrt{x}} + \frac{D_x y}{2\sqrt{y}} = 0$$

or

$$D_x y = -\sqrt{\frac{y}{x}},$$

and for the second derivative

$$D_x(D_xy) = -\frac{1}{2}\sqrt{\frac{x}{y}}\left[\frac{xD_xy - y}{x^2}\right] = \frac{1}{2}\sqrt{\frac{x}{y}}\frac{\sqrt{xy} + y}{x^2}$$

$$= \frac{1}{2}\frac{x + \sqrt{xy}}{x^2} = \frac{\sqrt{x} + \sqrt{y}}{2x^{3/2}} = \frac{1}{2x^{3/2}}.$$

The checklist is quite short:

x-intercept: $x = 1$.
y-intercept: $y = 1$.
Symmetry: with respect to the line $y = x$.
Interval where y decreases: $0 < x < 1$.
Interval of upward flexure: $0 < x < 1$.
$D_xy = 0$ at $(1, 0)$.

With the plotting of one additional point $(\frac{1}{4}, \frac{1}{4})$, the sketch is easily made;
See Figure 3.

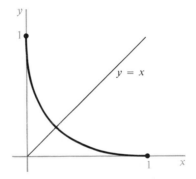

$y = x$

Figure 3

5.8 Exercises

1. Draw the graph of $f: x \to 4x^5 + 5x^4 - 20x^3 - 50x^2 - 40x$. (See 5.6b Example 1.)

2. Determine equations of the horizontal and vertical asymptotes, if any, of the graph of

 a. $xy + y = x$,
 b. $x^2y - 3x + 2 = 0$.

3. Find horizontal and vertical asymptotes, maxima, minima, and inflection points, for the graphs of the given functions. Show all tests used to identify each such point and draw the graph of each function.

 a. $f: x \to \dfrac{x}{x^2 + 1}$.   b. $f: x \to \dfrac{x^2}{x^2 + 1}$.   c. $f: x \to \dfrac{2(x - 2)}{x^2}$.

4. For a rational function given by

$$r(x) = \frac{a_p x^p + a_{p-1} x^{p-1} + \cdots + a_0}{b_q x^q + b_{q-1} x^{q-1} + \cdots + b_0}$$

where $a_p, b_q \neq 0$, find the horizontal asymptotes if they exist.

5. Show that the function $f: x \to (ax + b)/(cx + d)$ (assumed nonconstant) has no maxima or minima whatever the values of $a, b, c,$ and d.

6. Draw the graphs of the given functions making use of extrema and information about flexure.

   a. $f: x \to -x\sqrt{3 - x^2}$.

   b. $f: x \to \sqrt{\dfrac{x^3}{2 - x}}$.

   c. $f: x \to \cos^2 x + 2\cos x$.

   d. $f: x \to x \arcsin x$.

   e. $f: x \to x^{2/3}(x - 2)^2$.

7. a. Sketch the graph of the function

$$f: x \to \frac{x^2}{x - a}, \qquad\qquad a \neq 0,$$

   and determine all the horizontal, vertical, and slant asymptotes.

   b. Show for the function

$$f: x \to 1 + x - 2\sqrt{x}, \quad x \geq 0,$$

   that $\lim\limits_{x \to \infty} \dfrac{f(x)}{x}$ exists although the graph has no asymptotes.

8. Draw the graph of $x^2 y + xy^2 = 1$. Determine horizontal and vertical asymptotes, if any. Locate the axis of symmetry and the point of intersection of the curve with this axis. Show that the curve has one and only one extremum; locate and classify it.

⋏ 9. For what values of a does the function

$$f: x \to \frac{x^2 + 2x + a}{x^2 + 4x + 3a}$$

assume all real values? Sketch the graph of the function for typical cases.

10. Discuss and sketch the graph of

$$x^2 y + ax + by = 0.$$

Consider various cases.

5M MISCELLANEOUS EXERCISES

1. Does $f : x \to x - \sin x$ have any extrema? Justify your answer.

2. Does $f : x \to x/\sin x$ have any extrema in the open interval $(0, \frac{1}{2}\pi)$? Justify your answer.

3. Determine equations of the horizontal and vertical asymptotes, if any, of the graph of

   a. $xy^2 - 4y - x = 0$,   b. $xy - \cos x = 0$.

4. Show that there are two tangent lines to the graph $y = x^3 - 3x^2 + 3x$ which pass through the point $(4, 1)$. Find their equations.

5. Show that the tangent line to the conic section

$$ax^2 + 2bxy + cy^2 + 2dx + 2ey + f = 0$$

   at a point (x_0, y_0) on the curve has the equation

$$ax_0x + b(y_0x + x_0y) + cy_0y + d(x_0 + x) + e(y_0 + y) + f = 0.$$

6. For what points (h, k) can one draw two tangent lines, one tangent line, no tangent line to each of the following graphs?

   a. $x^2 + 3xy + y^2 = a^2$, $a > 0$.
   b. $3x^2 + xy + 3y^2 = a^2$, $a > 0$.
   c. $\sqrt{x} + \sqrt{y} = \sqrt{a}$, $a > 0$.
   Interpret geometrically.

7. Let m, n, and p be natural numbers, a, b, and c, any three real numbers.
   Sketch the graphs of

   a. $y = \dfrac{(x - a)^m}{(x - b)^n}$,   b. $y^2 = \dfrac{(x - a)^m}{(x - b)^n}$,

   c. $y = \dfrac{(x - a)^m (x - b)^n}{(x - c)^p}$,   d. $y^2 = \dfrac{(x - a)^m (x - b)^n}{(x - c)^p}$.

8. Show that the equation

$$x^7 - x^5 + 5x^2 - 1 = 0$$

   has no solution for $x > 1$.

9. On an interval, let the function f be the derivative of a function g. Prove that f has the Intermediate Value Property.

10. On a curve C given by the parametric equations

$$x = \phi(t), \qquad y = \psi(t),$$

   let Q be the point nearest to a point P not on the given curve. If Q is not an endpoint of C, and all necessary derivatives exist, prove that the line joining P to Q is perpendicular to C. (Compare 5.7 Exercise 6b.)

11. A man standing at the edge of a circular swimming pool wishes to reach a point $\frac{1}{4}$ of the way around the pool in the least possible time. He plans to run along the edge of the pool for some distance and then swim straight to his destination. If he can swim 20 feet per second and run 24 feet per second, how far should he run before diving in?

12. The position of a particle on a straight line at time t is given by the law of motion

$$s = 5 \sin 3t - 3 \sin 5t \qquad (t > 0).$$

Once it begins when does the particle first reach a stop? How far is it then from the starting point?

13. The location of an object on a straight line at time t, is given by the formula

$$S = At - (1 + A^4) t^2 \qquad (t > 0).$$

Show that when A is positive the object moves forward initially, but ultimately retreats. Show also that for different values of A the maximum possible distance that the particle can move forward is $\frac{1}{8}$.

14. A picture h feet high is placed on a wall with its base b feet above the level of the observer's eye. If he stands x feet from the wall, verify that the angle of vision ϕ subtended by the picture is given by

$$\phi = \operatorname{arccot} \frac{x}{h + b} - \operatorname{arccot} \frac{x}{b}.$$

Show that to get the "best" view of the picture; i.e., the largest angle of vision, the observer should stand $\sqrt{b(h + b)}$ feet away from the wall.

15. Let $[ABC]$ be a right triangle with AB perpendicular to BC, with $|AB| = h$, and with $|BC| = 2x$. Let $[AD]$ be the median to side $[BC]$. Determine x so that the angle θ between the median and the hypotenuse of triangle $[ABC]$ is a maximum.

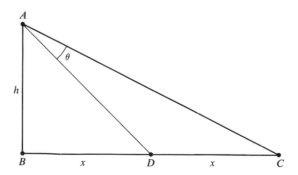

16. A conical cup with base radius r, height h, is filled with water. Find the radius R of the sphere which displaces the largest volume of water when jammed into the cup.

Appendices

For future reference, preparatory study, or review, these appendices summarize a number of topics preliminary to the main body of the calculus. The text assumes that you are already conversant with most of this material or will become so during the course. Chapter A1 introduces the real numbers axiomatically as a complete ordered field. Chapter A2 considers the concepts of function and graph of a function. Chapter A3 compactly presents the minimum of analytic geometry necessary for this text. Mathematical induction, the subject of Chapter A4, is an often neglected topic, but it is essential for mathematical literacy; it is needed for the solution of many exercises. Recognition of the pattern of an inductive argument will make for better understanding of certain parts of the text.

The idea of set is assumed to be familiar from earlier courses and will be used without comment in the text. Here, we give a cursory account mainly to explain the various notations we shall use.

The concept of *set*, a collection of objects called *elements* of the set, is a basic undefined term. The essential characteristic of a set is that it must be definite about any object, whether or not it is an element of the set.

Intuitively, the ideas of "a set" and "a classification" are the same. Even so simple an idea as "set" is a mathematical idealization and may be difficult to put to practical use. In biology, for example, the taxonomic problem is to classify living organisms into species, that is, nonoverlapping sets.

However carefully the concept of species is defined, there are always border-line individuals for whom it remains ambiguous whether or not they belong to a given species.

The statement "x is an element of the set S" is written

$$x \in S \, ;$$

the contrary, "x is *not* an element of S" is written

$$x \notin S \, .$$

If all the elements of S lie in a set T, we say "S is a subset of T" or "S is contained in T" and write

$$S \subset T \quad \text{or} \quad T \supset S \, .$$

In particular, $S \subset S$ is always true. Given two sets S and T, we define their *union*, written $S \cup T$, as the set that consists of the elements of S together with those of T. Observe that $S \cup T \supset S$ and $S \cup T \supset T$. The *intersection* of S and T, written $S \cap T$, consists of all elements common to both S and T. Since S and T may have no elements in common, we assume that $S \cap T$ is always defined by introducing the concept of the *empty set*, written $\emptyset$, the set that has no elements. The empty set is assumed to be a subset of every set. In general, $S \cap T \subset S$ and $S \cap T \subset T$.

We may describe a set by listing its elements; for example, the set of integers between 0 and 5 is written

$$\{1, 2, 3, 4\} \, .$$

Alternatively, we may describe a set by a property which is satisfied by its elements and by none other. For example, the set of nonnegative real numbers may be written as

$$\{x : x = y^2, \quad y \in \Re\}$$

(read, "the set of x such that $x = y^2$ where y is an element of $\Re$, the set of real numbers). In this text, we shall seldom be concerned with any sets other than those consisting of real numbers or points. In context, it is seldom necessary to state this restriction explicitly. For example, the set of nonnegative real numbers would be indicated simply by

$$\{x : x = y^2\} \, .$$

Similarly, the set of points in the plane on the horizontal line given by $y = 1$ would be written

$$\{(x, y) : y = 1\} \, .$$

A1

The Real Number System

The real numbers, through their representations as infinite decimals and as points of the number line, are assumed to be familiar. It is possible to define the real numbers in terms of the rational numbers.† Since the rational numbers may themselves be defined in terms of the natural numbers, the concept of real number may be made to rest ultimately on the concept of natural number. It is possible to begin only with axioms for the natural numbers and from these axioms laboriously construct the entire edifice of the number system.‡ For us, this would be an academic exercise. We begin immediately with axioms for the real number system, most of them familiar from experience, and consider the natural and rational numbers as special kinds of real numbers.

†See Richard Dedekind, *Essays on the Theory of Numbers*, translated by W. W. Bernan, Dover (New York, 1963).

‡See Edmund Landau, *Foundations of Analysis*, Chelsea (New York, 1960).

The material in A1.2 to A1.4 on inequalities, absolute value, intervals, and neighborhoods, which is used throughout the text, should be mastered thoroughly. Many of the results obtained in the exercises of these sections are cited in the text.

A1.1 ALGEBRAIC AXIOMS

Let $\mathcal{R}$ be the set of real numbers and represent the elements of $\mathcal{R}$ by lower case (italic) letters, $a, b, c, \ldots$. The real numbers form an algebraic system in which addition, multiplication, and their inverse operations, subtraction and division (except by zero) can be performed. Such a system is known as a *field*. The field properties of $\mathcal{R}$ are summarized in the following Axioms:

Closure

$$(1) \qquad (a + b) \in \mathcal{R}, \quad ab \in \mathcal{R}.$$

The sum and product of real numbers are real numbers.

Commutative laws

$$(2) \qquad a + b = b + a, \quad ab = ba.$$

A sum or product of two real numbers is independent of the order in which they are taken.

Associative laws

$$(3) \qquad a + (b + c) = (a + b) + c, \quad a(bc) = (ab)c.$$

A sum or product of three real numbers is independent of the way in which they are associated in pairs.

Distributive law

$$(4) \qquad a(b + c) = ab + ac.$$

Multiplication is distributed over a sum.

Identities

There exist real numbers 0 (the additive identity) and 1 (the multiplicative identity) such that

$$(5) \qquad a + 0 = a, \quad a \cdot 1 = a.$$

Inverses

Each real number a has an additive inverse, $-a$, "the negative of a," such that

(6a) $$a + (-a) = 0.$$

Each real number except 0 has a multiplicative inverse $\dfrac{1}{a}$, "the reciprocal of a," such that

(6b) $$a\left(\frac{1}{a}\right) = 1 \qquad\qquad (a \neq 0).$$

Finally, we require that 0 and 1 are not the same number.

(7) $$0 \neq 1.$$

The preceding axioms are sufficient to define the ordinary operations of arithmetic. We need not introduce further axioms for subtraction and division since we define these operations in terms of addition and multiplication. The operation of subtraction is defined by

(8a) $$a - b = a + (-b),$$

and division by

(8b) $$\frac{a}{b} = a\left(\frac{1}{b}\right) \qquad\qquad (b \neq 0).$$

We shall not attempt to derive the entire catalog of familiar properties of the real numbers implied by (1)–(8). The derivations of a number of these properties are left to exercises. There is one fact, however, to which we wish to give prominent attention:

Division by zero cannot be given any meaning.

If $b \neq 0$, then (8b) assures us that $\dfrac{a}{b}$ is a real number; concerning $b = 0$, the statement is mysteriously silent. If $b = 0$, we cannot assign a single definite value to $\dfrac{a}{b}$ consistent with (1)–(7). In proof, we show first that

(9) $$a \cdot 0 = 0.$$

For this, we use

$$a \cdot 0 + a \cdot 0 = a(0 + 0) \qquad \text{(Distributive Law)}$$
$$= a \cdot 0 \qquad \text{(Additive Identity)}.$$

Put $c = a \cdot 0$. By the preceding result,

$$c + c = c,$$

hence

$$(c + c) + (-c) = c + (-c),$$

and

$$c + (c + (-c)) = c + (-c) \quad \text{(Associative Law)},$$

and

$$c + 0 = 0 \quad \text{(Additive Inverse)};$$

that is,

$$c = 0 \quad \text{(Additive Identity)},$$

which is the result to be proved.

In order to define division by zero under the definition of (6b), we must be able to find a "reciprocal of zero," that is, a number a for which

$$0 \cdot a = 1.$$

However, from (9) we would then have

$$1 = 0 \cdot a = 0,$$

in contradiction to (7). It follows that division by zero cannot be made meaningful: the attempt to define division by zero leads to a contradiction.

A1.1 Exercises

Prove the following assertions.

1. a. The natural numbers do not form a field.
   b. The rational numbers form a field.
   c. The numbers $\dfrac{a + b}{2}$, where a and b are rational numbers, constitute a field.

2. For any real number a, $-(-a) = a$.

3. For any real number a, $(-1)a = -a$.

4. For any real numbers a and b, $-(a + b) = (-a) + (-b)$.

5. For any real numbers a and b, $(-a)(-b) = ab$.

6. The product of any real numbers a and b is zero, $ab = 0$, if and only if at least one of the factors is zero, $a = 0$ or $b = 0$.

A1.2 AXIOMS OF ORDER

Many number systems besides the field $\Re$ of real numbers satisfy the algebraic axioms of A1.1. Actually, many of the subsets of $\Re$, and particularly the set of rational numbers, are fields. (See A1.1 Ex. 1b and A1.2 Ex. 12.)

Furthermore, $\mathcal{R}$ itself is a subset of a number field, the field $\mathcal{C}$ of complex numbers, which may be thought of as the set of all numbers of the form $a + bi$ where a and b are real and $i^2 = -1$. The real number system differs from the complex number system in an important respect: it is possible to put the reals in a linear order. (See A1.2 Ex. 11.) Such an order obeys certain rules which supplement the field axioms for the real number system.

There is an order relation in $\mathcal{R}$, denoted by $a > b$ (read "a is greater than b") with the following properties:

Trichotomy

Each a and b satisfies one and no more than one of the following relations:

$$a > b, \quad a = b, \quad b > a.$$

Transitive Law

If $a > b$ and $b > c$, then $a > c$.

Addition Law

If $a > b$, then $a + c > b + c$.

Multiplication Law

If $a > b$ and $c > 0$, then $ac > bc$; if $a > b$ and $0 > c$, then $bc > ac$. (See Ex. 3.)

If $a > 0$, a is said to be *positive*; if $0 > a$, a is said to be *negative*; thus, from the law of trichotomy a real number is positive, zero, or negative.

It is often convenient to write $b < a$ (read "b is less than a") for $a > b$. Neither way of writing the relation is preferred above the other. We shall use the relation $a \geq b$ which may also be written $b \leq a$ (read "a is greater than or equal to b" and "b is less than or equal to a", respectively). The first of these, $a \geq b$, means that either $a > b$ or $a = b$; the second, $b \leq a$, means that either $b < a$ or $b = a$. The relations $a > b$ and $a \geq b$ are called *inequalities*; we occasionally emphasize the distinction between the two by calling $a > b$ a *strong inequality*, and the relation $a \geq b$ for which equality is permitted, a *weak inequality*.

By the law of trichotomy, each pair, a, b in $\mathfrak{R}$, satisfies one and no more than one of the following relations:

$$a \geq b, \qquad b > a.$$

Note that if $a > b$, then $a \geq b$; also, if $a = b$, then $a \geq b$.

By the transitive law:

a. If $a \geq b$ and $b \geq c$, then $a \geq c$.
b. If $a \geq b$ and $b > c$, then $a > c$.
c. If $a > b$ and $b \geq c$, then $a > c$.

Observe in (a) and in (b) that the symbol ">" representing strong inequality appears in the hypothesis, therefore we may use the strong inequality in the conclusion "$a > c$." In applications of the transitive law, the symbols ">," "$\geq$," and "=" may appear several times in a chain of inequalities; care must be exercised in selecting the symbol of inequality in the conclusion to insure its validity.

The transitive law permits us to write a chain of inequalities in a particularly simple form. For example, the inequality

$$a > b \geq c \geq d > e$$

stands for the inequalities $a > b$, $b \geq c$, $c \geq d$, and $d > e$. We shall never write a chain of inequalities in this fashion unless the first and last number are connected transitively. For example, we regard such an expression as $a > b < c$ as completely meaningless.

Example 1. If $a \geq b$, $b \geq c$, and $c = d$, then $a \geq d$. It is convenient to write

(1) $$a \geq b \geq c \geq d$$

so that the relation between the first and last number in the chain of inequalities is given by the last order symbol. If we had written

(2) $$a \geq b \geq c = d,$$

we would have to search farther back in the chain to find the relation between a and d. Thus (1) is the preferred form, and we shall avoid the form (2).

Example 2. If $a \geq b$, $b \geq c$, $c > d$, $d \geq e$, and $e = f$, then $a > f$. We write

$$a \geq b \geq c > d \geq e \geq f.$$

Here, as before, the last order symbol yields the correct relation $a \geq f$. Since there is a strong inequality in the chain we actually have the strong inequality $a > f$. If we need the strong result we must look back to see if there is a strong inequality in the chain of relations.

In our discussion of the transitive property, we have used the symbols $\geq$, $>$, and $=$, but the statements also hold if the symbols $\geq$ and $>$ are replaced by $\leq$ and $<$, respectively.

We leave the derivation of the well-known properties of order to exercises, but there is one property which we derive here as a useful example:

The square of a non-zero real number is positive.

If $a > 0$, then from the multiplication law

$$a \cdot a > 0 \cdot a,$$

that is,

$$a^2 > 0.$$

If $a < 0$, then from the addition law,

$$a + (-a) < 0 + (-a)$$

and from the properties of the additive inverse and identity we obtain

$$0 < -a.$$

Thus $(-a)$ is positive and by the preceding argument $(-a)^2 > 0$. We know, in general (see A1.1 Ex. 5), that $(-a)(-b) = ab$. Setting $b = a$ in the last relation, we have $(-a)^2 = a^2$. It follows that $a^2 > 0$ when a is negative, and our argument is complete.   ⌬

A1.2 Exercises

In each of the exercises 1 to 10, prove the given statement.

1. For any real number a,
   a. if $a > 0$, then $0 > -a$,
   b. if $0 > a$, then $-a > 0$.

2. For any real numbers a, b, c, d, if $a > b$ and $c > d$, then

$$a + c > b + d.$$

3. The second half of the Multiplication Law, "if $a > b$ and $0 > c$, then $bc > ac$", is not an independent condition, but can be derived from the remaining axioms of order and the field postulates.

4. a. Given that a and b are positive, $a > b$ if and only if $a^2 > b^2$.
   b. Given that a and b are negative, $a > b$ if and only if $b^2 > a^2$.

5. For any real number a and any positive number b,
   a. $a^2 \geq b$ if and only if $a \geq \sqrt{b}$ or $a \leq -\sqrt{b}$.
   b. $a^2 \leq b$ if and only if $-\sqrt{b} \leq a \leq \sqrt{b}$.

6. If $a > b > 0$ and $c > d > 0$, then $ac > bd$.

7. For any real numbers a and b if $ab > 0$, then a and b must be either both negative or both positive.

8. For any real number a,
   a. if $a > 0$, then $\dfrac{1}{a} > 0$;
   b. if $a < 0$, then $\dfrac{1}{a} < 0$.

9. For $bd < 0$, $\dfrac{a}{b} < \dfrac{c}{d}$ if and only if $ad > bc$.

10. If $ab > 0$ and $a > b$, then $\dfrac{1}{a} < \dfrac{1}{b}$.

11. Prove that the complex numbers form a field $\mathcal{C}$ and that there can be no order relation on $\mathcal{C}$.

12. The field $\mathcal{F}$ of numbers of the form $a + b\sqrt{2}$ where a and b are rational numbers has the ordering relation $>$ because $\mathcal{F}$ is a subset of R. Show that $\mathcal{F}$ is also ordered by the relation $\succ$ where $a + b\sqrt{2} \succ c + d\sqrt{2}$ means that $a - b\sqrt{2} > c - d\sqrt{2}$.

13. Show for all real numbers x and y that $x^2 + xy + y^2 \geq 0$.

14. a. Prove that $(x + y)^2 \geq 4xy$.
    b. For positive numbers a and b, show that the arithmetic mean is not less than the geometric mean which is, in turn, greater than or equal to the harmonic mean:
    $$\frac{a + b}{2} \geq \sqrt{ab} \geq \frac{2ab}{a + b}.$$

    When does equality hold in this relation?

15. Find all values of x for which
    $$ax^2 + 2bx + c \geq 0, \qquad a \neq 0.$$

    Discuss all possible cases.

16. Observe that
    $$(a_1x + b_1)^2 + (a_2x + b_2)^2 + \cdots + (a_nx + b_n)^2 \geq 0;$$

then use the solution of Exercise 15, to prove the Cauchy Inequality:

$$(a_1b_1 + a_2b_2 + \cdots + a_nb_n)^2 \leq (a_1^2 + a_2^2 + \cdots + a_n^2)(b_1^2 + b_2^2 + \cdots + b_n^2),$$

with equality, if and only if all $b_r = 0$, or $a_r = kb_r$, for all $r = 1, 2, \ldots,$ n and k, some constant.

17. If $a_1, a_2, \ldots, a_n$ are positive numbers, show that their arithmetic mean is greater than or equal to their harmonic mean, that is,

$$\frac{a_1 + a_2 + \cdots + a_n}{n} \geq \frac{n}{\dfrac{1}{a_1} + \dfrac{1}{a_2} + \cdots + \dfrac{1}{a_n}}.$$

(Compare Exercise 14b.)

18. Prove the general triangle inequality:

$$\sqrt{x_1^2 + x_2^2 + \cdots + x_n^2} + \sqrt{y_1^2 + y_2^2 + \cdots + y_n^2}$$
$$\geq \sqrt{(x_1 - y_1)^2 + (x_2 - y_2)^2 + \cdots + (x_n - y_n)^2}.$$

A1.3 ABSOLUTE VALUE AND INEQUALITY

The absolute value of a real number a, written $|a|$, is defined by

$$|a| = \begin{cases} a & \text{if } a > 0, \\ 0 & \text{if } a = 0, \\ -a & \text{if } a < 0. \end{cases}$$

If we represent real numbers as points on the number line, then $|a|$ is the

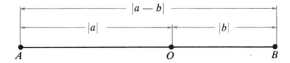

Figure 1

distance between 0 and a (Figure 1). In general, for any real numbers a and b, the distance between a and b is

$$|b - a| = |a - b|.$$

If x lies on the segment with endpoints $-\epsilon$ and ϵ, where $\epsilon > 0$, then $-\epsilon \leq x \leq \epsilon$ and x is no farther from the origin than ϵ; we must then have $|x| \leq \epsilon$. Conversely, if $|x| \leq \epsilon$, then

$$-\epsilon \leq x \leq \epsilon.$$

It follows immediately that

(1) $$-|x| \le x \le |x| .$$

(See Ex. 6a.)

From the inequalities

$$-|a| \le a \le |a| \quad \text{and} \quad -|b| \le b \le |b| ,$$

we obtain

$$-(|a| + |b|) \le a + b \le |a| + |b| ,$$

whence

(2) $$|a + b| \le |a| + |b| .$$

This relation is known as the "triangle inequality." In words, the absolute value of a sum of two terms is no greater than the sum of the absolute values of the terms. Since any sum can be built up by successive additions, this result holds in general, for example,

$$\begin{aligned} |a + b + c| &= |(a + b) + c| \\ &\le |a + b| + |c| \\ &\le |a| + |b| + |c| . \end{aligned}$$

We say that y is an *upper estimate* for x, and that x is a *lower estimate* for y if $x < y$. In (2) we found an upper estimate for the absolute value of the sum $a + b$. It is often useful to have a lower estimate for $|a + b|$ which is better than the obvious estimate 0. We can obtain such an estimate from (2) by setting $a = x + y$ and then $b = -x$ and $b = -y$ in turn. We thus obtain

$$|y| - |x| \le |x + y|$$

and

$$|x| - |y| \le |x + y| .$$

Since $||x| - |y||$ is one or the other of the values $|x| - |y|$ or $|y| - |x|$, we have a lower estimate, not necessarily 0, for the absolute value of a sum:

(3) $$||x| - |y|| \le |x + y| .$$

(See Ex. 9.)

The symbol $\max \{r_1, r_2, \dots, r_n\}$ denotes the largest of the numbers $r_1, r_2, \dots, r_n$; similarly, the symbol $\min \{r_1, r_2, \dots, r_n\}$ denotes the smallest of the numbers. For brevity, we put

$$\max_k \{r_k\} = \max \{r_1, r_2, \dots, r_n\}$$

when it is understood that the index k runs from 1 to n. The notation $\min_k \{r_k\}$ is used similarly.

Example 1.

$$\max \{2, 8, -3, -1\} = 8,$$

$$\min \{2, 8, -3, -10\} = -10,$$

$$\max \{-a, a\} = |a|,$$

$$\min \{x^2, x\} = \begin{cases} x & \text{for } x \geq 1, \\ x^2 & \text{for } 0 \leq x \leq 1, \\ x & \text{for } x < 0. \end{cases}$$

The maximum of two numbers can be expressed simply in terms of absolute values:

$$\max \{a, b\} = \tfrac{1}{2}(a + b + |a - b|);$$

a similar expression may be obtained for the minimum. (See Ex. 16b, c.)

A1.3 Exercises

1. a. For what real numbers x does $|x| = -x$?
   b. For what real numbers x does $|x^2 + 2x + 4| = x^2 + 2x + 4$?

2. Solve the equations:

   a. $|3 - x| = 1$.
   b. $|4x + 3| = 1$.
   c. $|x + 2| = x$.
   d. $|x + 1| = |x - 3|$.
   e. $|2x + 3| = |5 - x|$.
   f. $|2x + 5| + |5x + 2| = 0$.

3. For what values of x is each of the following true? (Express your answer in terms of inequalities satisfied by x.)

   a. $|x| \leq 0$.
   b. $|x| \neq x$.
   c. $|\sin x| > \dfrac{\sqrt{2}}{2}$.
   d. $|x - a| < \delta$.
   e. $0 < |x - a| < \delta$.
   f. $|x - 3| > 2$.
   g. $|2x - 3| < 1$.
   h. $|x - a| < |a|$.
   i. $|x - 1| < 2$ and $|x + 1| < \tfrac{3}{2}$.
   j. $|x - 1| < 2$ and $|2x - 1| < \tfrac{3}{2}$.
   k. $|x - 1| > |x - 3|$.
   l. $|x - 5| + 1 = |x + 5|$.
   m. $|x - 1| + |x - 2| = 1$.
   n. $|x^2 - 3| < 1$.
   o. $|x^2 - a^2| > 0$.
   p. $|(x - 2)(x - 3)| > 2$.
   q. $\sqrt{|x|} > \tfrac{1}{2}$.
   r. $\left|1 - \dfrac{1}{x}\right| < 1$.

4. Sketch the graphs of the following equations:

   a. $|x - 1| + |y| = 1$.
   b. $|x + y| + |x - y| = 2$.
   c. $y = |x - 1| + |x - 3|$.
   d. $y = |x - 1| + |x - 3| + 2|x - 4|$.

5. Prove for any real numbers a and b, that
   a. $|ab| = |a| \cdot |b|$,

   b. $\left|\dfrac{a}{b}\right| = \dfrac{|a|}{|b|}$, where $b \neq 0$.

6. a. Directly from the properties of order prove for any positive ϵ that $|x| < \epsilon$ if and only if $-\epsilon < x < \epsilon$.
   b. Prove that if x is an element of an ordered field and if $|x| < \epsilon$ for all positive numbers ϵ, then $x = 0$.

7. Show that if $|x - a| < \dfrac{|a|}{2}$, then $\dfrac{|a|}{2} < |x| < \dfrac{3|a|}{2}$ for all $a \neq 0$.

8. For all real x and y prove that $|x - y| \leq |x| + |y|$.

9. Under what conditions do the equality signs hold for

$$||a| - |b|| \leq |a + b| \leq |a| + |b| \, ?$$

10. Prove $x^2 \geq x|x|$ for all real x.

11. If $0 < x < 1$, then $x^2 < x$ (and, similarly, $x^3 < x^2$, $x^4 < x^3$, and so on). Use this result to show that if $0 < |x| < 1$, then

$$|x^2 + 2x| < 3|x| \, .$$

12. Prove the following inequalities

   a. $x + \dfrac{1}{x} \geq 2$, for $x > 0$.

   b. $x + \dfrac{1}{x} \leq -2$, for $x < 0$.

   c. $\left|x + \dfrac{1}{x}\right| \geq 2$, for $x \neq 0$.

13. Show for $|x| \leq 1$ that

$$|1 - \sqrt{1 + x}| \leq |x| \, .$$

14. Prove for positive a and b, where $a \neq b$, that

$$\frac{|b - a|^2}{4(a + b)} < \frac{a + b}{2} - \sqrt{ab} < \frac{|b - a|^2}{8\sqrt{ab}} \, .$$

15. a. Show that if $a > b > 0$, then $\dfrac{ab}{a + b} < b$.
   b. Thus, show that for positive numbers a and b, the condition

$$\delta \leq \min \{a, b\}$$

   is satisfied by $\delta = \dfrac{ab}{a + b}$.

16. a. Show for positive a, b that $\frac{1}{2}(a + b) < \max \{a, b\}$ if $a \neq b$.
    b. Prove for all a, b that

$$\max \{a, b\} = \frac{1}{2}(a + b + |a - b|).$$

c. Obtain a similar expression for $\min \{a, b\}$ and prove your result.

17. Show that
$$\max \{a, b\} + \max \{c, d\} \geq \max \{a + c, b + d\}.$$

18. Show that if $ab \geq 0$, then $ab \geq \min \{a^2, b^2\}$.

19. Show that if $a = \max \{a, b, c\}$, then $-a = \min \{-a, -b, -c\}$.

20. If $b_i > 0$, $i = 1, 2, \ldots, n$, prove that

$$\min_i \left|\frac{a_i}{b_i}\right| \leq \frac{a_1 + a_2 + \cdots + a_n}{b_1 + b_2 + \cdots + b_n} \leq \max_i \left|\frac{a_i}{b_i}\right|.$$

21. Prove that

$$\frac{1}{n} \leq \frac{1 + 2 + \cdots + n}{(n)^2 + (n - 1)^2 + \cdots + 2^2 + 1^2} \leq 1 \quad \text{for } n \text{ a positive integer.}$$

A1.4 INTERVALS AND NEIGHBORHOODS

An *interval* of the number line is any set of real numbers containing more than one element and having the property that if u and v are elements of the set, so is every real number x between them; that is, if $u < v$, every x for which $u < x < v$ is also in the interval. The following sets are easily proved to be intervals.

The segments (two endpoints). Given two real numbers a and b with $a < b$, there are four kinds of segments that have a and b as endpoints: the set of all x for which

a. $a \leq x \leq b$, also written $[a, b]$, called a *closed* interval,
b. $a < x < b$, also written (a, b), called an *open* interval,
c. $a \leq x < b$, sometimes written $[a, b)$,
d. $a < x \leq b$, sometimes written $(a, b]$.

We emphasize that when the symbols $[a, b]$ and (a, b) are used for intervals, it is assumed that $a < b$. (The sets defined by c and d are sometimes called *half-open* or *half-closed* intervals, but the concept is not particularly useful.)

The rays or half-lines (one endpoint). Given a real number a, there are four kinds of rays that have a as an endpoint:

a. $\{x : x \le a\} = (-\infty, a]$ and $\{x : x \ge a\} = [a, \infty)$ (closed rays),

b. $\{x : x < a\} = (-\infty, a)$ and $\{x : x > a\} = (a, \infty)$ (open rays).

The entire number line, $\Re = (-\infty, \infty)$.

We have listed all types of intervals. With the help of the Separation Axiom of A1.5 it is possible to show that the list is complete, but we are not concerned with that question.

In the text, we distinguish among the others primarily the closed and open intervals; these are intervals having two endpoints which are either simultaneously included in the interval or simultaneously excluded from it. A point of an interval which is not an endpoint is called an *interior* point of the interval.†

The *length* of an interval (whether open, closed, or other) with two endpoints a and b is the distance $|b - a|$ between a and b. The *midpoint* of an interval with endpoints a and b is the point $\frac{1}{2}(a + b)$. The closed interval with endpoints a and b is the set of real numbers x satisfying the weak inequality

$$|x - \tfrac{1}{2}(a + b)| \le \tfrac{1}{2}|b - a| \; ;$$

similarly, the open interval is the set of real numbers satisfying the corresponding strong inequality

$$|x - \tfrac{1}{2}(a + b)| < \tfrac{1}{2}|b - a| \, .$$

Given $\delta > 0$, the δ-*neighborhood* of a real number a is the set of all points x satisfying

$$|x - a| < \delta$$

and δ is called the *radius* of the neighborhood. The δ-neighborhood of a is the open interval

$$N_\delta(a) = \{x : a - \delta < x < a + \delta\}$$

of length 2δ with midpoint at a. Without specifying the radius δ, we often say only "a neighborhood" of a. Every open interval that contains the point a contains a neighborhood of a; conversely, every interval that contains with each of its points an entire neighborhood of the point, is open.

For many purposes we shall use the concept of a *deleted neighborhood* of a, that is, a δ-neighborhood with the center a deleted; namely, the set

$$\{x : 0 < |x - a| < \delta\} \, .$$

---

†In some texts any set $\{x : a \le x \le b\}$ is called a closed interval. If $a = b$, this admits closed intervals consisting of exactly one point and there are no interior points. For most of the purposes of this text, this degenerate case is not useful and we specifically exclude the possibility of a closed interval without interior points.

Sometimes we shall use the more general concept of *deleted open interval about* a, that is, a set $\{x: \ b < x < a \ \text{ or } \ a < x < c\}$, where $b < a < c$.

A1.4 Exercises

1. Use absolute value and inequalities to express the following statements.
   a. The point x is closer to -2 than is the point a.
   b. The point x is closer to point a than it is to the origin.

2. In each case, use absolute values and inequalities to express the condition that x is in the given interval.
   a. $[-5, -2]$.   b. $(-1, 5)$.
   c. $[5.9, 6.1]$.   d. $(-2.95, -2.85)$.

3. In each of the following express the set of values of x which satisfy the given inequality as an interval or union of intervals.
   a. $|x + 2| < 1$.   b. $0 < |x + 2| < 1$.
   c. $|x + a| < \dfrac{|a|}{2}$.   d. $0 < |x + a| < \dfrac{|a|}{2}$.

4. For each of the following statements give the interval or intervals on which the statement is true.
   a. $x^2 - x - 6 > 0$.
   b. $(x - a)(x - b)(x - c) \le 0$, for $a < b < c$.
   c. $\cos x > \sin x$.   d. $x + 1 \ge 2\sqrt{x}$.
   e. $|x^2 - 1| < \frac{1}{100}$.   f. $|x^2 - 1| < 100$.

5. In each of the following, for the given value of a find a neighborhood of a where the given inequality holds.
   a. $a = \frac{3}{2}$, $|2x - 3| < \frac{1}{7}$.
   b. $a = \dfrac{\pi}{2}$, $|\sin x - 1| < 1 - \dfrac{1}{\sqrt{2}}$.
   c. $a = -1$, $|x^2 + x| < \frac{1}{10}$.
   d. $a = -1$, $|x^2 + x| < \frac{1}{100}$.
   e. $a = -1$, $|x^2 + x| < \frac{1}{1000}$.

6. Given $\epsilon > 0$, find a positive δ such that $x \in N_\delta(a)$ and $y \in N_\delta(b)$ implies
   a. $x + y \in N_\epsilon(a + b)$,   b. $xy \in N_\epsilon(ab)$.

EA1.5 COMPLETENESS OF THE REAL NUMBER SYSTEM. THE SEPARATION AXIOM

As yet we do not have enough conditions to define the real number system. The axioms for an ordered field are satisfied not only by the real numbers, but also by the rational numbers and other fields (see A1.2 Ex. 12).

Among ordered fields, only the real number field can adequately represent the set of all points on the number line or the set of all infinite decimals. Other ordered fields inevitably have gaps; some points of the number line or some infinite decimals are always missing.

At first, an untutored intuition may rebel at the idea that an ordered field like the rational numbers may be inadequate to describe the number line. Since every point on the number line can be located in an interval with rational endpoints and an arbitrarily small length, any physical measurement — because no such measurement can be absolutely precise — is perfectly well described within the threshold of detectability by a rational number. It is not for the sake of measurement, but for the sake of having suitably general theories of geometry and analysis that we must go beyond the rational numbers.

For example, a right triangle with legs of unit length has a hypotenuse with the irrational length $\sqrt{2}$. If we restricted ourselves to the rational number system, a right triangle with legs of rational length could have a hypotenuse of no definable length. The Pythagorean Theorem would then make sense for only a very special class of right triangles and we should be forced to entertain the idea of a line segment to which we could not attribute a length. Again, the rational field does not include all infinite decimals. In the rational field, the concept of infinite decimal would be limited to terminating and periodic decimals; an infinite decimal like 0.101100111000 . . . with chains of ones and zeros of increasing length would be uninterpretable.

The system of rational numbers has theoretical gaps, but the real number system is complete in that real numbers are adequate to represent all the points on a line or all infinite decimals. This concept of completeness has a simple geometrical description. Consider two sets of points A and B on the number line such that every point of the one set A lies "leftward" of every point of the other set B (see Figure 1). More precisely, if $a \in A$

A   *s*   *B*

Figure 1

and $b \in B$ then $a \leq b$. (Note that weak inequality is allowed.) Intuitively, whatever the nature of the sets A and B, there exists a point s such that the points of A lie leftward of s and the points of B lie to the right of s. This is the property of the real numbers which we take as our axiom of completeness.

The Separation Axiom

Let A and B be nonempty sets of real numbers such that $a \leq b$ for every $a \in A$ and every $b \in B$. There then exists at least one real number s which separates A from B; that is, every $a \in A$ and $b \in B$ satisfy $a \leq s \leq b$.

As an example of sets satisfying the separation axiom consider

$$A = \{x : x \leq 0\}, \quad B = \{y : y \geq 1\}.$$

Any number s in the closed interval $[0, 1]$ separates these sets.

We already know the rational number field to be incomplete, and if the Separation Axiom implies completeness it must not hold for the rational number field. We cannot exhibit a failure of the Separation Axiom whenever the two sets are separated by an interval, as in the preceding example, because every interval contains rational numbers. The difficulties arise when the separation between the two sets is zero in the sense that, given any positive distance, there are always elements $a \in A$ and $b \in B$ closer together than that distance. For example, let A be the set of all positive rational numbers a satisfying $a^2 < 2$, and B, the set of all positive rational numbers b satisfying $b^2 > 2$. Given a positive distance, it is always possible to find elements of A and B separated by a smaller distance. (See 3.1 or A4.1 Ex. 14.) Any separation number s would have to satisfy $s^2 = 2$, but there is no rational number which has that property. (See Ex. 1c.) As we asserted, the Separation Axiom does not hold for the rational number field.

In the field of real numbers, the Separation Axiom implies that the two sets A and B of the preceding example do have a separation number. There can be only one such separation number and we could even define $\sqrt{2}$ as the unique real number which separates A and B. For that matter, any real number can be defined as the unique separation number for two suitably chosen sets of rational numbers. We need not restrict the defining sets to rational numbers; in general, any real number may be determined as the unique separation for some pair of sets satisfying the criterion of the following Lemma.

Lemma 1. Let A and B be sets of real numbers for which $x \leq y$ whenever $x \in A$ and $y \in B$. If for each positive ϵ there exist $a \in A$ and $b \in B$ such that $b - a < \epsilon$, then A and B have exactly one separation number. Conversely, if the separation number for A and B is unique, then for every positive ϵ there exist numbers a, b with $a \in A$, $b \in B$, and $b - a < \epsilon$.

Proof. Suppose first that, given ϵ, there are points $a \in A$ and $b \in B$ for which $b - a < \epsilon$. If s and t are separation numbers for A and B, then, since s and t lie in $[a, b]$, (see Figure 2), it follows

Figure 2

that $|s - t| \leq b - a < \epsilon$. For every positive ϵ, then, $|s - t| < \epsilon$. Consequently, (A1.3 Ex. 6b), $|s - t| = 0$; hence $s = t$ and uniqueness is proved.

To prove the converse, let s be the one point separating A and B. For each positive ϵ there must exist points a in A and b in B for which

(1) $\qquad\qquad s - \tfrac{1}{2}\epsilon < a \quad \text{and} \quad b < s + \tfrac{1}{2}\epsilon$

(Figure 3); for should the first of these inequalities fail for all $a \in A$, then

Figure 3

$s - \tfrac{1}{2}\epsilon$ would be a separation number and if the second should fail for all $b \in B$, then $s + \tfrac{1}{2}\epsilon$ would be a separation number. For a and b satisfying (1), we conclude that $b - a < \epsilon$. $\qquad\qquad\square$

From the Separation Axiom, we now derive two principles which can be used as alternate formulations of the idea of completeness.

A sequence of closed intervals $[a_n, b_n]$, $n = 1, 2, 3, \ldots$, is said to be *nested* if and only if

$$[a_{n+1}, b_{n+1}] \subset [a_n, b_n]$$

for each natural number n. Observe for such a nested sequence that

$$a_1 \leq a_2 \leq a_3 \leq \cdots \leq a_n \leq \cdots$$

and

$$b_1 \geq b_2 \geq b_3 \geq \cdots \geq b_n \geq \cdots.$$

Theorem 1. The Nested Interval Principle. There is at least one point common to all the intervals of a nested sequence.

Proof. Let $[a_n, b_n]$, $n = 1, 2, 3, \dots$, denote the intervals of a nested sequence. Let $A = \{a_n : n = 1, 2, 3, \dots\}$ be the set of all lower end-points of the given intervals and $B = \{b_n : n = 1, 2, 3, \dots\}$, the set of all upper endpoints. For any $a_i \in A$ and $b_j \in B$ we have $a_i < b_j$ since, for $k = \max \{i, j\}$,

$$a_i \leq a_k < b_k \leq b_j .$$

The sets A and B satisfy all conditions of the Separation Axiom and there exists a number s which separates the two. Thus, $a_n \leq s \leq b_n$ for $n = 1, 2, 3, \dots$.

Example 1. Any infinite decimal may be written in the form

(2) $$c_0 . c_1 c_2 c_3 \dots ,$$

where c_0 is an integer and each of $c_1, c_2, c_3, \dots$, is a *digit*, one of the integers $0, 1, 2, \dots, 9$. Such a decimal is interpreted as the real number r which satisfies the inequalities

(3 a) $$a_n \leq r < b_n \qquad\qquad (n = 1, 2, 3, \dots),$$

where

(3 b)
$$a_n = c_0 + \frac{c_1}{10} + \frac{c_2}{10^2} + \frac{c_3}{10^3} + \cdots + \frac{c_n}{10^n} ,$$
$$b_n = a_n + \frac{1}{10^n} .$$

From the Nested Interval Principle, we show that at least one such real number r exists and we show that r is unique. First, since $a_n < b_n$, the interval $[a_n, b_n]$ is defined. Furthermore, from (3b),

$$a_{n+1} = a_n + \frac{c_{n+1}}{10^{n+1}} \geq a_n$$

and

$$b_{n+1} = a_n + \frac{c_{n+1}}{10^{n+1}} + \frac{1}{10^{n+1}} \leq a_n + \frac{10}{10^{n+1}} \leq a_n + \frac{1}{10^n} \leq b_n ,$$

we have $a_n \leq a_{n+1} < b_{n+1} \leq b_n$ and we conclude that the intervals $[a_n, b_n]$ define a nested sequence. There must then exist at least one real number r common to all the intervals of the sequence. To prove that r is unique we need only observe that r is the separation number for the sets $\{a_n\}$ and $\{b_n\}$, and for any positive ϵ , that

$$b_n - a_n = \frac{1}{10^n} < \epsilon ,$$

provided n is large enough (Ex. 2c). By Lemma 1, r must be unique.

We have shown that every infinite decimal has an unambiguous interpretation as a real number, but leave to Ex. 4d the complementary proof that every real number has an infinite decimal representation (2). With these results in mind, we make no further distinction between a real number and its representation as an infinite decimal.

A number M is said to be an *upper bound* for the set S if $x \leq M$ for every element x of S . Similarly, a number m is a *lower bound* for S if $x \geq m$ for every element x of S . If S has an upper bound, S is said to be *bounded above;* if S has a lower bound, *bounded below.* If S has both upper and lower bounds, then S is said to be *bounded.*

Theorem 2. The Least Upper Bound Principle.   If a nonempty set A of real numbers is bounded above, it has a *least upper bound*, an upper bound that is less than any other.

Proof. Let B denote the set of upper bounds of A . The sets A and B satisfy the conditions of the Separation Axiom. It follows that there exists at least one separation number s for A and B . Since s is a separation number, it is an upper bound of A and is by definition an element of B . Since s is also a lower bound for B , it is the least element of B and, therefore, it is the least upper bound of A .

The least upper bound of A is also called the *supremum* of A and is commonly denoted either by lub A or sup A .

Observe that the least upper bound is unique since only one upper bound can be least. From this observation, the following corollary is easily proved.

Corollary a.   If sup $A = M$, then for each positive ϵ there exists at least one $a \in A$ such that $a > M - \epsilon$. (Ex. 6.)

Example 2. Given the infinite decimal (2), we may write the real number r which it represents as $r = \sup \{a_n\}$ where a_n is defined as in (3b). We have already verified that r lies in all the intervals $[a_n, b_n]$, hence that $a_n \leq r$ for all a_n , or that r is an upper bound for $\{a_n\}$. Furthermore, $r \leq b_n \leq a_n + \dfrac{1}{10^n}$ · We conclude that r is the least upper bound for if there were a lesser upper bound s , from

$$a_n \leq s < r \leq a_n + \frac{1}{10^n},$$

we would have $0 < r - s < \dfrac{1}{10^n}$ for all n . Consequently, $r - s$ is less than every positive number, which is a contradiction.

Just as we have introduced the idea of least upper bound, we may consider the greatest of the lower bounds of a set and prove the following corollary to Theorem 2.

Corollary b. Any nonempty set of real numbers which is bounded below has a greatest lower bound (Ex. 7).

The greatest lower bound or *infimum* of a set A is denoted by glb A or inf A .

The Least Upper Bound Principle, the Nested Interval Principle, and the Separation Axiom are alternate ways of expressing the completeness of the real numbers. They are equivalent in that any one of them may be taken as an axiom supplementing the axioms of an ordered field and the other two may then be derived as consequences. To show that the three are equivalent, it is necessary to prove further that the Least Upper Bound Principle and the Nested Interval Principle each imply the Separation Axiom. The proofs are left to Exercises 8 and 9, respectively.

A1.5 Exercises

1. a. Consider the sets A of positive rational numbers α satisfying $\alpha^2 < 2$, and B of positive rational numbers β satisfying $\beta^2 > 2$. Prove if $\alpha \in A$ and $\beta \in B$ that $\alpha < \beta$.
   b. Show that a separation number s for the sets A and B must satisfy $s^2 = 2$; i.e., $s = \sqrt{2}$.
   c. Prove that $\sqrt{2}$ is irrational.

2. a. Prove for each real number a , that there is an integer n greater than a (Principle of Archimedes).
   b. Prove that given any positive ϵ there is an integer n such that

$$0 < \frac{1}{n} < \epsilon.$$

   c. Prove for any given positive ϵ that for all sufficiently large natural numbers n , $0 < \dfrac{1}{10^n} < \epsilon$.

3. Prove that every real number has a unique infinite decimal representation given by (2).

4. An infinite decimal $c_0 . c_1 c_2 c_3 \ldots$ is said to be periodic if for a fixed value p, the *period* of the decimal, we have $c_{n+p} = c_n$ for all n satisfying $n \geq n_0$, where we require that p is the smallest positive integer satisfying this condition. In words, from some place on, the decimal consists of the cyclic repetition of the same p digits. For example,

$$\tfrac{1}{3} = .33333 \ldots , \text{ where } n_0 = 0 , \quad p = 1 ,$$
$$\tfrac{15}{44} = .34090909 \ldots , \text{ where } n_0 = 3 , \quad p = 2 ,$$

are periodic decimals. It is convenient to indicate a cycle of p digits by underlining, rather than repetition; e.g.,

$$\tfrac{1}{3} = .\underline{3}, \qquad \tfrac{15}{44} = .34\underline{09} .$$

   a. Prove that every periodic decimal represents a rational number. (Hint: Consider the decimal as a geometric progression.)
   b. Prove that every rational number has a periodic decimal representation. (A "terminating" decimal for which every place beyond a certain point is zero is considered as a special periodic decimal.) If $r = s/t$ represents a rational number given in lowest terms, find the largest possible period of the infinite decimal representation of r in terms of the denominator t.

   From Parts a and b we conclude that a decimal which is not periodic represents an irrational number, and conversely.
   c. Prove for every positive prime α other than 2 and 5 that there exists an integer, all of whose digits are ones, for which α is a factor; i.e., α is a factor of some number of the form

$$10^n + 10^{n-1} + 10^{n-2} + \cdots + 10 + 1 .$$

   d. The *integer part* of any real number x is defined as the one integer $[\![x]\!]$ for which $[\![x]\!] \leq x < [\![x]\!] + 1$ (see A2.2, p. 259). Given a real number r we define its decimal representation recursively in terms of integer parts as follows:

$$c_0 = [\![r]\!]$$
$$c_n = \left[10^n \left(r - c_0 - \frac{c_1}{10} - \frac{c_2}{10^2} - \cdots - \frac{c_{n-1}}{10^{n-1}} \right) \right] .$$

   Show that the inequality (3a) is satisfied for this choice of c_n. Show also that this representation does not yield decimals consisting entirely of 9's from some point on. For example, we obtain $2 = 2.000 \ldots$ but not $2 = 1.999 \ldots$.

5. a. Consider a polynomial with integer coefficients:

$$a_n x^n + a_{n-1} x^{n-1} + \cdots + a_1 x + a_0 \qquad (a \neq 0) .$$

   Prove that if $\dfrac{p}{q}$ is a rational root of this polynomial given in lowest terms, then p is a factor of a_0 and q is a factor of a_n.

  b. Prove that if $\sqrt{n}$ is rational then it is integral.

  c. Prove that $\sqrt{3} - \sqrt{2}$ is irrational.

6. Prove Corollary 2a. If sup $A = M$, then for each positive ϵ there exists at least one $a \in A$ such that $a > M - \epsilon$.

7. Prove Corollary 2b. Any nonempty set of real numbers which is bounded below has a greatest lower bound.

8. Prove that an ordered field in which the Least Upper Bound Principle holds, also obeys the Separation Axiom.

9. Prove that an ordered field in which the Nested Interval Principle holds also obeys the Separation Axiom.

10. Prove

  a. inf $\{x + y : x \in S, \ y \in T\} = $ inf $S +$ inf T.

  b. For $\lambda \geq 0$, inf $\{\lambda X : x \in S\} = \lambda$ inf S.
     What is the corresponding expression for

$$\text{inf } \{\lambda x : x \in S\} \quad \text{when} \quad \lambda < 0 \ ?$$

  Prove your assertion.

Functions

EA2.1 RELATIONS

The concept of a relation among several elements is one of the primitive concepts of mathematics. Every axiomatic mathematical system can be described abstractly as a set of postulated properties of relations among the elements of certain sets. We can define a relation by a general statement about elements of the sets. For example, in plane geometry the sets might be the set of points P and the set of lines L, and the relation that of incidence:

(1) $\qquad\qquad$ $\mathbf{I}:$ $\quad p$ lies on ℓ,

where $p \in P$ and $\ell \in L$. If the statement is true for $p_1 \in P$ and $\ell_1 \in L$, we say the relation holds for $p = p_1$ and $\ell = \ell_1$ and write $\mathbf{I}(p_1, \ell_1)$; if false, we say the relation does not hold for $p = p_1$ and $\ell = \ell_1$ and we write $\mathbf{\cancel{I}}(p_1, \ell_1)$. Note that $\mathbf{\cancel{I}}$ is itself a relation:

(2) $\qquad\qquad$ $\mathbf{\cancel{I}}:$ $\quad p$ does not lie on ℓ.

One typical form of axiom is a rule for the derivation of further relations from stated relations; for example,

(3)   if $I(p_1, \ell_1)$, $I(p_2, \ell_1)$ and $I(p_1, \ell_2)$, $I(p_2, \ell_2)$
    and $p_1 \neq p_2$, then $\ell_1 = \ell_2$.

In English, this axiom says that at most one line passes through any two points. (Later we shall discuss the relation of equality which appears in this axiom.) Another typical form of axiom asserts the existence of elements which satisfy certain of the stated relations; for example,

for any $p_1, p_2 \in P$ there exists an
$\ell_0 \in L$ such that $I(p_1, \ell_0)$ and $I(p_2, \ell_0)$.

In English, this axiom says that at least one line passes through the points†
p_1 and p_2.

The statements in (1) and (2), which are considered in this discussion as general forms, become meaningful only if the symbols refer to specific elements. We shall write $I(P, L)$ for the form   "p lies on ℓ." In using the sets P and L we indicate only that I expresses a relation between elements of P and L. We ask whether the relation is true or false only with respect to specific elements; $I(P, L)$ is neither true nor false, it is a blank form which acquires meaning only when its spaces are filled in with elements from the indicated sets. Thus, we see that the symbols p and ℓ which appear in (1) do not stand for a specific point and a specific line, but are generic symbols for elements of P and L, respectively. In the same way, the word "person" does not symbolize you or me, but represents any member of the genus *homo*. A generic symbol for any element of a set is called a *variable*. In some elementary texts, a variable appearing in the statement that defines a relation is called a "placeholder," indicative of a blank in the form which is to be filled in with any specific element of the set. A specific element of the set will be called a *value* of the variable.

The concept of relation is a mathematical idealization. A relation is assumed to be defined if and only if for each assignment of values to the variables in its statement its truth or falsity is unambiguous. In practical situations, such precision may be difficult to achieve. Consider, for example, the relation defined by "a and b are animals of the same species." For borderline individuals it is not obvious whether the relation is true or false.

---

†The use of the plural in this text allows the possibility, $p_1 = p_2$. If we refer to "the *two* items p_1 and p_2" we do mean to imply $p_1 \neq p_2$.

Observe that the same set may appear several times in the statement of a relation. For example, the order relation $\mathbf{O}(\Re, \Re)$ on the set $\Re$ of real numbers is defined by

$$\mathbf{O}: \quad x > y, \text{ where } x, y \in \Re.$$

The axioms of order in A1.2 may then be written formally as follows.

Trichotomy: If $a, b \in \Re$ then either $a = b$, or $\mathbf{O}(a, b)$, or $\mathbf{O}(b, a)$,
    and if $\mathbf{O}(a, b)$ then $a \neq b$ and $\cancel{\mathbf{O}}(b, a)$.
Transitive Law: If $\mathbf{O}(a, b)$ and $\mathbf{O}(b, c)$, then $\mathbf{O}(a, c)$.
Addition Law: If $c \in \Re$ and $\mathbf{O}(a, b)$, then $\mathbf{O}(a + c, b + c)$.
Multiplication Law: If $\mathbf{O}(a, b)$ and $\mathbf{O}(c, 0)$, then $\mathbf{O}(ac, bc)$.

In writing the postulates of a mathematical system as a set of symbolic rules for deriving relations we conceive of the system as completely formal and abstract. The elements that are related and the relations themselves are not defined and have no intrinsic meaning apart from the operations performed upon them. Such abstraction has several virtues offset by certain disadvantages. When we give an interpretation to the undefined elements and relations of a mathematical system, the colorful details of such a realization may obscure the essential pattern revealed by the abstract formulation. Furthermore, as frequently happens, a single abstract system may have several realizations, and anything proved for the abstract system is simultaneously valid for all of them. This generality of application is what makes mathematics so powerful a tool for the theoretical scientist. It is also a virtue of the abstract formulation that it forces us to express our arguments in terms of directly verifiable formal steps, and so helps us to avoid logical errors. As compared with a realization or model, however, there are disadvantages to abstraction: it neither suggests what concepts it would be fruitful to define nor offers any criterion by which we may appraise the significance of any theorem.

Thus far, we have tacitly assumed the properties of the relationship of *equality;* now we spell these out. Let $a, b, c, \ldots$, be symbols representing elements of some given set S. Two or more symbols may stand for the same element; for example, the symbols $1, 4 - 3, 2^0$ all represent the same number. In any given discussion, equality $\mathbf{E}(S, S)$ is defined by

$$\mathbf{E}: \quad a \text{ and } b \text{ represent the same element of } S.$$

The statement $\mathbf{E}(a, b)$ is more familiar in the form $a = b$. We give the properties of equality in the abstract form:

Reflexivity: $E(a, a)$ for all $a \in S$.
Symmetry: If $E(a, b)$ then $E(b, a)$.
Transitivity: If $E(a, b)$ and $E(b, c)$, then $E(a, c)$.

One implication of the reflexive property is that a symbol always has the same meaning within any given discussion. It places us under an obligation to avoid giving the same name to different objects in the same context.

Any relation that is reflexive, symmetric, and transitive is called an *equivalence*. There is one further property of equality which is not true of equivalences in general. This is the formal substitution rule: if $E(a, b)$ then b may be substituted for a wherever a appears in a given context; that is, any symbol for an element may be replaced by any other symbol for the same element.

Example. Let $\mathfrak{N}$ be the set of integers and consider the relation

$$\mathbf{R}: \quad a - b \text{ is even, where } a, b \in \mathfrak{N}.$$

The statement $\mathbf{R}(\mathfrak{N}, \mathfrak{N})$ can be expressed alternatively as, "there exists a z such that $x - y = 2z$"; here x, y, z are integer variables. We shall verify that $\mathbf{R}$ is an equivalence. Clearly $\mathbf{R}(a, a)$ holds for all $a \in \mathfrak{N}$ since $a - a = 0 = 2 \cdot 0$. Further, $\mathbf{R}(a, b)$ implies the existence of an integer c such that $a - b = 2c$; hence $b - a = -2c = 2(-c)$ or $\mathbf{R}(a, b)$ implies $\mathbf{R}(b, a)$. Finally, if $\mathbf{R}(a, b)$ and $\mathbf{R}(b, c)$, there exist integers m and n for which $a - b = 2m$ and $b - c = 2n$; hence, $a - c = (a - b) + (b - c) = 2(m + n)$ and $\mathbf{R}(a, c)$ holds. The relation $\mathbf{R}$ therefore is an equivalence.

Scientific endeavor is aimed at uncovering relations that can be analyzed logically or quantitatively. What is the relation between the number of people who have been told a story by time t_0 and the number who have heard it by time t? What is the relation between the temperature and the average time it takes for a newborn tadpole to become a frog? If a man is in the habit of smoking a certain number of cigarettes a day, what is the probability that he will die of lung cancer? What is the relation between the rate of a chemical reaction and the proportions of the reagents? How is the position of a satellite at a given time related to the initial speed and direction in which it was launched? Each of these questions contains a suggestion of a causal relationship. More precisely, in each of the relations sought it is hinted that any choice of values for some of the variables unambiguously determines the value for each of the remaining variables. For example, for the question about the time for a tadpole to grow into a frog, it may be expected that for any fixed water temperature the average time will be the same (or very nearly so) for all sample populations, provided the samples are not too small.† The use of the word "causal" is not in the familiar idiom. It is not implied, for example, that the number of people who know a story at one time is a "cause" of the number of people who know it at another, perhaps earlier, time. Cigarette manufacturers challenge any assertion of a causal relation between smoking and lung cancer; many of us on seeing the data will refrain from smoking and others will mutter something about "lies, damn lies, and statistics" and go on to smoke. Instead of "causal" relation, we shall use a neutral term, *function*, for any relation in which the choice of values for certain of the variables uniquely specifies the values of the remaining variables for which the relation holds.

As an example of a function, consider the position (x, y, z) of a satellite at a given time t. If other factors are fixed, such as the position of the launching site and the time of launching, the position (x, y, z) is determined by the laws of mechanics, provided the velocity $\mathbf{v}_0$ (speed and direction) at which the satellite was launched and the time t are given. The time and initial velocity are called the independent variables of this function, the coordinates x, y, z of position are the dependent variables. It is convenient to lump the independent variables together in the ordered pair $(\mathbf{v}_0, t)$ and the dependent variables in the ordered triple (x, y, z), and to refer to the ordered pair $(\mathbf{v}_0, t)$ as *the* independent variable, and the triple (x, y, z) as *the* dependent variable; this will be our customary usage.

The specification of a function includes a choice of independent and dependent variables. The same relation may define several functions. For example, the relation involving the pressure p, volume V, and temperature T of a perfect gas is given by

$$pV = cT,$$

where c is a constant which depends on the chemical composition of the gas. Any two of the variables in the perfect gas law may be taken as independent, the remaining one, as dependent.

---

†In any realistic problem, of course, other variables than the ones considered may affect the outcome. Part of the scientific problem is to recognize these variables and either to take direct account of their influence or to hold them fixed and so avoid the effects of unregulated factors. For example, an experiment to observe the dependence of the growth time of tadpoles upon temperature would undoubtedly be conducted entirely with samples of tadpoles all of the same species, with similar nutrients available to all samples, with equal concentrations of dissolved oxygen in the water, and any other conceivably important relevant variable held constant.

A2.1 Exercises

1. Show as a consequence of the incidence axiom that two lines intersect in no more than one point.

2. Consider the following relations:

   A: the person m is an ancestor of person n ,

   B: the real number a is greater than or equal to real number b ,

   C: $m - n$ is divisible by q , where m , n are integer variables and q is a fixed integer,

   D: the square of the real number x is the real number y ,

   E: right thumbprint u could only be made by person v ,

   F: the person a is married to the person b .

   a. Which of these relations is reflexive? symmetric? transitive?

   b. For which of these relations is it possible to define functions by a choice of independent and dependent variables? Specify which are the dependent variables for each function.

3. Show that the three given properties of an equivalence are independent; that is, for each of the properties, there is a relation which does not have that property but does satisfy the other two.

A2.2 FUNCTIONS AND THEIR GRAPHS

The concept of function is basic to all of mathematics. For the calculus, it is imperative to have a clear understanding of the concept, a command of the notations which describe functions and of the operations upon them, and facile knowledge of certain special classes of functions — monotone functions, polynomial functions, the absolute value function, the circular functions, and others. We shall take the concept of function as one of our primitive ideas and explain it as much by example as by the following description.

A function is a relation between the elements of sets A and B with the property that for each $a \in A$ there is precisely one element $b \in B$ for which the relation holds. We call a an *antecedent* of b and b the *image* of a .

Example 1. The relation " $y = 2x$ " for $x , y \in \Re$ describes a function. Here $A = B = \Re$. For each pair of real numbers x, y the relation must be definitely true or definitely false. Given a value of x , there is only one value of y which makes the relation true, namely $y = 2x$. Observe also that for each value of y there is only one value of x which makes the relation true, namely $x = y/2$.

In Example 1, we see that a relation may not define precisely which is antecedent and which is image. We shall not consider a function to be specified unless the roles of antecedent and image are clearly distinguished. It will not do to specify only the set A of antecedents and the set B which contains the images because, as in the preceding example, A and B may be the same. To indicate the relation between antecedent and image, we draw an arrow from antecedent to image:

(1) $$x \rightarrow 2x \,,$$

or

(2) $$y \rightarrow y/2 \,.$$

The rules (1) and (2) describe different functions. If 2 is taken as the antecedent in these relations, each function yields a different image, the image 4 by (1) and the image 1 by (2).

Three things are required to specify a function: a set A of all antecedents in the functional relation, a set B containing all the images of the elements of A (and which may contain other elements), and a single unambiguously defined image in B for each element of A. The set A of antecedents is called the *domain* of the function, the set C of images of A is called the *range*. It is often more convenient to specify some appropriate set B which contains the range than to give the range precisely. For example, we may take $\Re$ as the domain of the function

$$x \rightarrow x^4 - x^3 + 1$$

with range contained in $\Re$. At this point, we have no obvious way of determining the exact range of this function (we shall develop ways of doing so later), and for the purpose of some particular problem we may not need that information.

Example 2. Let $\Re$ be the domain of the function $x \rightarrow x^2$ with range in $\Re$. The range of the function is not all of $\Re$, but simply the set of nonnegative real numbers $\mathscr{P} = \{y \; : \; y \in \Re, \, y \geq 0\}$.

The function $x \rightarrow x^2$ is one expression of the relation "$y = x^2$." We may well ask whether the reverse association

(3) $$x^2 \rightarrow x$$

is meaningful, that is, whether it is a function. We may specify the domain of (3) as the set $\mathscr{P}$ of nonnegative real numbers, but now we have difficulties with the range. If we take 4 as the value of the antecedent x^2 in (3), we have two possibilities for its image, $x = 2$ or $x = -2$.

Thus (3) is meaningless unless we specify the range so as to eliminate the ambiguity. We may restrict the range to $\mathcal{P}$ so that (3) is the *square-root function*

(4) $$y \to \sqrt{y}.$$

There are infinitely many other ways of choosing the range so that (3) defines a function as you may wish to show (Ex. 5).

It is common to denote a function by the letter f; we shall also use other letters as needed: typically, $g, h, F, G, H, \phi, \psi$. We write

(5) $$f : x \to y$$

to indicate that y is the image of x for the function f. We also write (5) in the form

(6) $$y = f(x).$$

For $f(x)$, read "the value of the function f at x" or simply, "f of x." It is helpful to regard a function f as mapping each element of its domain upon one and only one element of its range. This notion is illustrated in Figure 1 where elements of the domain A and the range C

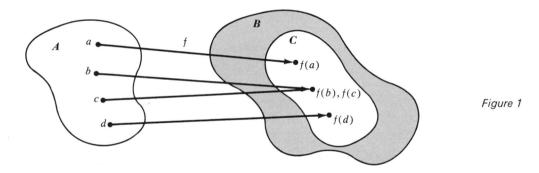

Figure 1

are represented by points and the mapping is suggested by arrows from points of the domain to corresponding points of the range. Note for this figure, that each point of the domain must be the initial point of exactly one arrow; this is the requirement that every point of the domain have precisely one image. At the same time, as for the function $x \to x^2$ of Example 2, several arrows may end at the same point of the range; a given point of the range may have more than one antecedent in the domain. Influenced by this pictorial concept of function, we sometimes refer to a function as a *mapping*. We then say that a function maps each element of its domain upon one and only one element of its range. We read the expression $f : x \to y$

as "f maps x upon y." In the situation of Figure 1, we say that f maps its domain A *onto* its range C, but *into* any set B which contains C.

In (5) and (6), the symbol x does not indicate a specific element of the domain A, nor does y indicate a specific element of the range C. The expressions (5) and (6) have the nature of a blank form to which we assign a value, true or false, only when the blanks are filled in; that is, when x is replaced by a specific $a \in A$ and y by a specific $b \in B$ where B is some appropriate set containing the range. We call x and y *variables*, meaning symbols indicating the general types "element of A" and "element of B," respectively, rather than any particular individual elements. When x and y are replaced by specific elements, a and b, respectively, we say that a is a *value* of x and b a *value* of y. To indicate the existence of a function $f : x \to y$, we refer to x as the *independent variable* or *argument* of f, and y as the *dependent variable*. When we wish to indicate the functional dependence of y on x without naming the function, we say that y *is a function of* x (please note, this does not mean that y is a function); this is a particularly convenient locution when y stands for a physical variable such as the velocity of a particle which we might wish to consider as a function of different variables, say time or position, in different contexts. We indicate that a value is being assigned to x by using such expressions as "take $x = a$" and "for $x = a$"; the corresponding value of the independent variable is called "the value of y at $x = a$."

Example 3. Consider the function

(7) $$f : x \to 2x^2 - 3$$

from $\Re$ into $\Re$. We have

$$f(x) = 2x^2 - 3,$$
$$f(3) = 15,$$
$$f(0) = -3,$$
$$f(-1) = -1,$$

and, for $b \geq 0$,

$$f(a + \sqrt{b}) = 2(a + \sqrt{b})^2 - 3.$$

Since $2x^2$ may be any nonnegative real number, $2x^2 - 3 \geq -3$ and the range of f is $\{y : y \geq -3\}$.

Note that for the function f defined by (7), the relation

$$f : x \to y$$

permits any meaningful assignment of values, but that it is false for some assignments of values. Thus, it is *not* true that $f : -2 \to -4$ and we could indicate this by $-2 \nrightarrow -4$ or $f(-2) \neq -4$; the latter form is the one commonly used.

In this text, without an explicit indication to the contrary, it is to be assumed that any function referred to is a mapping from $\mathcal{R}$ into $\mathcal{R}$; such a function is called "a real valued function of a real variable" or, briefly, "a real function." As we have already mentioned, the domain of a function must be specified to give a complete description of the function. For any real function defined by a formula, however, if no information about the domain is explicitly given, you are to assume that the domain includes every real number for which the formula has a real value. For example, if a domain is not specified for the function $f : x \to \dfrac{2x}{x^2 - 9}$, then the domain is assumed to be the set of all real numbers except 3 and -3. Similarly, if g is given by $g(x) = \sqrt{4 - x^2}$, we assume, in the absence of any other information, that the domain is the closed interval $[-2, 2]$. Note that two functions are equal $f = g$ if and only if they have the same domain and $f(x) = g(x)$ at every point of that domain. Thus, the function $f : x \to 1$ is not the same as the function $g : x \to \dfrac{x}{x}$; the function f has all of $\mathcal{R}$ as its domain, while the domain of g excludes the point $x = 0$. When, as in this example, the domain of f contains the domain of g, we say that f is an *extension* of g (here, to the domain of all real numbers) and that g is a *restriction* of f (here, to the domain of all nonzero real numbers).

The graph of a function or of any relation between two real variables is often its most illuminating representation. The graph of a relation between the real variables x and y is the set of points (x, y) with coordinates for which the relation holds. In the depiction of a relation by its graph, many of its important properties are visible at a glance.

Example 4. Consider the relation

$$x > y.$$

The graph of this relation, the set $\{(x, y) : x > y\}$, is shown in

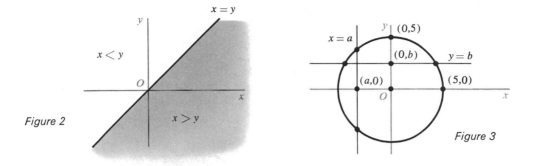

Figure 2

Figure 3

Figure 2 as the shaded region to the right of and below the line $x = y$.

Example 5. The graph of the relation given by

(8) $$x^2 + y^2 = 25$$

is a circle with radius 5 and center at the origin (Figure 3). If $|x| < 5$ there are two values of y which satisfy the relation for any given value of x. Similarly, if $|y| < 5$ there are two values of x which satisfy (8) for any given value of y. Geometrically, these multiple values correspond to multiple intersections of the vertical line $x = a$ and the horizontal line $y = b$, (for $|a|, |b| < 5$), with the graph.

For the graphs of relations between two real variables it is generally irrelevant which variable is taken as the abscissa and which the ordinate. For the graphs of functions it is convenient to indicate the distinction between the independent and dependent variables by a consistent assignment of coordinates, the abscissa for the independent variable, the ordinate for the dependent variable. *The graph of a function f is defined as the set of all points $(x, f(x))$ where x lies in the domain of f.* Since a function maps each element of its domain onto precisely one element of its range, the graph of the function cannot contain points (x_1, y_1) and (x_1, y_2) with $y_1 \neq y_2$. In other terms, no vertical line $x = a$ meets the graph of a function at more than one point. Conversely, if every vertical line intersects a graph in at most one point, the graph is that of a function.

Example 6. Since some vertical lines may intersect the circle $x^2 + y^2 = 25$ in two points (Example 5), it follows that the circle cannot be the graph of a function. However, nothing keeps us from separating the circle into two semicircles, the graphs of the functions

$$x \to \sqrt{25 - x^2} \quad \text{and} \quad x \to -\sqrt{25 - x^2}.$$

The graph of the function $x \rightarrow \sqrt{25 - x^2}$ is the semicircle shown in Figure 4. The graph not only provides a clear picture of the mapping of each element of the domain upon its image in the range, but also immediately displays the extents of domain and range. It is clear from the figure that the domain is $\{x : -5 \leq x \leq 5\}$ and the range, $\{y : 0 \leq y \leq 5\}$. These sets are represented by the heavy bars along the x- and y-axis in Figure 4.

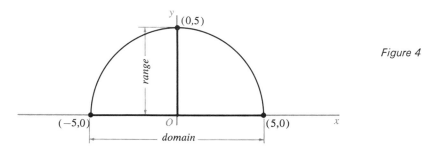

Figure 4

The graph of the function f is described precisely as the set

$$\{(x, y) : y = f(x)\} .$$

Since the context is usually understood, there will be no ambiguity or confusion in referring to "the graph $y = f(x)$", just as no confusion resulted from our reference to "the circle $x^2 + y^2 = 25$" in the first sentence of Example 6. We shall use this abbreviated form from now on without further comment.

We end this section with descriptions of some of the basic functions used in the text.

Constant functions

If a is any real number, the function $x \rightarrow a$ which maps every real number upon the number a is called a *constant function*. More generally, any function whose range contains exactly one element is a constant function. The graph of the constant function $x \rightarrow a$ on the domain $\Re$ of all real numbers is the line parallel to, and a units above, the x-axis if $a > 0$, and $-a$ units below the x-axis if $a < 0$.

The identity function

The mapping from $\Re$ onto $\Re$,

$$f : x \rightarrow x$$

is called the *identity function*. More generally, any function that maps each element of its domain upon itself is an identity function. For the domain $\mathcal{R}$, the graph is the line $y = x$.

The absolute value function

This function maps each real number upon its absolute value (see A1.3):†

$$f: x \rightarrow |x| = \begin{cases} x & \text{for } x \geq 0, \\ -x & \text{for } x < 0. \end{cases}$$

The graph of f is shown in Figure 5; it is the union of two rays issuing from the origin.

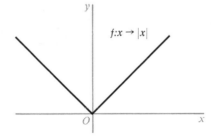

Figure 5

The linear functions

A function f is said to be linear if it has the form

$$f: x \rightarrow ax + b.$$

The graph of f is a straight line with slope a and y-intercept b. The constant functions are linear functions with $a = 0$. With the exception of the vertical lines, and these are not graphs of functions, every line is the graph of a linear function.

The polynomial functions

A polynomial function has the form

(9) $\qquad p: x \rightarrow a_n x^n + a_{n-1} x^{n-1} + a_{n-2} x^{n-2} + \cdots + a_0.$

A polynomial is an expression of the form

$$p(x) = a_n x^n + a_{n-1} x^{n-1} + a_{n-2} x^{n-2} + \cdots + a_1 x + a_0.$$

†Alternative definitions:
$$f: x \rightarrow |x| = \max \{x, -x\} ;$$
$$f: x \rightarrow |x| = \sqrt{x^2} .$$

Since the formula for a polynomial defines a real number for every real value of x, the domain of p is all of $\mathcal{R}$. The real number a_k (for $k = 0, 1, 2, \ldots, n$) is called the coefficient of order k. The degree of the polynomial $p(x)$ or of the polynomial function p, written $\deg p$, is the highest order among the nonvanishing coefficients:

$$\deg p = \max \{k : a_k \neq 0\} .$$

Under this definition, the zero function $x \to 0$ is not assigned a degree.† If $a_n \neq 0$ in (9), then $\deg p = n$ and we call $a_n x^n$ the *leading term* of the polynomial and a_n the leading *coefficient*. The constant functions, except the zero function, are the polynomial functions of degree zero. The linear functions are the zero function and the polynomial functions of degree no more than 1. We may also introduce the *quadratic*, *cubic*, and *quartic* functions, as well as functions of higher degree; these classes of functions comprise the polynomial functions of degree $2, 3$, and 4, respectively. The graph of a quadratic function

$$x \to ax^2 + bx + c \qquad\qquad (a \neq 0),$$

is a parabola (A3.5c Fig. 7).

The rational functions

These are functions of the form

(10)
$$r : x \to \frac{p(x)}{q(x)}$$

where $p(x)$ and $q(x)$ are polynomials. Since the domain of a polynomial function is the set $\mathcal{R}$ of all real numbers, the domain of the rational function r in (10) consists of all $\mathcal{R}$ except those points where the denominator $q(x) = 0$. Thus the rational function

$$x \to \frac{1}{x^2 + x - 6} = \frac{1}{(x + 3)(x - 2)}$$

has as its domain $\{x : x \neq -3, x \neq 2\}$, whereas all of $\mathcal{R}$ is the domain of the rational function

$$x \to \frac{x}{1 + x^2} .$$

†In algebra this is sometimes expressed by saying the zero polynomial has degree "minus infinity," written $-\infty$. The conventions concerning this symbol are that $-\infty < n$ where n is any integer, and consistent with this symbolic inequality, $-\infty + n = -\infty$. With these conventions, the formulas for the degrees of the sum and the product of two polynomials remain valid for the zero polynomial (see Ex. 15). We shall not adopt this convention.

The integer part function

For every real number x there is a unique integer n such that

$$n \le x < n+1 \,.$$

For example,

$$\text{if } x = 5 \,, \quad n = 5 \,;$$

$$\text{if } x = \sqrt{7} \,, \quad n = 2 \,;$$

$$\text{if } x = -\frac{8}{3} \,, \quad n = -3 \,.$$

We call n the *integer part* of x and write $n = [\![x]\!]$. The function $x \to [\![x]\!]$ is called the *integer part function*. The graph of this function is shown in Figure 6.

Figure 6

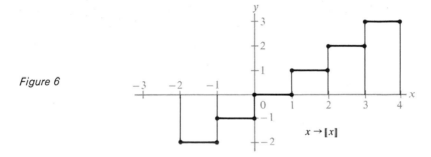

$$x \to [\![x]\!]$$

The signum function

With each real number x we may associate its *signum* or sign, now defined as a real number: 1 if x is positive, 0 if x is zero, -1 if x is negative. We define the *signum function*, $x \to \operatorname{sgn} x$, by

$$\operatorname{sgn} x = \begin{cases} 1, & \text{for } x > 0 \,, \\ 0, & \text{for } x = 0 \,, \\ -1, & \text{for } x < 0 \,. \end{cases}$$

Observe that $\operatorname{sgn} x = |x|/x$ for $x \ne 0$. You may sketch the graph of this function as an exercise (Ex. 8e).

Even and odd functions

Let f be a function whose domain contains $-x$ whenever it contains x. The function f is said to be *even* if $f(-x) = f(x)$. For example, the function $x \to x^2$ is even since $(-x)^2 = x^2$ for all x. The graph of an even function is symmetric to the y-axis.

The function f is said to be *odd* if $f(-x) = -f(x)$. For example, the function $x \to x^3$ is odd since $(-x)^3 = -x^3$ for all x. The graph of an odd function is symmetric to the origin.

Periodic functions

Functions having the property that their values recur cyclically at constant intervals, as in Figure 7, are called *periodic*. This important class

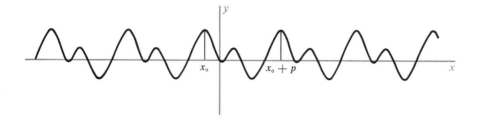

Figure 7

includes the circular (trigonometric) functions which will be discussed in A2.6. We say a function f is *periodic* and has a *period* p, $p \neq 0$, if and only if, for all x in the domain of f, $x + p$ is also in the domain and

(11) $$f(x + p) = f(x).$$

From the definition we note that each successive addition or subtraction of p to the argument of f brings us back to $f(x)$ again. For example,

$$f(x + 2p) = f((x + p) + p)$$
$$= f(x + p)$$
$$= f(x),$$

and

$$f(x - p) = f((x - p) + p)$$
$$= f(x).$$

In general, any multiple of a period of f is also a period; that is, for any integer n

$$f(x + np) = f(x).$$

For a constant function

$$f : x \to c,$$

it is immediate that f is periodic with any period p, since

$$f(x + p) = c = f(x).$$

It can be shown under very general conditions† that for any nonconstant periodic function there is a least positive value p for which (11) is true; this value is called the *fundamental period* or simply *the* period of the function.

Example 7. The *fractional part* r of a real number x is defined by

$$r = x - [\![x]\!].$$

Observe that $0 \le r < 1$. We show that the *fractional part function* $f : x \to x - [\![x]\!]$ is periodic with period 1. Since

$$[\![x]\!] + 1 \le x + 1 < ([\![x]\!] + 1) + 1,$$

we have $[\![x + 1]\!] = [\![x]\!] + 1$, and conclude that

$$f(x + 1) = (x + 1) - [\![x + 1]\!] = x - [\![x]\!] = f(x).$$

The periodicity of f is apparent in its graph, Figure 8.

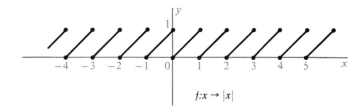

Figure 8

$$f{:}x \to |x|$$

A2.2 Exercises

1. Which of these figures represent functions?

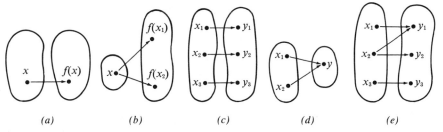

(a)   (b)   (c)   (d)   (e)

2. Which of the following statements are always true for any function f and numbers x_1 and x_2 in the domain of f?

†The function must be *continuous* at some point of its domain. The proof of existence of a fundamental period is left to 3.5 Ex. 13b after the discussion of continuity.

a. If $x_1 = x_2$, then $f(x_1) = f(x_2)$.
b. If $x_1 \neq x_2$, then $f(x_1) \neq f(x_2)$.
c. If $f(x_1) = f(x_2)$, then $x_1 = x_2$.
d. If $f(x_1) \neq f(x_2)$, then $x_1 \neq x_2$.

3. For each following example of an association between elements of two sets decide whether it may properly represent a function. Specify the domain and range for each function. Note that there may be more than one choice for independent variable and function.

a. With each nonnegative integer n associate the number $2n - 5$.
b. With each real number x associate the number 7.
c. With each complex number $z = x + iy$ associate the ordered pair of real numbers (x, y).
d. With each pair of distinct points in the plane associate the distance between them.
e. $\quad y = -3$ for all x.
f. $\quad x = 4$ for all y and z.
g. $\quad x + y = 2$.
h. $\quad y = 2x^2 + 3$.
i. $\quad y^2 - 4 = x$.
j. $\quad y < 2x - 1$.
k. $\quad f(x) = -\sqrt{16 - x^2}$.

4. Sketch the graphs for Exercise 3, Parts e through k.

5. Choose ranges in infinitely many ways other than as in (4) for each of which the association (3) is meaningful; that is, for each choice of range, (3) should define a function.

6. Which of the following functions are even, which are odd, and which are neither?

a. $\quad x \rightarrow 3x$.
b. $\quad x \rightarrow -2x^2 + 5$.
c. $\quad x \rightarrow x^2 - 4x + 4$.
d. $\quad x \rightarrow -2x + 1$.
e. $\quad x \rightarrow x^3 + 4$.
f. $\quad x \rightarrow x^3 - 2x$.
g. $\quad x \rightarrow 2^{1/x}$.
h. $\quad x \rightarrow 2^{1/x^2}$.

7. Can a function be both even and odd?
What can you say about the evenness or oddness of the product of:

a. an even function and an even function?
b. an even function and an odd function?
c. an odd function and an odd function?

8. Specify the domain and range of each function and sketch its graph.

a. $\quad x \rightarrow -|x|$.
b. $\quad x \rightarrow 1 - |x|$.
c. $\quad x \rightarrow |1 - x|$.
d. $\quad x \rightarrow |x| - x$.

e. $\quad x \rightarrow \begin{cases} \dfrac{x}{|x|}, & \text{for } x \neq 0. \\ 0, & \text{for } x = 0. \end{cases}$

f. $\quad x \rightarrow |1 - x^2|$.
g. $\quad x \rightarrow |x^2 - 2x - 3|$.

9. Sketch the graph of each function.

    a. $H : x \to \dfrac{1 + \text{sgn } x}{2}$

    This function H is the *Heaviside Unit* function.†

    b. $x \to H(x) + H(x - 2)$.
    c. $x \to H(x) \, H(x - 2)$.
    d. $x \to (x - 2)^2 \, H(x)$.
    e. $x \to H(x) + H(x - 2) + H(x - 4)$.
    f. $x \to H(x^2 - 2)$.

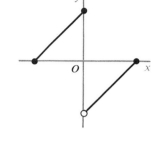

10. For the function f whose graph is shown, sketch the graphs of

    a. $x \to -f(x)$,
    b. $x \to f(-x)$,
    c. $x \to |f(x)|$,
    d. $x \to f(|x|)$,

11. For each of the given pairs of functions f and g state whether $f = g$. Justify your answer.

    a. $f : x \to x$, $g : x \to \dfrac{x^2}{x}$.

    b. $f : x \to \dfrac{1}{x}$, $g : x \to \dfrac{x}{x^2}$.

    c. $f : x \to \dfrac{x^2}{x}$, $g : x \to \dfrac{x}{x^2}$.

    d. $f : x \to \dfrac{|x|}{x}$, $g : x \to \dfrac{x}{|x|}$.

    e. $f : x \to \dfrac{[\![x]\!]}{x}$, $g : x \to \dfrac{x}{[\![x]\!]}$.

12. Specify the domain and range of each function and sketch the graph.

    a. $x \to [\![-x]\!]$.   b. $x \to \dfrac{[\![x]\!]}{x}$.

    c. $x \to \dfrac{x}{[\![x]\!]}$.   d. $x \to x[\![x]\!]$.

    e. $x \to (x - 1)^2 \text{ sgn } x + x^2 \text{ sgn } (x - 1)$.

13. Sketch the graph of each function and indicate which are even or odd.

    a. $x \to 2x^2 - [\![2x^2]\!]$.
    b. $x \to 2x^2 - 2[\![x^2]\!]$.
    c. $x \to 2x^2 - 2[\![x]\!]^2$.

14. Sketch the graphs of the following functions. Give the periods of those functions that are periodic.

    †Oliver Heaviside (1850–1925) used the unit function, now named after him, to solve problems involving electrical circuits by algebraic methods.

    a. $x \to ax - [\![ax]\!]$, $a > 0$.

    b. $x \to 5x - [\![2x]\!] - [\![3x]\!]$.

    c. $x \to x(\sqrt{2} + 1) - [\![x\sqrt{2}]\!] - [\![x]\!]$.

15. Let p and q be nonzero polynomial functions. Show

    a. if $\deg p \neq \deg q$, then $\deg(p + q) = \max\{\deg p, \deg q\}$,

    b. $\deg pq = \deg p + \deg q$.

    What can be said of the degrees of the sum and product if one or both of p and q is the zero function? Is the result of Part a necessarily true when $\deg p = \deg q$? Discuss $\deg(p + q)$ for the case

$$\deg p = \deg q$$

    in detail.

16. a. Show that the polynomial function

$$p : x \to a_n x^n + a_{n-1} x^{n-1} + \cdots + a_0$$

    is the zero function if and only if all coefficients are zero, $a_k = 0$ for $k = 0, 1, 2, \ldots, n$. (Hint: show if $a_n \neq 0$ that for sufficiently large x the magnitude of the leading term is greater than that of the sum of all the other terms.)

    b. Show that two polynomial functions are equal if and only if they have the same coefficients for each order.

17. If f and g are periodic functions of periods m and n, respectively, where m and n are integers, show that $f + g$ and $f \cdot g$ are also periodic. Give examples to show that the period of $f + g$ can either be greater or less than both m and n. Repeat the same for the product $f \cdot g$.

18. Show that every function whose domain contains $-x$ whenever it contains x can be expressed as the sum of an even function and an odd function.

19. Find functions f satisfying the equation $f(x)f(-x) = 1$. (This is an example of a functional equation that is, an equation whose solutions are functions rather than numbers.) Suggestion: use Ex. 18.

20. Prove that no periodic function other than a constant can be a rational function.

A2.3 ALGEBRA OF FUNCTIONS

    Given functions f and g on a common domain, we may combine them by the rational operations; addition, subtraction, multiplication, and division to obtain new functions:

$$f + g : x \to f(x) + g(x),$$
$$f - g : x \to f(x) - g(x)$$
$$f \cdot g : x \to f(x)g(x),$$

$$f/g : x \to \frac{f(x)}{g(x)}, \; g(x) \neq 0 .$$

The product of a real number c and a function f is defined as the function

$$cf : x \to cf(x) .$$

The function cf may be thought of as the product of the constant function $x \to c$ with the function f.

In the algebra of functions there is one operation which has no counterpart in the algebra of numbers, the operation of *composition*. If a function g maps its domain into the domain of f, the function f may be applied to the images under the mapping g to define a composite function on the domain of g. We frame the concept of composition more generally.

Definition 1. The *composition* fg of two functions f and g is the function

$$fg : x \to fg(x) = f(g(x)) .$$

The domain of fg is the set of all elements x in the domain of g for which $g(x)$ is in the domain of f.

Example 1. The function $x \to \sqrt{1 - x^2}$ can be considered as the composition fg of the functions $g : x \to 1 - x^2$ and $f : y \to \sqrt{y}$. Although the domain of f is the set of nonnegative real numbers and the domain of g is all of $\Re$, the domain of fg is the closed interval $[-1, 1]$.

From the definition it is clear that the domain of the composition fg is a subset of the domain of the inner function g. For example, the composition fg of $g : x \to \sqrt{x}$ and $f : y \to y^2$ is *not* the function $h : x \to x$ on the domain $\Re$, but the restriction of h to the domain of nonnegative numbers.

At first it may seem that there are two ways to define the composition of three functions h, g, f in the given order. The function h might be employed first and then fg applied to h, or gh might be employed first and then f applied to gh; we indicate the two modes of forming the composition by $fg(h)$ and $f(gh)$, respectively. However, the interpretation of the two modes is the same: first apply the mapping h, then the mapping g, then the mapping f. In other words, composition is associative; that is, in forming the composition of more than two functions in a given order it does not matter how we insert parentheses to express the ultimate composite function as the result of pairwise compositions. We may therefore omit the association parentheses in a composition of three or more functions altogether. In particular, we define $fgh(x)$ as the result of the successive mappings h, g, and f in that order:

$$x \to h(x) \to g(h(x)) \to f(g(h(x))) \,;$$

that is,

$$fgh : x \to fgh(x) = f(g(h(x))) \,.$$

In this text, we use a dot to indicate the product of two functions $f \cdot g : x \to f(x)g(x)$ and write the compositions of f and g simply as $fg : x \to f(g(x))$ and $gf : x \to g(f(x))$. Some texts do just the reverse. In each case, you will have to determine the usage of the text.

A2.3 Exercises

1. Given the functions $f : x \to \dfrac{x}{1+x^2}$ and $g : x \to 1 + x^2$ find

   a. $f(0) + g(0)$,   b. $f(0)\,g(0)$,

   c. $fg(0)$,   d. $gf(0)$,

   e. $f\left(\dfrac{1}{x}\right) g\left(\dfrac{1}{x}\right)$, $x \neq 0$.

2. Show that composition is not commutative; that is, there exist functions f and g for which $fg \neq gf$.

3. For each pair of functions f and g, find the composite functions fg and gf and specify the domain and range of each.

   a. $f : x \to \dfrac{1}{x}$, $g : x \to 2x - 6$.

   b. $f : x \to \dfrac{1}{x}$, $g : x \to x^2 - 4$.

   c. $f : x \to \dfrac{1}{x}$, $g : x \to \sqrt{x}$.

   d. $f : x \to x^2$, $g : x \to \sqrt{x}$.

   e. $f : x \to x^2$, $g : x \to \sqrt{4 - x}$.

   f. $f : x \to -x^2 - 1$, $g : x \to \sqrt{x}$.

4. For each pair of functions f and g solve the equation $fg(x) = gf(x)$.

   a. $f : x \to 2x + 1$, $g : x \to x^2$

   b. $f : x \to x^2 + 3$, $g : x \to \sqrt{x + 2}$.

   c. $f : x \to x^2 + 3$, $g : x \to \sqrt{x - 2}$.

5. Let $f : x \to \sqrt{x}$ and $g : x \to 2 - \sqrt{x+1}$. Sketch the graph of the composition fg.

6. For each pair of functions f and g find the compositions fg and gf and specify the domain and range of each. Sketch the graphs of fg and gf.

   a. $f : x \to x \operatorname{sgn} x$, $\quad g : x \to [\![x]\!]$.

   b. $f : x \to |x|$, $\quad g : x \to \operatorname{sgn}(x - 2)$.

   c. $f : x \to |x|$, $\quad g : x \to 2 \operatorname{sgn}(x - 2) - 1$.

7. What can you say, if anything, about the evenness or oddness of the composition of

   a. two even functions?

   b. an even and an odd function?

   c. two odd functions?

8. Given any arbitrary function g (not necessarily periodic) and the periodic function f, what can you say, if anything, of the periodic character of the compositions fg and gf, assuming these exist? Illustrate by examples.

9. If the functions f and g are each periodic, then the composite functions fg and gf (assumed to exist) are also periodic. Can the period of either one be less than that of both f and g?

⋏10. A sequence $a_0, a_1, a_2, \dots, a_n, \dots$ is defined by the equation

$$a_{n+1} = f(a_n), \quad n = 0, 1, 2, 3, \dots$$

where f is a given function and a_0 is a given number. If $a_0 = 0$ and $f : x \to \sqrt{2 + x}$, then

$$a_1 = f(a_0) = \sqrt{2},$$

$$a_2 = f(a_1) = ff(a_0) = \sqrt{2 + \sqrt{2}}.$$

$$a_3 = f(a_2) = ff(a_1) = fff(a_0) = \sqrt{2 + \sqrt{2 + \sqrt{2}}}.$$

Show that for any n,

   a. $a_n < 2$.

   b. $a_n > 2 - \dfrac{1}{2^{n-1}}, \quad n > 0$.

11. If $a_{n+1} = f(a_n)$, $n = 0, 1, 2, \dots$ and $a_0 = c$, find a_n as a function of c and n, for the following functions:

   a. $x \to a + bx$,

   b. $x \to x^m$,

   c. $x \to \sqrt{|x|}$,

   d. $x \to \sqrt{1 - x^2}$,

   e. $x \to (1 - x)^{-1}$.

A2.4 INVERSE FUNCTIONS

Recall the vertical line test for the graph of a function (A2.2): if every line parallel to the y-axis intersects a graph in no more than one point, the graph is that of a function. Thus, in Figure 1, a and b illustrate graphs of functions, and c is the graph of a relation that is not a function. This figure also illustrates an important distinction between two classes of functions: for graph a there are lines parallel to the x-axis which intersect the graph in more than one point; this is not the case for graph b. The latter is typical of a class of functions called one-to-one functions: not only is each element in the domain mapped upon one and only one image in the range, but each element in the range has only one antecedent in the domain. In other words, a function of this kind establishes a one-to-one pairing of elements of the domain with elements of the range.

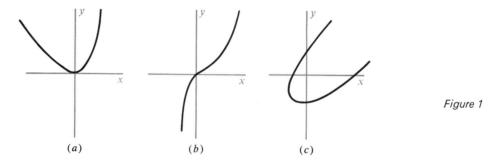

Figure 1

(a)　　　　　　　(b)　　　　　　　(c)

Definition 1. A function f is *one-to-one* if $f(x_1) = f(x_2)$ implies $x_1 = x_2$.

Note the distinction between the general definition of a function and that of a one-to-one function. The former states for any function f, that if $x_1 = x_2$, then $f(x_1) = f(x_2)$, whereas the latter states with respect to a one-to-one function f that $f(x_1) = f(x_2)$ if and *only if* $x_1 = x_2$.

In a loose way of speaking, for every one-to-one function there is a function that undoes the work of the given function. For example, if f is the function of A2.2 Example 1 which maps each real number onto its double, $f: x \rightarrow 2x$, then there is a function g, called the inverse of f, which reverses this mapping and takes each real number onto its half, namely, $g: y \rightarrow \frac{1}{2}y$.

Definition 2. If a function $f: x \rightarrow f(x)$ is one-to-one, the function

$$g : f(x) \rightarrow x ,$$

whose domain is the range of f, is called the *inverse* of f.

The functions f and g represent the same relation with the roles of the variables interchanged; the domain of g is the range of f and the range of g is the domain of f. Furthermore, g is itself one-to-one and its inverse is f.

The statement that the inverse g of the function f "undoes the work of f" is best understood in terms of the compositions of the two functions. If f maps x into y, then g maps y back into x; in other terms, if $y = f(x)$, then $x = g(y)$. Hence,

$$gf(x) = g(y) = x, \text{ for all } x \text{ in the domain of } f,$$

and

$$fg(y) = f(x) = y, \text{ for all } y \text{ in the range of } f.$$

Thus, fg is the identity function on the domain of g, and gf the identity function on the domain of f. Observe that the restriction of the domain of g to coincide with the range of f is part of the definition of the inverse.

Example 1. Consider the one-to-one function $f : x \rightarrow 2x - 3$; what is its inverse? Here, f is described by the instruction, "take a number, double it, and then subtract 3." In order to reverse this procedure, we must add 3 and then divide by 2. This suggests that the inverse of f is the function $g : x \rightarrow \dfrac{x + 3}{2}$. To prove this, we must show that g satisfies Definition 2, that is, we must show that g maps $f(x)$ upon x for all x in the domain of f. By substitution,

$$gf(x) = g(2x - 3) = \frac{(2x - 3) + 3}{2} = x;$$

hence g is the inverse of f. Furthermore, in the opposite direction,

$$fg(x) = f\left(\frac{x + 3}{2}\right) = 2\left(\frac{x + 3}{2}\right) - 3 = x$$

for all x in the domain of g. Hence, f is the inverse of the function g, as expected.

The graph of the inverse g of a function f is easily found from the graph of f. If f maps a upon b, then g maps b upon a. It follows that the point (a, b) is on the graph of f if and only if (b, a) is on the graph of g. Figure 2 shows three points $(1, 3)$, $(2, 1)$, and $(4, 2)$ on the graph of a function f, and their corresponding points, obtained by interchange of coordinates, on the graph of g.

In this figure, we see that the points (a, b) and (b, a) are sym-

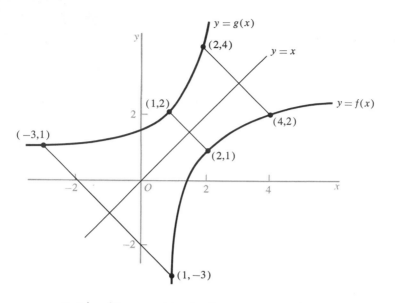

Figure 2

metric with respect to the line $y = x$; that is, the line segment determined by these two points is perpendicular to, and bisected by, the line $y = x$. We call (b, a) the *reflection* of (a, b) *in the line* $y = x$.

Example 2. Consider the functions $f : x \to \sqrt{x + 2}$, $x \ge -2$, and $g : x \to x^2 - 2$. The function f is one-to-one; g is not one-to-one and, hence, cannot be the inverse of f. By Definition 2, the domain of the inverse must be the range of f, namely, the set of nonnegative real numbers. Hence, the inverse of f is $h : x \to x^2 - 2$, $x \ge 0$ (Figure 3). By forming their compositions, we may verify that f and h are inverse to each other:

$$fh : x \to fh(x) = \sqrt{(x^2 - 2) + 2} = x \qquad (x \ge 0),$$
$$hf : x \to hf(x) = (\sqrt{x + 2})^2 - 2 = x \qquad (x \ge -2).$$

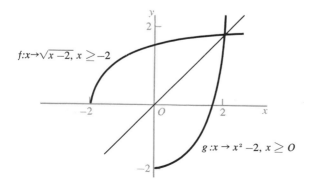

$f : x \to \sqrt{x - 2}, \ x \ge -2$

$g : x \to x^2 - 2, \ x \ge 0$

Figure 3

The relationship between the coordinates of a point (a, b) and the coordinates of its reflection (b, a) in the line $y = x$ suggests a formal method for obtaining a formula for the inverse of a given function, assuming that the inverse exists.

Example 3. Consider the function from the set $\mathcal{R}$ of all real x onto $\mathcal{R}$,

$$f : x \rightarrow y = 3x + 5.$$

If we interchange x and y in the equation

$$(1) \qquad\qquad y = 3x + 5,$$

we obtain

$$(2) \qquad\qquad x = 3y + 5.$$

For every pair of numbers (a, b) in the set of solutions of (1), a pair (b, a) is in the set of solutions of (2). Hence, (2) defines the inverse of the given function f. In order to represent the inverse in explicit form, we solve (2) for y in terms of x and obtain

$$y = \frac{x - 5}{3}.$$

The inverse of f is, therefore,

$$g : x \rightarrow g(x) = \frac{x - 5}{3} \qquad\qquad \text{for all real } x.$$

You should verify the fact that $gf(a) = a$ for any a in the domain of f, and that $fg(b) = b$ for any b in the domain of g (range of f).

Example 4. If the given equation defines a quadratic function, the problem of finding an inverse is more complicated. In the first place, the given function must be restricted to a domain which gives a one-to-one function; in the second place, the details of interchanging the variables x and y in the given equation and then solving for y are more involved.

Consider the function

$$f : x \rightarrow x^2 + 2x + 3$$

whose graph is a parabola with vertex at $(-1, 2)$ and opening upward. The restriction of f to the domain $\{x : x \geq -1\}$ is a function f_1 which is one-to-one and hence has an inverse g_1. The range of f_1 is $\{y : y = f_1(x) \geq 2\}$, and this is the domain of g_1.

We proceed to find a formula for g_1. For $y = f_1(x)$ we have

$$y = x^2 + 2x + 3,$$

and we interchange the variables to obtain

$$x = y^2 + 2y + 3.$$

We now solve for y in the quadratic equation

$$y^2 + 2y + (3 - x) = 0,$$

to obtain

$$y = -1 + \sqrt{x - 2} \quad \text{or} \quad y = -1 - \sqrt{x - 2}.$$

Which of these formulas defines the function g_1? Here y represents any element in the range of the inverse function; since this range must be the domain of f_1, we see that $y \geq -1$ is required. Hence,

$$y = -1 + \sqrt{x - 2}$$

defines the inverse function

$$g_1 : x \rightarrow -1 + \sqrt{x - 2}$$

whose domain is $\{x : x \geq 2\}$. (Note, again, that this is the range of f_1.)

A sketch of the graphs of the two inverse functions clearly shows the relationships between their domains and ranges; see Figure 4. From the

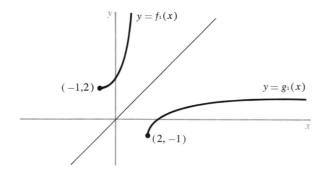

Figure 4

graph of the original function f, you may also see how its domain may be restricted in infinitely many ways to yield infinitely many different one-to-one functions, each of which has a unique inverse function.

A2.4 Exercises

1. What is the reflection of the line $y = f(x) = 5x$ in the line $y = x$? Write an equation defining the inverse of f.

2. Which points are their own reflections in the line $y = x$? What is the graph of all such points?

3. a. Find the slope of the segment joining (a, b) to (b, a), and prove that the segment is perpendicular to the line $y = x$.
   b. Prove that the segment joining (a, b) to (b, a) is bisected by the line $y = x$.

4. What is the reflection of the point $(1, 1)$ in the line

a.	$x = 0$?	b.	$y = 0$?
c.	$y = -x$?	d.	$y = 2$?
e.	$x = -3$?		

5. Describe any function or functions you can think of which are their own inverses.

6. For each of the following find the inverse of f. Sketch the graph of f and its inverse.
   a. $f : x \rightarrow 3x + 6$.
   b. $f : x \rightarrow x^3 - 5$.
   c. $f : x \rightarrow \dfrac{2}{x} - 3$.

7. Which of the following functions have inverses? Describe each inverse by means of a graph or equation and give its domain and range.

a.	$x \rightarrow x^2$.	b.	$x \rightarrow \sqrt{x}$.
c.	$x \rightarrow |x|$.	d.	$x \rightarrow [\![x]\!]$.
e.	$x \rightarrow x|x|$.	f.	$x \rightarrow \operatorname{sgn} x$.

8. For each of the functions $x \rightarrow \sqrt{4 - x^2}$ and $x \rightarrow x^2 - 4x$:
   a. Sketch the graph and show that the function does not have an inverse.
   b. Divide the domain of the function into two intervals such that its restriction to either one has an inverse.
   c. Write an equation defining each inverse function in Part b and sketch its graph.

9. An equation or an expression is said to be symmetric in x and y if the equations or the expressions remain unaltered by an interchange of x and y; for example, $x^2 + y^2 = 0$, $x^3 + y^3 - 3xy$, $|x - y| = |x + y|$, $x - xy + y$. It follows that graphs of symmetric equations are symmetric about the line $y = x$. Geometrically, we can consider the line $y = x$ as a mirror, and symmetry in x and y implies that for each point of the graph there must be a counterpart that is its mirror image. The equation

   $$x^4 + y^4 = a^4$$

   is obviously symmetric with respect to the line $y = x$. What other axes of symmetry (mirror type) does it have?

10. The expression

    $$a + b + |a - b| + 2c + \left| a + b + |a - b| - 2c \right|$$

is obviously symmetric in a and b. Show that it is also symmetric in a and c.

11. Given that $f(x) = 3x - 2$ and $g(x) = -2x + k$, find k such that $fg(x) = gf(x)$. For this value of k are f and g inverse to one another? Give reasons for your answers.

12. Show that $f: x \to x^2 - 4x + 5$ $(x \geq 2)$ and $g: x \to 2 + \sqrt{x - 1}$ $(x \geq 1)$ are inverse to one another by showing that $fg(y) = y$ for all y in the domain of g, and that $gf(x) = x$ for all x in the domain of f.

13. If $f(x) = (2x^3 + 1)^7$, find at least two functions g such that

$$fg(x) = gf(x).$$

A2.5 MONOTONE FUNCTIONS

The functions $f: x \to \sqrt{x}$ and $g: x \to \sin x$ have notably different behavior: as x increases, the values of f increase, while the values of g sometimes increase, sometimes decrease. Geometrically, this means that as we survey it from left to right (the direction of increasing x) the graph of f is continually rising, whereas the graph of g undulates like a wave, now rising, now falling. The graph of a function may also contain horizontal portions (parallel to the x-axis), where the values of the function remain constant on an interval, like the function $x \to [\![x]\!]$.

Example 1. The function h, defined by

$$h(x) = \begin{cases} -x^2, & 0 \leq x \leq 1, \\ -1, & 1 \leq x \leq 2, \\ \dfrac{-x^3}{8}, & 2 \leq x, \end{cases}$$

has the graph shown in Figure 1. The value of h decreases as x increases except on the interval $[1, 2]$ where it remains constant. The function h is said to be weakly decreasing on its entire domain. Taken as a class, the increasing, decreasing, weakly increasing, and weakly de-

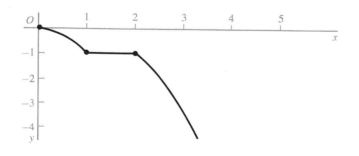

Figure 1

creasing functions are called monotone (compare with monotonous) because as x increases the change in the values of such a function never reverses direction. The ideas of increasing, weakly increasing, decreasing, and weakly decreasing are defined precisely as follows.

Definition 1. Let f be a function defined on the domain D. If for each pair of numbers $x_1, x_2 \in D$ with $x_1 < x_2$ the corresponding function values satisfy the inequality:

a. $f(x_1) < f(x_2)$, then f is an *increasing function;*
b. $f(x_1) > f(x_2)$, then f is a *decreasing function;*
c. $f(x_1) \leq f(x_2)$, then f is a *weakly increasing function;*
d. $f(x_1) \geq f(x_2)$, then f is a *weakly decreasing function.*†

In brief, this definition states that a function that preserves order relations is increasing; a function that reverses order relations is decreasing. Note particularly that an increasing function is a special kind of weakly increasing function; similarly, a decreasing function is a special kind of weakly decreasing function.

Definition 2. A function that is weakly increasing or weakly decreasing is called *monotone.* A function that is either increasing or decreasing is called *strongly monotone.*

For example, the function h of Example 1 is monotone over its entire domain and strongly monotone on the closed interval $0 \leq x \leq 1$ as well as on the interval $x \geq 2$.

The graph of a strongly monotone function indicates that such a function must be one-to-one, hence must have an inverse.

Theorem 1. If a function is strongly monotone, it has an inverse which is strongly monotone in the same sense.

Proof. We prove the theorem for f increasing; the proof for f decreasing is entirely similar.

By Definitions 1 and 2, $f(x_1) = f(x_2)$ if and only if $x_1 = x_2$. Hence, by A2.4, Definition 1, f is one-to-one, and by A2.4, Definition 2, f has an inverse

$$g : f(x) \to x$$

defined for all values $f(x)$ in the range of f.

---

†In some texts the term "nondecreasing" is used instead of "weakly increasing" and "nonincreasing" instead of "weakly decreasing."

Finally, g is an increasing function, hence strongly monotone, by Definitions 1 and 2.   □

Example 2. The function

$$f : x \to x^n ,$$

where n is a natural number, is strongly monotone (increasing) for all real nonnegative x. (See 3.7a Ex. 13.) Hence, f has the inverse function

(1) $g : x^n \to x$ $(x \geq 0)$,

which is also an increasing function. For an arbitrary element y in the domain of g, we denote $g(y)$ by $\sqrt[n]{y}$; thus (1) may be rewritten

(2) $g : y \to \sqrt[n]{y}$ $(y \geq 0)$.

Comparing (1) and (2), we see that $\sqrt[n]{y}$ is the unique positive solution x of the equation $x^n = y$; we call $\sqrt[n]{y}$ the n-th root of y for all real $y \geq 0$.

If the natural number n is odd, the function $f : x \to x^n$ is strongly monotone for all real x, and so is its inverse function. This means that every real number has a unique n-th root for n odd. For example, for n odd and a real, $\sqrt[n]{-a^n} = -a$.

If n is even, $f : x \to x^n$ is decreasing for all real $x \leq 0$, and increasing for all real $x \geq 0$. If f_1 is the restriction of f to the domain $x \geq 0$ and f_2 the restriction of f to $x \leq 0$, then each of these functions has an inverse, namely

$$g_1 : y \to \sqrt[n]{y}$$

and

$$g_2 : y \to -\sqrt[n]{y} ,$$

respectively, for n even and all real $y \geq 0$. For n even, the positive n-th root of a nonnegative real number is sometimes called its *principal* n-th root. The symbol $\sqrt[n]{y}$ always means the principal n-th root.

A2.5 Exercises

1. Prove that $f : x \to x^2$ $(x \geq 0)$ is an increasing function. (Hint: $x_1 > x_2$ implies $x_1 - x_2 > 0$. Use this to show that $x_1^2 > x_2^2$.)

2. Which of the following functions are weakly decreasing? weakly increasing? decreasing? increasing? In each case the domain is the set of real numbers unless otherwise restricted.

a. $x \to c$, for c constant.
b. $x \to x$.
c. $f : x \to |x|$.
d. $g : x \to [\![x]\!]$.
e. $x \to \operatorname{sgn} x$.
f. $x \to -x^2$, $x \le 0$.
g. $x \to -\sqrt{x}$, $x \ge 0$.
h. $x \to x|x|$.
i. $x \to x + |x|$.
j. $x \to |x| + |x - 1|$.
k. $x \to |x - 1| + |x - 3|$.
l. $x \to fg(x)$. (See Parts c and d.)
m. $x \to gf(x)$. (See Parts c and d.)

3. For each function in Exercise 2 which is not monotone, divide its domain into parts such that its restriction to any of these parts is monotone.

4. Prove that any function which is both weakly increasing and weakly decreasing must be constant.

5. We are given that f_1 is weakly increasing, f_2 is increasing, g_1 is weakly decreasing, and g_2 is decreasing, on a common domain. What is the monotone character, if any, of the following functions?

a. $f_1 + f_2$.
b. $f_2 + g_1$.
c. $g_1 + g_2$.
d. $g_2 + f_1$.
e. $f_1 \cdot f_2$.
f. $f_2 \cdot g_1$.
g. $g_1 \cdot g_2$.
h. $g_2 \cdot f_1$.
i. $f_1 f_2$.
j. $f_2 f_1$.
k. $f_2 g_1$.
l. $g_1 f_2$.
m. $g_1 g_2$.
n. $g_2 g_1$.
o. $g_2 f_1$.
p. $f_1 g_2$.

A2.6 THE CIRCULAR FUNCTIONS

We shall treat the circular (or trigonometric) functions (sin, cos, etc.) not so much as geometrical functions, but as purely numerical functions apart from the ideas of geometry. The advantage of approaching the circular functions analytically through the number concept rather than through geometrical concepts is that we can then develop systematic computational techniques for their use and greatly expand their range of application. The property of the circular functions essential to higher analysis is their periodicity, a property which the considerations of elementary geometry and trigonometry scarcely foreshadow. In our understanding of natural phenomena the role of periodicity is profound (see 1.3). The circular functions describe the simplest periodic motions, the turning of a wheel or the motion of a particle transcribing a circle at uniform speed. Yet combinations of these same elementary circular functions can be used to represent the most intricate periodic phenomena. (To obtain such representations and demonstrate their properties is the province of Fourier analysis; the elements of this subject will be within reach when you have completed the calculus.)

The concept of circular function is based upon ideas, like the idea of limit, which are not usually stated precisely before the calculus. Nonetheless, the circular functions are too important to neglect. We shall use them freely, assuming all the properties which are familiar from earlier courses without concern for a logical derivation of these properties. In fact, as the situation warrants, we shall also argue geometrically and intuitively to obtain other properties we may need. Eventually (Chapter 8), we shall be able to define the circular functions purely analytically and derive all the properties used earlier. It is tempting to try to be systematic and to develop the theory of circular functions from the beginning by means of a precise definition, but it is doubtful that such an approach could be made meaningful without the prior intuitively based exploration.

The following fundamental properties† of the sine and cosine functions are then to be taken initially as assumptions until we can do better and prove them from a precise definition. It is assumed in the following that the domain of $\sin x$ and $\cos x$ is the set $\mathcal{R}$ of all real numbers.

(1) $$\sin x > 0, \quad \text{for} \quad 0 < x < \frac{\pi}{2}.$$

The sine function is odd:

(2) $$\sin(-x) = -\sin x.$$

The function cos is defined by

(3) $$\cos x = \sin\left(x + \frac{\pi}{2}\right).$$

(4) $$\sin(x + y) = \sin x \cos y + \cos x \sin y.$$

These four properties are sufficient for the derivation of all the common trigonometric formulas. Most of those we shall use are listed here or left for proof in the exercises.

(5) $$\sin 0 = 0.$$

(6) $$\cos 0 = 1.$$

(7) $$\sin\frac{\pi}{2} = 1.$$

(8) $$\cos\left(-\frac{\pi}{2}\right) = 0.$$

(9) $$\cos x = \cos(-x).$$

†In this text we use radian measure only, as in Properties (1) and (3).

(10) $$\cos\left(\frac{\pi}{2}\right) = 0 .$$

(11) $$\sin \pi = 0 .$$

(12) $$\cos\left(-\pi\right) = -1 .$$

(13) $$\cos \pi = -1 .$$

(14) $$\sin\left(x + \pi\right) = -\sin x .$$

From (14) it follows that

(15) $$\sin\left(x + 2\pi\right) = \sin x ;$$

that is, sin is periodic with period 2π.

(16) $$\cos^2 x + \sin^2 x = 1 .$$

(17) $$\cos\left(x + y\right) = \cos x \cos y - \sin x \sin y .$$

(18) $$\sin 2x = 2 \sin x \cos x .$$

(19) $$\cos 2x = \cos^2 x - \sin^2 x .$$

(20) $$\sin\frac{x}{2} = (-1)^{[\![\frac{x}{2\pi}]\!]} \sqrt{\frac{1 - \cos x}{2}} .$$

(21) $$\cos\frac{x}{2} = (-1)^{[\![\frac{x+\pi}{2\pi}]\!]} \sqrt{\frac{1 + \cos x}{2}} .$$

Formulas (5) through (21) have been arranged so that any one of them can easily be derived with the help of the preceding formulas. The proofs are left to the exercises.

It is convenient to introduce the tangent function

(22) $$\tan : x \rightarrow \frac{\sin x}{\cos x} .$$

The function tan has the following properties:

(23) $$1 + \tan^2 x = \frac{1}{\cos^2 x} ,$$

(24) $$\tan x = -\tan\left(-x\right) ,$$

(25) $$\tan\left(x + y\right) = \frac{\tan x + \tan y}{1 - \tan x \tan y} ,$$

(26) $$\tan\frac{x}{2} = \frac{1 - \cos x}{\sin x} = \frac{\sin x}{1 - \cos x} .$$

In American and English texts it is customary to introduce the reciprocals of the circular functions, the secant, cosecant, and cotangent functions by

(27) $\sec : x \rightarrow \dfrac{1}{\cos x}$,

(28) $\csc : x \rightarrow \dfrac{1}{\sin x}$,

(29) $\cot : x \rightarrow \dfrac{1}{\tan x}$.

The reciprocal functions are not much used in continental Europe.
    We shall have uses for the observation that a linear combination

$$\alpha \cos x + \beta \sin x$$

can be written in the form

$$A \sin (x + a)$$

where

$$\sin a = \frac{\alpha}{A}, \quad \cos a = \frac{\beta}{A},$$

and

$$A = \sqrt{\alpha^2 + \beta^2} .$$

A2.6 Exercises

    In the following exercises, you may assume the properties (1) to (4) given on
page 278. You may also assume for the proof of any particular result, any result
that is cited earlier or any result that you may have already proved yourself.

1. Derive the statements (5) through (19) from the assumed properties (1)
   through (4).

2. Derive (23) through (25).

3. Prove

   a. $\cos 2x = 2 \cos^2 x - 1 = 1 - 2 \sin^2 x$,

   b. $\tan \dfrac{z}{2} = \dfrac{1 - \cos z}{\sin z} = \dfrac{\sin z}{1 + \cos z}$,

   c. $\left| \cos \dfrac{z}{2} \right| = \sqrt{\dfrac{1 + \cos z}{2}}$,

   d. $\left| \sin \dfrac{z}{2} \right| = \sqrt{\dfrac{1 - \cos z}{2}}$.

4. Show that

   a. $\cos \left(x + \dfrac{\pi}{2} \right) = -\sin x$,

   b. $\cos (x + \pi) = -\cos x$,

   c. $\tan (x + \pi) = \tan x$;   that is, tan is periodic with period π .

d.   Let f be any circular function and let cof be its cofunction. (The following are pairs of cofunctions: sin and cos, tan and cot, sec and csc.) Show that

$$cof(x) = f\left(\frac{\pi}{2} - x\right).$$

5. Prove

a. $\sin 3t = 3 \sin t - 4 \sin^3 t$,

b. $\cos 3t = 4 \cos^3 t - 3 \cos t$.

6. Show that

a. $\sin p - \sin q = 2 \cos \dfrac{p+q}{2} \sin \dfrac{p-q}{2}$,

b. $\cos p - \cos q = -2 \sin \dfrac{p+q}{2} \sin \dfrac{p-q}{2}$.

7. a. Prove that $\sin x > 0$, for $0 < x < \pi$, and that $\cos x > 0$, for $-\frac{1}{2}\pi < x < \frac{1}{2}\pi$.

b. Prove

$$\sin x > 0 \quad \text{for} \quad 2n\pi < x < (2n+1)\pi,$$
$$\sin x = 0 \quad \text{for} \quad x = n\pi,$$
$$\sin x < 0 \quad \text{for} \quad (2n-1)\pi < x < 2n\pi,$$

where n is any integer.

8. Prove the half-angle formulas (20) and (21).

9. Express each of the following numerically

a.	$\sin \frac{3}{2}\pi$,	b.	$\cos \frac{13}{6}\pi$,
c.	$\tan \frac{5}{3}\pi$,	d.	$\sin \left(-\frac{1}{4}\pi\right)$,
e.	$\sin \frac{5}{12}\pi$,	f.	$\tan \frac{1}{6}\pi$,
g.	$\cos \frac{5}{8}\pi$,	h.	$\sin \frac{1}{16}\pi$,
i.	$\cos^3 \frac{3}{8}\pi$,	j.	$\tan \frac{1}{5}\pi$.

10. Prove that the sine is increasing on $[-\frac{1}{2}\pi, \frac{1}{2}\pi]$ and that the cosine is decreasing on $[0, \pi]$.

11. Show that 2π is the fundamental period of the sine; namely that the sine has no smaller period than 2π.

12. Sketch the graph of each of the following functions. State which of these functions are periodic, and give their periods. State which functions are even, which odd.

a.	$x \rightarrow \sin x + \cos x$.	b.	$x \rightarrow \sin \frac{2}{3}\pi x + \cos \pi x$.
c.	$x \rightarrow \sin x + \cos x\sqrt{2}$.	d.	$x \rightarrow \sin 2x$.
e.	$x \rightarrow |\sin 3\pi x|$.	f.	$x \rightarrow \cos^2 \pi x$.
g.	$x \rightarrow 2 \sin x^2$.		

13. a. What is the period of $x \rightarrow \sin ax$, $a \neq 0$?

b. What is the period of $x \rightarrow \sin (ax + b)$, $a \neq 0$? For what values of a and b is this function odd? even?

14. For each pair of functions f and g find the composite functions fg and gf and specify the domain and range (if possible) of each. Also, sketch the graph of each, and give the period (fundamental) if it is periodic.

    a. $f : x \rightarrow \sin \pi x$, $g : x \rightarrow \operatorname{sgn} x$.
    b. $f : x \rightarrow \sin a\pi x$ $(a > 0)$, $g : x \rightarrow \operatorname{sgn} x$.
    c. $f : x \rightarrow 3 |\sin x|$, $g : x \rightarrow [\![x]\!]$.
    d. $f : x \rightarrow \max \{\sin \pi x, \ x - [\![x]\!]\}$, $g : x \rightarrow \min \{x, x^2\}$.

15. For x in $[0, 2\pi]$ solve $\sin^m x + \cos^m x = 1$, where m is an integer greater than 2.

16. Show how to solve the cubic equation $4x^3 - 3x = a$, where $|a| \leq 1$, trigonometrically.

17. Which properties of the trigonometric functions are considered fundamental is a matter of taste. We could have begun with properties known to be true for acute angles only and shown that any functions having these properties for *all* real values must satisfy the other trigonometric relations; for example,

    (i) $\sin x > 0$,   for $0 < x < \frac{1}{2}\pi$,
    (ii) $\sin 0 = 0$,
    (iii) $\cos x = \sin (\frac{1}{2}\pi - x)$,
    (iv) $\sin (x + y) = \sin x \cos y + \cos x \sin y$.

    These properties follow from (1) to (4):

    (i), (ii), and (iv) are the same as (1), (5), and (4), respectively, and (iii) is to be proved in Exercise 4d. Conversely, derive the properties (1) to (4) from (i) to (iv) and thereby prove that the two sets of properties are equivalent.

Analytic Geometry

INTRODUCTION

Analytic geometry is the wonderful invention of Descartes.† What seems wonderful about it at first is that analytic geometry translates geometrical problems into numerical ones. In classical geometry, the solution of a new problem always demands a fresh insight, an original inspiration; there are no standard procedures for grinding out geometrical solutions. With the introduction of analytic geometry, presumably even a dull mathematician could become a geometer if only he were reasonably adept at computation. In practice, Descartes' ideas have been quite as fertile in the opposite direction. Many a problem which seems intractable if posed as a computational question can be nicely solved if restated in geometrical terms. Thus, the problem posed in 1.1, to maximize a function, could be attacked systematically once it was recognized that the graph of the function at a maximum

†René Descartes (1596–1650), French mathematician and philosopher.

must be horizontal. The problems of both 1.1 and 1.2 show how cartesian geometry, as Descartes' geometry is called, permits the facile interplay of geometrical (synthetic) and numerical (analytical) ideas.

The notations used here for lines, planes, and other sets of points may not be those used in your geometry text. For any two points A and B, we use AB or BA for the line that contains the two points, (AB) or (BA) for the *open segment* with endpoints A and B, and $[AB]$ or $[BA]$ for the *closed segment* with the same endpoints. As for open and closed intervals, the open segment (AB) contains only the points between A and B on the line AB, not the endpoints themselves; the closed segment $[AB]$ consists of (AB) *and* the endpoints. In addition, we shall use the *directed* or oriented *segment* $\overrightarrow{AB}$ for which we introduce a preferred direction, the direction of B from the point A. The point A is called the *initial point* and B the *terminal point* of $\overrightarrow{AB}$. The length for each of the segments, $[AB]$, (AB), and $\overrightarrow{AB}$, with endpoints A and B is the same real number, the distance between A and B, and it is written $|AB|$. Occasionally, it is convenient to employ the concept of *ray* or *half-line*. The *open ray* $(AB$ consists of the points of the line AB which lie in the direction of B from A; the closed ray $[AB$ consists of $(AB$ together with the initial point A.

Let A, B, C be three *noncollinear* points, that is, points not all of the same line. Then ABC will represent the plane that contains the three points. The *angle* with vertex A and *sides* in the directions of B and C from A is written $\angle BAC$ or $\angle CAB$. In this text, $\angle BAC$ is the union of all closed segments with endpoints on the sides.† The *triangle* with vertices A, B, and C is written $[ABC]$. The *sides* of the triangle are the closed segments $[AB]$, $[BC]$, and $[CA]$. The triangle is the union of all closed segments with endpoints on the sides.

A3.1 VECTORS AND TRANSLATIONS

In this section, a vector $\mathbf{V}$ is thought of as a mapping of space E^3 onto itself,‡ a translation in which every point is displaced the same distance in the same direction (later the concept of vector will be seen to have many

---

†In some texts, $\angle BAC$ is defined as the broken line $[AB \cup [AC$. Here, a geometrical angle is a planar region. Similarly, some texts define the triangle as the union of its sides.

‡We use the word *space* here to denote the euclidean three-dimensional space E^3. Euclidean two-dimensional space E^2 will be referred to as "the plane" and one-dimensional space E^1 as "the line."

other interpretations). If **V** maps the point P onto the point Q, we write

$$\mathbf{V} : P \to Q,$$

or

$$\mathbf{V}(P) = Q.$$

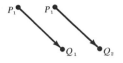

Consequently, if $\mathbf{V}(P_1) = Q_1$, and $\mathbf{V}(P_2) = Q_2$ the directed line segments $\overrightarrow{P_1Q_1}$ and $\overrightarrow{P_2Q_2}$ are parallel and have the same length; see Figure 1.† This length is a positive number called the *length* of **V** and is written $|\mathbf{V}|$.

Figure 1

In three-dimensional space E^3, two nonintersecting lines may fail to be parallel. We say two nonintersecting lines in E^3 are parallel if they lie in the same plane. It is also said that any line is parallel to itself. A plane is any set of points $\mathcal{P}$ which satisfies the following properties:

1. $\mathcal{P}$ contains at least three noncollinear points.
2. If $\mathcal{P}$ contains the two points A and B, then $\mathcal{P}$ contains the entire line AB joining A and B.
3. There exists at least one point of E^3 which is not contained in $\mathcal{P}$.

Two directed line segments $\overrightarrow{P_1Q_1}$ and $\overrightarrow{P_2Q_2}$ are said to be parallel if P_1Q_1 and P_2Q_2 are either parallel lines or the same line and if the orientations of the segments are the same.

Directed segments $\overrightarrow{P_1Q_1}$ and $\overrightarrow{P_2Q_2}$ that have the same length and direction will be called *equivalent*.

The vector **V** is determined by the way in which it maps just one point, since any directed segment $\overrightarrow{PQ}$, where $Q = \mathbf{V}(P)$, defines the direction and length of **V**. The points P, Q are called, respectively, the *initial* and *terminal* points of $\overrightarrow{PQ}$. A convenient mental picture of **V** is as a directed segment floating in space, an arrow of specific length and direction, which may be attached to any initial point P to yield a terminal point Q.

Given a vector **V** and a positive real number λ, we denote the vector in the direction of **V**, with length λ times that of **V**, by $\lambda\mathbf{V}$. In particular, $1\mathbf{V} = \mathbf{V}$. For any point X in the direction of **V** from a fixed point P, there is a real number λ such that $X = \lambda\mathbf{V}(P)$. The set of points

$$\{X : X = \lambda\mathbf{V}(P), \quad \lambda > 0\}$$

is the open ray or half-line in the direction of **V** from the initial point P.

---

†In referring to $\overrightarrow{P_1Q_1}$ as a directed segment, we assume $P_1 \neq Q_1$.

In order to describe the ray from P in the direction opposite to $\mathbf{V}$, we define $\lambda\mathbf{V}$ for $\lambda < 0$ as the vector in the direction opposite to $\mathbf{V}$ with length $-\lambda$ times that of $\mathbf{V}$. Thus, the open ray with initial point P directed oppositely to $\mathbf{V}$ is the set of points

$$\{X : X = \lambda\mathbf{V}(P), \quad \lambda < 0\} .$$

Finally, for $\lambda = 0$ we define $\lambda\mathbf{V} = \mathbf{O}$ where the *null vector* $\mathbf{O}$ is the identity mapping,

$$\mathbf{O} : P \rightarrow P ,$$

which maps each point of space onto itself. It is convenient to consider the mapping $\mathbf{O}$ as a vector of length zero, but we assign no definite direction to $\mathbf{O}$. In any case, for the length $|\lambda\mathbf{V}|$ of the vector $\lambda\mathbf{V}$,

(1) $$|\lambda\mathbf{V}| = |\lambda|\,|\mathbf{V}| .$$

It is easy to show for any real numbers λ and μ that

$$\lambda(\mu\mathbf{V}) = (\lambda\mu)\mathbf{V}$$

(see Ex. 4). This is a form of the associative law and it permits us to omit the parentheses altogether. The line containing P and all points in the direction of $\mathbf{V}$ or in the opposite direction from P is the set of points

$$\{X : X = \lambda\mathbf{V}(P), \quad \lambda \in \mathfrak{R}\} ;$$

we refer to this set briefly as the line $X = \lambda\mathbf{V}(P)$. For a given point P and vector $\mathbf{V}$ there is a one-to-one correspondence between points X on the line $X = \lambda\mathbf{V}(P)$ and real numbers λ. Thus, the line

$$X = \lambda\mathbf{V}(P)$$

can be considered as the number line with origin at P and 1 at $\mathbf{V}(P)$. On a given geometrical line there are clearly many realizations of the number line. To obtain such a realization it is only necessary to choose any given point P of the line as 0 and any other point Q as 1. If $\mathbf{V}$ is the vector that maps P onto Q, the realization is given by $X = \lambda\mathbf{V}(P)$ and $|\mathbf{V}|$ is the unit of length.

If vectors $\mathbf{U}$ and $\mathbf{V}$ have the same or opposite directions we say that $\mathbf{U}$ and $\mathbf{V}$ are collinear. More generally, we say that $\mathbf{U}$ and $\mathbf{V}$ are *collinear* if either $\mathbf{V} = a\mathbf{U}$ or $\mathbf{U} = b\mathbf{V}$ for some real a or b. By this definition, the null vector $\mathbf{O}$ is collinear with every vector. If $\mathbf{U}$ and $\mathbf{V}$ are nonnull and collinear, then the line $X = \lambda\mathbf{V}(P)$ is the same as the line $X = \mu\mathbf{U}(P)$, $\mu \in \mathfrak{R}$. (Ex. 5.)

If $\mathbf{V}$ is a nonnull vector let us see what happens when the vectors

$a\mathbf{V}$ and $b\mathbf{V}$ are applied successively to the point P. Set $Q = a\mathbf{V}(P)$ and $R = b\mathbf{V}(Q)$. The point $Q = a\mathbf{V}(P)$ is a point of the line

$$\ell_1 = \{X : X = \lambda\mathbf{V}(P)\} \; .$$

The line

$$\ell_2 = \{Y : Y = \mu\mathbf{V}(Q)\}$$

is parallel to ℓ_1 but meets ℓ_1 at the point Q ; therefore $\ell_1 = \ell_2$. It follows that

$$R = b\mathbf{V}(Q) = c\mathbf{V}(P)$$

for some c. Since the signed distance of Q from P is $a|\mathbf{V}|$, and that of R from Q is $b|\mathbf{V}|$, the signed distance of R from P is the sum of the two,

$$c|\mathbf{V}| = (a + b)|\mathbf{V}| \; .$$

Thus, $c = a + b$ and

(2) $$b\mathbf{V}[a\mathbf{V}(P)] = (a + b)\mathbf{V}(P) \; .$$

From (2) it follows that the two ways of forming the composition of a pair of collinear vectors define the same vector; see Ex. 6. We shall see that this result is true of noncollinear vectors too. From (2) it also follows that $(-1)\mathbf{V}$, which we write simply as $-\mathbf{V}$, is the inverse mapping to $\mathbf{V}$: if $Q = \mathbf{V}(P)$, then $P = -\mathbf{V}(Q)$; see Ex. 7. Thus, $-\mathbf{V}$ is the vector of the same length as $\mathbf{V}$, but in the opposite direction.

The range of any translation is the entire space E^3 and so may be taken as the domain of a further translation. The compositions of vectors are, therefore, always defined and again are one-to-one mappings of E^3 onto E^3. The composition $\mathbf{UV}$ applied to a point P has a simple interpretation. First apply $\mathbf{V}$ to P to obtain $Q = \mathbf{V}(P)$, then apply $\mathbf{U}$ to Q to obtain $R = \mathbf{U}(Q)$. We may think of $\mathbf{V}$ as attached to the initial point P to yield the terminal point Q, and $\mathbf{U}$ as attached to the terminal point of the directed segment $\overrightarrow{PQ}$ to yield the final point R ; see Figure 2. There is a unique translation $\mathbf{W}$ which maps P onto R. Furthermore, $\mathbf{UV}$ is another mapping of P onto R. If, as we prove next, the mapping $\mathbf{UV}$ is a translation, it must be the same mapping as $\mathbf{W}$. To show that $\mathbf{UV}$ is a translation, we need only prove

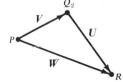

Figure 2

Theorem 1. If $\mathbf{UV}(P_1) = R_1$ and $\mathbf{UV}(P_2) = R_2$, the directed segments $\overrightarrow{P_1 R_1}$ and $\overrightarrow{P_2 R_2}$ are parallel and equal in length.

Proof. Let $\mathbf{T}$ be the translation that maps P_1 onto P_2. We give

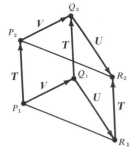

Figure 3

the proof for the case when **T** is not collinear with either **U** or **V** and leave the proof for **T** collinear with **U** or **V** to Ex. 8. Since $Q_1 = V(P_1)$ and $Q_2 = V(P_2)$, the directed segments $\overrightarrow{P_1Q_1}$ and $\overrightarrow{P_2Q_2}$ are equivalent. Since the two directed segments are parallel, they are contained in a plane. Because these segments are equal in length, they determine a parallelogram with the endpoints P_1, Q_1, P_2 and Q_2 as vertices; see Figure 3. It follows that the translation T which maps P_1 onto P_2 also maps Q_1 onto Q_2. In exactly the same way, we conclude from $R_1 = U(Q_1)$ and $R_2 = U(Q_2)$ that R_1, Q_1, R_2, Q_2 are vertices of a parallelogram and, from $T(Q_1) = Q_2$, that $T(R_1) = R_2$. But now, since $T(P_1) = P_2$ and $T(R_1) = R_2$, the points P_1, P_2, R_1, R_2 are vertices of a parallelogram and, therefore $\overrightarrow{P_1R_1}$ and $\overrightarrow{P_2R_2}$ are equivalent directed segments as asserted.   ☐

Since translations are mappings of E^3 onto E^3, a composition of translations is a composition of functions and therefore associative:

$$\mathbf{U(VW) = (UV)W}$$

(see A2.3). In general, we do not expect the composition of functions to be commutative, but for translations, in particular,

Theorem 2. The composition of any two translations is independent of order; namely, **UV = VU**.

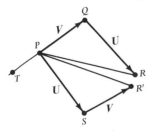

Figure 4

Proof. Let P be any point. Set $Q = V(P)$, $R = U(Q)$, $S = U(P)$, and $R' = V(S)$; see Figure 4. To prove that **UV = VU**, we must show that $R' = R$. We have already seen that the composition of collinear vectors is commutative. Now assume that **U** and **V** are not collinear. Observe first, since $\vec{U}$ and $\vec{V}$ are noncollinear, that the points P, Q, S are noncollinear. Therefore, there is a unique plane $\mathcal{P}$ that contains the three points. Now, since $Q = V(P)$ and $R' = V(S)$, the directed segments $\overrightarrow{PQ}$ and $\overrightarrow{SR'}$ are parallel, hence coplanar; therefore $R' \in \mathcal{P}$. Similarly, since $R = U(Q)$ and $S = U(P)$, we also have $R \in \mathcal{P}$. Consequently, all five points P, Q, R, S, R' are coplanar and Figure 4 represents a plane figure. Moreover, since the lines QR and PS are parallel, as are PQ and SR', the exterior angle $\angle TPS$ is congruent to $\angle PQR$ and $\angle R'SP$. From $|PQ| = |R'S|$ and $|QR| = |SP|$

we further conclude that $[PQR]$ is congruent to $[R'SP]$. Therefore, $|PR| = |R'P|$. Furthermore, $\angle QPR = \angle SR'P$. But from the parallelism of PQ and SR', we have $\angle SR'P = \angle QPR'$ and conclude that $\angle QPR = \angle QPR'$. The point R' lies in the same direction at the same distance from P as R; hence $R' = R$. $\square$

The commutative law is known also as the "parallelogram law" for the composition of vectors. In the geometrical representation of the commutative law, the points R and R' of Figure 4 are the same and the figure $[PQRS]$ is a parallelogram for which the directed diagonal $\overrightarrow{PR}$ represents $\mathbf{UV}$ and $\mathbf{VU}$; see Figure 5.

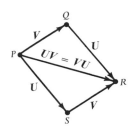

Figure 5

We have introduced two operations upon vectors. The first, $\mathbf{V} \to \lambda\mathbf{V}$, multiplies a vector by a number. If λ is positive, multiplication by λ leaves the directions of all vectors unchanged but multiplies all lengths by λ. Thus multiplication by a positive λ amounts only to a change of scale. In Figure 2, for example, multiplication of the scale by λ yields a triangle similar to $[PQR]$, or

(3) $(\lambda\mathbf{U})(\lambda\mathbf{V}) = \lambda(\mathbf{UV})$.

This last result holds also for $\lambda \leq 0$ (see Ex. 9). When a number λ is used to multiply a vector it is called a *scalar*. If $\lambda > 0$, scalar multiplication $\mathbf{V} \to \lambda\mathbf{V}$ is simply a change of scale, and if $\lambda < 0$, it is a reversal of direction and a change of scale.

The second operation, composition of two translations, behaves in many ways like the addition of two numbers. Because of this analogy, it is customary to write the composition of two vectors as a sum,

$$\mathbf{UV} = \mathbf{U} + \mathbf{V}.$$

In the preceding discussion, we have been guided by the geometrical idea of translation, but there are many other interpretations of vectors than the one we have chosen. The basic algebraic structure which we have obtained for the two operations, multiplication of translations by scalars and addition (composition) of translations, defines the concept of vectors in general. Specifically, a set Λ is called a *linear vector space* over the real numbers and its elements are called *vectors* if there are two operations, addition of vectors and multiplication of vectors by a scalar, which obey the following laws.

For each pair of vectors $\mathbf{U}$ and $\mathbf{V}$ in Λ there is a vector $\mathbf{U} + \mathbf{V}$

in Λ, called the *sum* of **U** and **V** which has the following properties.†

A1. Commutativity: $\mathbf{U} + \mathbf{V} = \mathbf{V} + \mathbf{U}$.

A2. Associativity: $(\mathbf{U} + \mathbf{V}) + \mathbf{W} = \mathbf{U} + (\mathbf{V} + \mathbf{W})$.

A3. There exists a vector **O** in Λ, called the *null vector* such that $\mathbf{V} + \mathbf{O} = \mathbf{V}$ for each vector **V** in Λ.

A4. For each vector **V** in Λ there exists a vector $-\mathbf{V}$ such that $\mathbf{V} + (-\mathbf{V}) = \mathbf{O}$.

Like the difference of two numbers, the *difference of two vectors* is defined by

$$\mathbf{U} - \mathbf{V} = \mathbf{U} + (-\mathbf{V}).$$

For each scalar (real number) λ and each vector **V** in Λ there is a vector $\lambda\mathbf{V}$ in Λ, called the *product* of λ and **V**, with the following properties.‡

M1. $1\mathbf{V} = \mathbf{V}$.

M2. $\lambda(\mu\mathbf{V}) = (\lambda\mu)\mathbf{V}$.

Multiplication of vectors by scalars is distributive over addition of scalars,

D1. $(\lambda + \mu)\mathbf{V} = \lambda\mathbf{V} + \mu\mathbf{V}$.

Multiplication by scalars is distributive over addition of vectors,

D2. $\lambda(\mathbf{U} + \mathbf{V}) = \lambda\mathbf{U} + \lambda\mathbf{V}$.

For the realization of the sum of two vectors as the composition of translations, it is a minor exercise to verify that the algebraic properties A1 to D2 hold.

The postulates for a linear vector space include spaces which we might not at first connect with our geometrical model. For example, the set of all polynomials with real coefficients form a linear vector space; the set of all real functions on a given domain forms another. For present purposes, however, the geometrical model is sufficient. Some of the simpler algebraic consequences of the vector space postulates are left for proof in the exercises.

A3.1 Exercises

1. In Figure 5, one diagonal corresponds to the sum of $\mathbf{U} + \mathbf{V}$. What vector corresponds to the other diagonal?

---

†The properties A1–A4 define an algebraic structure, an *abelian* or *commutative group*, which appears in many different mathematical contexts.

‡In this text, the product of a scalar and a vector is always written with the scalar on the left.

2. Give the geometrical justification for the inequality

$$|\mathbf{U} + \mathbf{V}| \le |\mathbf{U}| + |\mathbf{V}| \,.$$

3. For any nonnull vector $\mathbf{A}$ obtain an expression for the *unit vector* (vector of length 1) in the direction of $\mathbf{A}$.

4. Prove the associative law for the multiplication of vectors by real numbers:

$$\lambda(\mu\mathbf{V}) = (\lambda\mu)\mathbf{V} \,.$$

5. Let $\mathbf{U}$ and $\mathbf{V}$ be collinear nonnull vectors. Show that the lines $X = \lambda\mathbf{V}(P)$ and $X = \mu\mathbf{U}(P)$ are the same.

6. Prove, as asserted in the text, that Equation (2) implies that the two ways of forming the composition of a pair of collinear vectors define the same vector.

7. Prove if $Q = \mathbf{V}(P)$ then $P = -\mathbf{V}(Q)$.

8. In the proof of Theorem 1 we proved if $\overrightarrow{P_1Q_1}$ and $\overrightarrow{P_2Q_2}$ are equivalent and noncollinear, $\overrightarrow{P_1P_2}$ and $\overrightarrow{Q_1Q_2}$ are equivalent; namely, if $Q_1 = \mathbf{V}(P_1)$, $Q_2 = \mathbf{V}(P_2)$, and $P_2 = \mathbf{T}(P_1)$ where $\mathbf{T}$ and $\mathbf{V}$ are noncollinear, then $Q_2 = \mathbf{T}(Q_1)$. Prove this result when $\mathbf{T}$ and $\mathbf{V}$ are collinear; hence prove Theorem 1 in general.

9. Derive (3) for $\lambda \le 0$.

10. Give a geometrical derivation for the associative law A2 for the addition of vectors.

11. From the properties A_1 to D_2, which define a vector space, derive the following consequences.
    a. $\quad \lambda\mathbf{O} = \mathbf{O}$.
    b. $\quad 0\mathbf{V} = \mathbf{O}$.
    c. $\quad$ If $\lambda \ne 0$ and $\mathbf{V} \ne \mathbf{O}$, then, $\lambda\mathbf{V} \ne \mathbf{O}$.
    d. $\quad (-1)\mathbf{V} = -\mathbf{V}$.
    e. $\quad$ If $\lambda \ne 0$, the vector equation $\lambda\mathbf{X} + \mathbf{U} = \mathbf{V}$ has the unique solution $\mathbf{X} = \dfrac{1}{\lambda}(\mathbf{V} - \mathbf{U})$.

12. a. Let Λ_1 and Λ_2 be linear vector spaces over the real numbers. Show that the set of ordered pairs

$$\Lambda_1 \oplus \Lambda_2 = \{(\mathbf{V}_1, \mathbf{V}_2) : \mathbf{V}_1 \in \Lambda_1 \,, \ \mathbf{V}_2 \in \Lambda_2\}$$

is a linear vector space over the real numbers, where, for $\mathbf{U}_1, \mathbf{V}_1 \in \Lambda_1$ and $\mathbf{U}_2, \mathbf{V}_2 \in \Lambda_2$ addition and multiplication by a scalar in $\Lambda_1 \oplus \Lambda_2$ are defined by

$$(\mathbf{U}_1, \mathbf{U}_2) + (\mathbf{V}_1, \mathbf{V}_2) = (\mathbf{U}_1 + \mathbf{V}_1, \mathbf{U}_2 + \mathbf{V}_2)$$

and

$$\lambda(\mathbf{V}_1, \mathbf{V}_2) = (\lambda\mathbf{V}_1, \lambda\mathbf{V}_2) \,.$$

The space $\Lambda_1 \oplus \Lambda_2$ is known as the direct sum of Λ_1 and Λ_2.

b. Show that $\Re$, the real number field, is a linear vector space over the real numbers, where addition and multiplication are now, respectively, ordinary addition and multiplication of numbers. The set $\Re$ considered as a linear vector space with a length defined as $|x|$ for $x \in \Re$ is denoted by E^1 (one-dimensional euclidean space).

c. Show that euclidean two-dimensional space E^2 is given by

$$E^2 = E^1 \oplus E^1 ,$$

where the length $|\mathbf{A}|$ for $\mathbf{A} = (a, b)$ with $a, b \in E^1$, is defined by

$$|\mathbf{A}| = \sqrt{a^2 + b^2} .$$

Similarly, show that euclidean three-dimensional space E^3 is given by

$$E^3 = E^2 \oplus E^1$$

where length for $\mathbf{V} \in E^3$, given in the form $\mathbf{V} = (\mathbf{A}, c)$ with $\mathbf{A} \in E^2$, $c \in E^1$, is defined by

$$|\mathbf{V}| = \sqrt{|\mathbf{A}|^2 + c^2} .$$

A3.2 VECTOR GEOMETRY

A vector $\mathbf{V}$ can be represented by any one of the infinitely many directed segments $\overrightarrow{PQ}$ where $Q = \mathbf{V}(P)$, the initial point P being entirely arbitrary. If the initial point P is fixed, however, then for each terminal point Q, there is only one vector $\mathbf{V}$ such that $Q = \mathbf{V}(P)$. Thus, all vectors $\mathbf{V}$ can be represented, one-to-one, by the directed segments emanating from a single initial point. The one initial point in such a representation is called the *origin* and is usually denoted by O. Given a point A, there is a unique translation which maps O onto A; this translation is called the *position vector* $\mathbf{A}$. We say that A is the point with position vector $\mathbf{A}$ and represent the position vector $\mathbf{A}$ by the point A onto which $\mathbf{A}$ maps the origin; conversely, we may represent the point A, by the position vector $\mathbf{A}$ which maps O onto A. Given either point or vector, the other is determined. This one-to-one correspondence between points and vectors depends only on the choice of origin.

The relation between point and position vector extends to translation of points and addition of vectors: the point $\mathbf{A}(B)$ has the position vector $\mathbf{A} + \mathbf{B}$. This is immediate from

$$\mathbf{A}(B) = \mathbf{A}\mathbf{B}(O) = [\mathbf{A} + \mathbf{B}](O) .$$

For this reason, it is possible to introduce the concept of sum for points and to write $A + B$ for the point with position vector $\mathbf{A} + \mathbf{B}$. Thus,

$$A + B = \mathbf{A}(B) = \mathbf{B}(A).$$

Similarly, for any real λ, we may introduce the point λA as the point with position vector $\lambda \mathbf{A}$. Observe, however, that the points $A + B$ and λA are not defined in terms of A and B alone, but depend on the choice of origin.

With these ideas, we shall be able to give simple descriptions of such geometrical objects as line, ray, segment, and plane, and to prove theorems about them, often with greater ease than in synthetic geometry.

Preliminary to further discussion, we choose an origin O so that we may represent points by position vectors.

We shall make frequent use of the following lemma.

Lemma 1. If $\mathbf{V}(P) = Q$, then

$$\mathbf{V} = \mathbf{Q} - \mathbf{P},$$

where $\mathbf{P}$ and $\mathbf{Q}$ are the position vectors of P and Q, respectively.

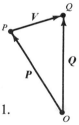

Figure 1

Proof. Since $P = \mathbf{P}(O)$, we have

$$[\mathbf{V} + \mathbf{P}](O) - Q = \mathbf{Q}(O);$$

hence, $\mathbf{V} + \mathbf{P}$ maps O on the same point as $\mathbf{Q}$; see Figure 1. Therefore,

(1) $$\mathbf{V} + \mathbf{P} = \mathbf{Q}.$$

From the algebraic laws governing the addition of vectors (p. 290), we obtain

$$(\mathbf{V} + \mathbf{P}) + (-\mathbf{P}) = \mathbf{V} + [\mathbf{P} + (-\mathbf{P})]$$
$$= \mathbf{V} + \mathbf{O}$$
$$= \mathbf{V};$$

whence, from (1) and the definition of subtraction,

$$\mathbf{V} = \mathbf{Q} + (-\mathbf{P}) = \mathbf{Q} - \mathbf{P}.$$

(Compare this result with that of A3.1 Exercise 1.)   ▯

Lemma 2. The distance between P and Q is $|\mathbf{Q} - \mathbf{P}|$.

Lemma 2 is an immediate corollary of Lemma 1, since $\mathbf{Q} - \mathbf{P}$ is the translation that maps P onto Q.

In order to preserve the one-to-one correspondence between points and position vectors, it is necessary to refer all position vectors to the single origin O. At the same time, we are completely free to choose the origin to suit our own convenience. We need to express the position vector of a point P referred to a new origin A in terms of the position vector of P referred to the old origin O. The directed segment $\overrightarrow{AP}$ represents the position vector of P with respect to the origin A and therefore, by Lemma 1, $\mathbf{P} - \mathbf{A}$ is the position vector of P referred to A; see Figure 2. From this, we see that a change of origin from O to A is expressed algebraically in the same way as a translation of the plane by $-\mathbf{A}$. Any vector expression of a geometrical property must be independent of the choice of origin. For a vector expression to be independent of choice of origin, it should not be affected by a transformation of the form

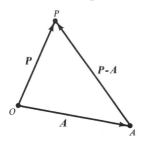

Figure 2

$$\mathbf{X} \to \mathbf{X} - \mathbf{A} .$$

For example, the distance between P and Q, which is given by Lemma 2 as $|\mathbf{Q} - \mathbf{P}|$, is not affected if $\mathbf{Q}$ is replaced by $\mathbf{Q} - \mathbf{A}$ and $\mathbf{P}$ by $\mathbf{P} - \mathbf{A}$ (see Ex. 6).

Given any two points of a line, we can immediately apply Lemma 1 to obtain its equation. First, from A3.1 we recall that the equation of a line through a point P parallel to a nonnull vector $\mathbf{V}$ can be written in the form

$$X = \lambda V(P)$$

where λ is any real number. In terms of position vectors, since

$$\lambda V(P) = \lambda VP(O) = [\lambda V + P](O) ,$$

the equation takes the form

(2) $$\mathbf{X} = \mathbf{P} + \lambda \mathbf{V} , \qquad \lambda \text{ real.}$$

(We may, of course, replace the bold face symbols in (2) by italic type to indicate points instead of position vectors.) Now, let Q be a point of line (2) other than P. The line PQ is parallel to the vector $\mathbf{V}$ represented by the directed segment $\overrightarrow{PQ}$. Thus, a point X of the line may be represented as the result of a translation from O to P followed by a translation in the direction of $\mathbf{V}$ or its inverse $-\mathbf{V}$. In particular, we observe that if $O \leq \lambda \leq 1$ in (2), then X is a point on segment

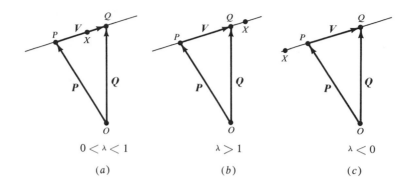

Figure 3

$$0 < \lambda < 1 \qquad\qquad \lambda > 1 \qquad\qquad \lambda < 0$$

(a) $\qquad\qquad$ (b) $\qquad\qquad$ (c)

$[PQ]$ and λ represents the ratio of $|PX|$ to $|PQ|$; see Figure 3a. If $\lambda > 1$, then Q lies between P and X (see Figure 3b) and if $\lambda < O$, then P is between X and Q (see Figure 3c). We observe also that $\mathbf{V} = \mathbf{Q} - \mathbf{P}$. Using this result and (2), we obtain the *two-point equation* of the line in the vector form,

$$(3) \qquad\qquad \mathbf{X} = (1 - \lambda)\mathbf{P} + \lambda\mathbf{Q} .$$

Here, $|\lambda|$ has the geometrical meaning of the ratio of the length of $\overrightarrow{PX}$ to that of $\overrightarrow{PQ}$, λ being positive if Q and X lie in the same direction from P, negative if Q and X lie in opposite directions from P. For example, the midpoint of the segment $[PQ]$ is given by $\lambda = \frac{1}{2}$:

$$(4) \qquad\qquad \mathbf{X} = \tfrac{1}{2}(\mathbf{P} + \mathbf{Q}) .$$

Now, we show how the concept of position vector may be used to prove geometrical theorems.

Example 1. The line segment that joins the midpoints of two of the sides of a triangle is parallel to and half as long as the third side.

Proof. Let A, B, C be the vertices of the triangle and let M_1 be the midpoint of $[AB]$, M_2 the midpoint of $[BC]$; see Figure 4. From (4), we have for the corresponding position vectors

$$\mathbf{M}_1 = \tfrac{1}{2}(\mathbf{A} + \mathbf{B}), \qquad \mathbf{M}_2 = \tfrac{1}{2}(\mathbf{B} + \mathbf{C}) .$$

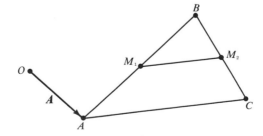

Figure 4

According to Lemma 1, the directed segment $\overrightarrow{M_1M_2}$ represents the vector

$$\mathbf{M}_2 - \mathbf{M}_1 = \tfrac{1}{2}(\mathbf{C} - \mathbf{A}).$$

Consequently, $\overrightarrow{M_1M_2}$ is parallel to $\overrightarrow{CA}$ and $|M_1M_2| = \tfrac{1}{2}|AC|$ as we sought to prove. □

Example 2. The midpoints of the sides of a quadrilateral are vertices of a parallelogram.

Proof. Let A, B, C, D be the successive vertices of the quadrilateral. The midpoint M_1 of $[AB]$ is given by (4):

$$\mathbf{M}_1 = \tfrac{1}{2}(\mathbf{A} + \mathbf{B}).$$

Similarly, the midpoints of the remaining sides are given, successively, by

$$\mathbf{M}_2 = \tfrac{1}{2}(\mathbf{B} + \mathbf{C}), \quad \mathbf{M}_3 = \tfrac{1}{2}(\mathbf{C} + \mathbf{D}), \quad \mathbf{M}_4 = \tfrac{1}{2}(\mathbf{D} + \mathbf{A});$$

see Figure 5. The figure $[M_1M_2M_3M_4]$ is a parallelogram if $\overrightarrow{M_1M_4}$

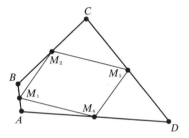

Figure 5

and $\overrightarrow{M_2M_3}$ are equivalent, that is, if $\mathbf{M}_4 - \mathbf{M}_1 = \mathbf{M}_3 - \mathbf{M}_2$ (see the proof of A3.1 Theorem 1). Since

$$\mathbf{M}_4 - \mathbf{M}_1 = \tfrac{1}{2}(\mathbf{D} - \mathbf{B}) = \mathbf{M}_3 - \mathbf{M}_2,$$

the result is proved. □

The foregoing proof (Example 2) is completely general; for example, the quadrilateral $ABCD$ may be self-intersecting; it need not even lie in a plane.

The *centroid* C of n points P_1, P_2, ..., P_n is defined as the point whose position vector $\mathbf{C}$ is the arithmetic average of the n position vectors P_i, where $i = 1, 2, ..., n$;

$$\mathbf{C} = \frac{1}{n}(\mathbf{P}_1 +_2 \mathbf{P} + \mathbf{P}_3 + \cdots + \mathbf{P}_n).$$

Example 3. The three medians of a triangle intersect at the centroid of the vertices. Furthermore, the distance from the centroid to any vertex is twice its distance to the opposite side.

Proof. Let P_1, P_2, P_3 be the vertices of the triangle and Q_1, Q_2, Q_3 the respective midpoints of the opposite sides; see Figure 6. The

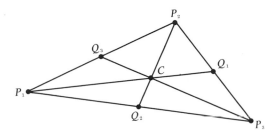

Figure 6

equation of the median line P_1Q_1 is given by (3) as

$$X = (1 - \lambda)P_1 + \lambda Q_1 ,$$

and, since $Q_1 = \frac{1}{2}(P_2 + P_3)$,

$$X = (1 - \lambda)P_1 + \frac{1}{2}\lambda(P_2 + P_3) .$$

The centroid C of the vertices lies on the median if and only if there is some value of λ for which $X = C$; that is,

$$\tfrac{1}{3}(P_1 + P_2 + P_3) = (1 - \lambda)P_1 + \tfrac{1}{2}\lambda P_2 + \tfrac{1}{2}\lambda P_3 ,$$

or, equivalently,

$$(\tfrac{2}{3} - \lambda)P_1 + (\tfrac{1}{2}\lambda - \tfrac{1}{3})P_2 + (\tfrac{1}{2}\lambda - \tfrac{1}{3})P_3 = O .$$

The final equation is clearly satisfied by $\lambda = \frac{2}{3}$. We conclude that the centroid does lie on the median and that it subdivides the segment $[P_1Q_1]$ in the asserted ratio. The same argument may be applied to each of the other medians to complete the proof. ⬜

Given any two points, the vector equation (3) describes the line containing those points. We now seek a vector description of the plane that contains any three noncollinear points A, B, C. The plane ABC must contain, with any two of its points, the entire line that joins them. In particular, ABC must contain the two lines

(5)
$$AB = \{X : X = A + \lambda(B - A), \quad \lambda \text{ real}\},$$
$$AC = \{Y : Y = A + \mu(C - A), \quad \mu \text{ real}\}.$$

Furthermore, if X is any point of AB and Y any point of AC, then ABC contains the line

(6)
$$XY = \{Z : Z = (1 - \nu)X + \nu Y, \quad \nu \text{ real}\}.$$

Consequently, from (5) and (6), ABC contains the set

(7)
$$S = \{Z : Z = A + (1 - \nu)\lambda(B - A)$$
$$+ \nu\mu(C - A), \quad \lambda, \mu, \nu \text{ real}\}.$$

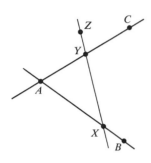

Figure 7

The set S given by (7) is actually the plane ABC. To prove this, we need show only that S contains ABC, since we already know that ABC contains S. Let Z be any point of ABC other than A and take any line through Z in ABC which does not pass through A and is parallel to neither AB nor AC (see Ex. 1). Such a line will meet AB at a point X, and AC at a second point Y; see Figure 7. Since Z lies on the line XY, it can be expressed in the form given by (7) and, therefore, is an element of S. Since we have proved any point of ABC to be a point of S, we conclude that $ABC \subset S$.

The representation of the plane ABC by (7) shows that any point Z of the plane can be given by an expression of the form

(8)
$$Z = A + x(B - A) + y(C - A),$$

where x and y are real numbers satisfying

$$x = (1 - \nu)\lambda \quad \text{and} \quad y = \nu\mu$$

to agree with (7). This is no restriction, however, for if x and y are any real numbers whatever, we may take $\nu = \frac{1}{2}$, $\lambda = 2x$, $\mu = 2y$ to obtain (8) from (7). We shall, therefore, take (8) as our basic representation of ABC.

Equation (8) has a simple geometrical interpretation. Let A be the origin and set $U = B - A$ and $V = C - A$. The position of the point Z of the plane ABC is given by the *generalized coordinates* (x, y), where Z is determined by the translation xU applied to the point A, followed by the translation yV; see Figure 8. The lines $Z = A + xU$ and $Z = A + yV$, corresponding to the respective conditions $y = 0$ and $x = 0$, are called the x-axis and y-axis, respectively. The point A with generalized coordinates $(0, 0)$ is called

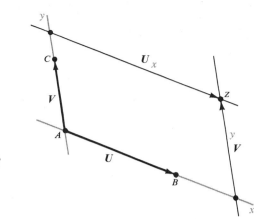

Figure 8

the origin of the coordinate system. This representation of the plane in terms of generalized coordinates is a straightforward generalization of the conventional rectangular coordinate representation. In conventional rectangular coordinates, **U** and **V** are perpendicular and the unit is the same for both axes; that is, $|\mathbf{U}| = |\mathbf{V}|$ (see A3.3). We leave the proof that there is a one-to-one correspondence between the points Z of the plane ABC and their generalized coordinates (x, y) to Ex. 2.

In general, we cannot assume that four points will not all lie in one plane. If four given points are coplanar, we say that the position vectors of any three of them, referred to the fourth as origin, are coplanar. Thus, if O, A, B, C lie in a plane, we say that the vectors **A**, **B**, **C** are *coplanar*. By this definition, if the vectors **A**, **B**, **C** include the null vector **O** among them, they are coplanar.

Theorem 1. The vectors **U**, **V**, **Z** are coplanar if and only if there exist scalars a, b, c, not all zero, such that

(9) $$a\mathbf{U} + b\mathbf{V} + c\mathbf{Z} = \mathbf{O}.$$

Proof. Suppose, first, that there exist scalars a, b, c, not all zero, such that (9) holds. If $c \neq 0$, say,

$$\mathbf{Z} = -\frac{a}{c}\mathbf{U} - \frac{b}{c}\mathbf{V}.$$

This has the form of (8) with **A** = **O**, **U** = **B** − **A**, and **V** = **C** − **A**; therefore, if **U** and **V** are noncollinear, **Z** lies in the plane OUV. If **U** and **V** are collinear, **Z** will also be collinear with **U** and **V**. In this case, all planes that contain the points O, U, and V will also contain Z.

Conversely, suppose that $\mathbf{U}$, $\mathbf{V}$, and $\mathbf{Z}$ are coplanar. If any two of the vectors are collinear, say $\mathbf{U} = \lambda\mathbf{V}$, then

$$\mathbf{U} - \lambda\mathbf{V} + 0\mathbf{Z} = \mathbf{O},$$

so that there exist scalars, not all zero, for which (9) is satisfied. If $\mathbf{U}$ and $\mathbf{V}$ are not collinear, the points O, U, and V are contained in only one plane, and by (8), any point Z which lies in the plane satisfies

$$\mathbf{Z} = a\mathbf{U} + b\mathbf{V}.$$

Consequently,
$$a\mathbf{U} + b\mathbf{V} - \mathbf{Z} = \mathbf{O};$$

thus (9) is satisfied with $c = -1$. $\square$

In this text, we shall employ the euclidean spaces of one, two, and three dimensions, namely, the number line E^1, the plane E^2, and space E^3, respectively. From (3), with $\mathbf{P} = \mathbf{O}$ and $\mathbf{Q} = \mathbf{U}$, we see that any point X in E^1 is given by

$$\mathbf{X} = \lambda\mathbf{U},$$

where $\mathbf{U} \neq \mathbf{O}$. Similarly, any point X in E^2 can be expressed by (8) in the form
$$\mathbf{X} = \lambda\mathbf{U} + \mu\mathbf{V},$$

where $\mathbf{U}$ and $\mathbf{V}$ are noncollinear vectors, and where we have set $\mathbf{A} = \mathbf{O}$, $\mathbf{B} - \mathbf{A} = \mathbf{U}$, and $\mathbf{C} - \mathbf{A} = \mathbf{V}$ in (8). Any expression of the form
$$c_1\mathbf{U}_1 + c_2\mathbf{U}_2 + c_3\mathbf{U}_3 + \cdots + c_n\mathbf{U}_n$$

is called a *linear combination* of the vectors $\mathbf{U}_1$, $\mathbf{U}_2$, $\mathbf{U}_3$, ..., $\mathbf{U}_n$. We have seen that each position vector in E^1 is a linear combination of any one nonnull vector, each position vector in E^2 is a linear combination of any two noncollinear vectors, and we shall prove that each position vector in E^3 is, similarly, a linear combination of any three noncoplanar vectors. This last property can be used to define three-dimensional space. We shall define three-dimensional space in another way and derive this property as a consequence.

A line is said to be *parallel* to a plane if it is parallel to some line in the plane. By the requirement that a plane does not contain every point of space (p. 285), we have guaranteed that space has at least three dimensions. The assertion that space has exactly three dimensions is a consequence of the following postulate.

Dimension postulate for E^3 . If a line is not parallel to a given plane, then the line intersects that plane at precisely one point.

Theorem 2. Given any four vectors **A** , **B** , **C** , **D** , there exist scalars a , b , c , d , not all zero, such that

(10) $$a\mathbf{A} + b\mathbf{B} + c\mathbf{C} + d\mathbf{D} = \mathbf{O} .$$

Proof. If any three of the vectors, say **A** , **B** , **C** , are coplanar, then, by Theorem 1, there is a linear combination of the three which is null:

(11) $$a\mathbf{A} + b\mathbf{B} + c\mathbf{C} = \mathbf{O} ,$$

where at least one of the scalars a , b , c is not zero. In that case, (10) follows from (11) with $d = 0$.

Now, assume **A** , **B** , **C** are noncoplanar. We consider two cases, that **D** is parallel to the plane ABC , or that any line parallel to **D** meets the plane at exactly one point.

If **D** is parallel to ABC , there exists a directed segment $\overrightarrow{P_1 P_2}$ in the plane which represents **D** . From (8), there exists scalars λ_i , μ_i for which

$$\mathbf{P}_i = \mathbf{A} + \lambda_i(\mathbf{B} - \mathbf{A}) + \mu_i(\mathbf{C} - \mathbf{A}) \qquad (i = 1 , 2) ;$$

hence, by Lemma 1,

(12) $$\mathbf{D} = \mathbf{P}_2 - \mathbf{P}_1 = (\lambda_2 - \lambda_1)(\mathbf{B} - \mathbf{A}) + (\mu_2 - \mu_1)(\mathbf{C} - \mathbf{A}) .$$

This last relation can be put immediately in the form of (10).

If **D** is not parallel to ABC , the line $\{\xi\mathbf{D} : \xi \in \Re\}$ must meet the plane at exactly one point, say at $d\mathbf{D}$. Furthermore, $d \neq 0$ since the plane ABC does not contain the origin (**A** , **B** , **C** were assumed to be noncoplanar). Now, by (8) there exist scalars λ and μ such that

(13) $$d\mathbf{D} = \mathbf{A} + \lambda(\mathbf{B} - \mathbf{A}) + \mu(\mathbf{C} - \mathbf{A}) ,$$

and this relation is readily put in the form of (10).   ⬚

Corollary a. If **A** , **B** , **C** are noncoplanar vectors, then any vector **X** in E^3 can be represented as a linear combination of **A** , **B** , and **C** .

The proof of the corollary is left to Exercise 3.

A3.2 Exercises

1. Let A , B , C be noncollinear points and let Z be any point of the plane ABC . Show, if $Z \neq A$, that through Z at least one line in ABC does not pass through A and is parallel to neither AB nor AC .

2. Let A , B , C be any three noncollinear points. Prove that there is a one-to-one correspondence between ordered pairs of real numbers (x, y) , (generalized coordinates) and the points Z of the plane ABC given by (8).

3. Prove Corollary 2a.

4. For any two noncollinear position vectors $\mathbf{A}$ and $\mathbf{B}$, the angle $\angle AOB$ is defined as the set of points consisting of the two closed rays $[OA$ and $[OB$ with initial point O in the directions of $\mathbf{A}$ and $\mathbf{B}$, respectively, together with all segments having one endpoint on $[OA$ and the other on $[OB$. Describe $\angle AOB$ in terms of linear combinations of $\mathbf{A}$ and $\mathbf{B}$.

5. Let $\mathbf{A}$ and $\mathbf{B}$ be noncollinear vectors. Determine the equation of the ray that bisects $\angle AOB$.

6. Verify that the results of (3), (4), (8) and Examples 1, 2, 3 do not depend on the choice of origin.

7. Let A and B be any given points. Characterize geometrically each of the sets of points

a. $\{X : |\mathbf{X} - \mathbf{A}| = r\}$.   e. $\{X : \mathbf{X} = \lambda \mathbf{A}, \ \lambda \geq 0\}$.

b. $\{X : |\mathbf{X} - \mathbf{A}| < r\}$.   f. $\{X : \mathbf{X} = \mathbf{A} + \lambda \mathbf{B}, \ \lambda \geq 0\}$.

c. $\{X : |\mathbf{X} - \mathbf{A}| > r\}$.   g. $\{X : \mathbf{X} = \mathbf{A} + \lambda \mathbf{B}, \ \lambda \ \text{real}\}$.

d. $\{X : \mathbf{X} = \lambda \mathbf{A}, \ \lambda \ \text{real}\}$.   h. $\{X : |\mathbf{X} - \mathbf{A}| = |\mathbf{X} - \mathbf{B}|\}$.

8. The statement of Theorem 2 implies that any four vectors are linearly dependent, namely that at least one can be expressed as a linear combination of the other three. Show from the assumption that E^3 is not wholly contained in a plane, that there do exist three linearly independent vectors in E^3 , that is, vectors $\mathbf{A}$, $\mathbf{B}$, $\mathbf{C}$ for which the equation

$$a\mathbf{A} + b\mathbf{B} + c\mathbf{C} = 0$$

is satisfied only if all three scalars a , b , c are zero.

9. Prove if $\mathbf{A}$, $\mathbf{B}$, $\mathbf{C}$ are not coplanar that any vector $\mathbf{D}$ can be represented as a linear combination

$$\mathbf{D} = a\mathbf{A} + b\mathbf{B} + c\mathbf{C}$$

and the representation is unique.

10. Show if $\mathbf{U}$ and $\mathbf{V}$ are not collinear that $\mathbf{X} = \mathbf{A} + p\mathbf{U} + q\mathbf{V}$ is the equation of a plane passing through the point A and parallel to the vectors $\mathbf{U}$ and $\mathbf{V}$.

11. In the accompanying figure, R is any point on the line AB . Determine scalars a and b such that $\mathbf{R} = a\mathbf{A} + b\mathbf{B}$, and determine $|AR|/|RB|$ in terms of a and b .

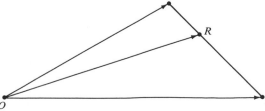

12. Let $[OABC]$ be a parallelogram, D the midpoint of $[BC]$, and E the midpoint of $[CO]$. Show that the lines AD and AE divide the diagonal $[OB]$ in thirds.

13. In the accompanying figure, O is any point not on an extended side of the triangle. Set

$$\mathbf{R} - \mathbf{B} = \alpha(\mathbf{A} - \mathbf{R}), \qquad \mathbf{P} - \mathbf{C} = \beta(\mathbf{B} - \mathbf{P}),$$
$$\mathbf{Q} - \mathbf{A} = \gamma(\mathbf{C} - \mathbf{Q}).$$

Show that

$$\alpha\beta\gamma = 1.$$

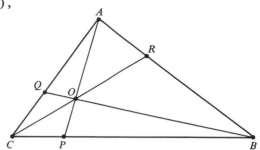

This result together with its converse (namely, if P, Q, R divide their respective sides so that this relation holds, the lines AP, BQ, and CR are concurrent) is Ceva's Theorem.†

14. Prove that the bisectors of the interior angles of a triangle are concurrent.

15. For any three noncollinear points A, B, C, the triangle $[ABC]$ may be defined as the intersection of the angles $\angle ABC$, $\angle BCA$, $\angle CAB$, (see Exercise 4). Describe $[ABC]$ in terms of linear combinations of A, B, C.

16. a. Let A, B, C be three noncollinear points. Show that $[ABC]$ (see preceding exercise), is the set of all points contained in the closed segments with one endpoint at A and the other endpoint on the closed segment $[BC]$.

    b. For any four noncoplanar points, A, B, C, D, the tetrahedron $[ABCD]$ is defined as the union of all closed segments with one endpoint on $[ABC]$ and the other at D. Describe $[ABCD]$ in terms of linear combinations of A, B, C, and D.

17. A median of a tetrahedron joins any one vertex to the centroid of the other three. Show that the medians of the tetrahedron are concurrent at the centroid of its four vertices. Show also that the segment of any median between the centroid and vertex is $3/4$ of the total length of the median.

18. The segment joining the midpoint of any edge of a tetrahedron to the midpoint of the opposite edge is bisected by the centroid of the four vertices.

19. The six planes, each containing one edge and bisecting the opposite edge of a tetrahedron, are concurrent.

20. Let A, B, C be any three noncollinear points. Let ℓ be any line in the plane ABC which contains no vertex of the triangle $[ABC]$ and which is parallel to no side. Let P, Q, and R be the intersections of ℓ with the lines BC, CA, and AB, respectively

†Giovanni Ceva, Italian mathematician (1647–1736).

(see figure). If α, β, and γ are defined by

(i) $$\mathbf{R} - \mathbf{A} = \alpha(\mathbf{B} - \mathbf{R}), \qquad \mathbf{P} - \mathbf{B} = \beta(\mathbf{C} - \mathbf{P}),$$
$$\mathbf{Q} - \mathbf{C} = \gamma(\mathbf{A} - \mathbf{Q}),$$

prove that $\alpha\beta\gamma = -1$. Conversely if P, Q, and R are points of the respective lines, BC, CA, and AB, such that $\alpha\beta\gamma = -1$, then the points are collinear. This is Meneläus's Theorem.†

A3.3 RECTANGULAR COORDINATES

In this section, we make the first significant uses of the idea of distance in euclidean spaces of more than one dimension. Let $\mathbf{A}$ and $\mathbf{B}$ be nonnull position vectors and let θ be the angle between them; see Figure 1.‡ The distance between the points A and B is then given by

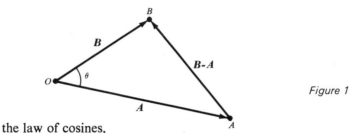

Figure 1

the law of cosines,

(1) $$|AB|^2 = |\mathbf{B} - \mathbf{A}|^2 = |\mathbf{A}|^2 + |\mathbf{B}|^2 - 2|\mathbf{A}|\,|\mathbf{B}|\cos\theta.$$

The expression $|\mathbf{A}|\,|\mathbf{B}|\cos\theta$, which appears in the law of cosines, is called the *dot product* (or inner product, or scalar product) of $\mathbf{A}$ and $\mathbf{B}$ and is written $\mathbf{A} \cdot \mathbf{B}$. Thus,

(2) $$\mathbf{A} \cdot \mathbf{B} = |\mathbf{A}|\,|\mathbf{B}|\cos\theta.$$

If either $\mathbf{A}$ or $\mathbf{B}$ is null, the angle θ is not defined, but then we define $\mathbf{A} \cdot \mathbf{B} = 0$. With this interpretation, the law of cosines (1) in the form

(3) $$|\mathbf{B} - \mathbf{A}|^2 = |\mathbf{A}|^2 + |\mathbf{B}|^2 - 2\mathbf{A} \cdot \mathbf{B}$$

is valid for any choice of $\mathbf{A}$ and $\mathbf{B}$.

The dot product has another frequently useful geometrical interpretation. Take $\mathbf{B} \neq \mathbf{O}$ and consider the perpendicular projection of the position

†Meneläus, Greek geometer and astronomer (c. 100). Author of the earliest known work on spherical trigonometry.

‡More precisely, θ is the measure of the geometrical angle, $\angle AOB$, but the distinction between the geometrical angle and its measure is usually clear from the context and this text, like many others, uses the word "angle" in both senses.

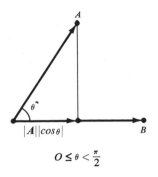

Figure 2

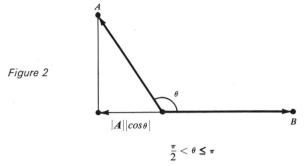

$$0 \leq \theta < \frac{\pi}{2}$$

$$\frac{\pi}{2} < \theta \leq \pi$$

vector **A** on the line OB ; see Figure 2. This projection is a vector of length

$$|\mathbf{A}|\ |\cos \theta|$$

which has the direction of **B** if $\cos \theta > 0$ $(0 \leq \theta < \frac{1}{2}\pi)$, and oppo-site to **B** if $\cos \theta < 0$ $(\frac{1}{2}\pi < \theta \leq \pi)$. Thus, the dot product **A · B** is $|\mathbf{B}|$ times the signed length of the projection of **A** on **B**. The projection of **A** on **B** is called the *component of A in the di-rection of* **B**, or the *component of A parallel to* **B** and is written $\mathbf{A_B}$. We have

(4)
$$\mathbf{A_B} = \frac{\mathbf{A \cdot B}}{|\mathbf{B}|^2} \mathbf{B}$$

(compare Exercises 5 and 6).

If $\mathbf{A_B} = \mathbf{O}$, either $\cos \theta = 0$, in which case $\theta = \frac{1}{2}\pi$ and **A** is perpendicular to **B**, or $\mathbf{A} = \mathbf{O}$. We adopt the convention that the null vector **O** is perpendicular to every vector† so that $\mathbf{A \cdot B} = 0$ if and only if **A** and **B** are perpendicular.

Lemma 1. If **C** is nonnull, the component of $\mathbf{A + B}$ in the direction of **C** is the sum of the components of **A** and **B** in the direction of **C** ; that is,

$$[\mathbf{A + B}]_\mathbf{C} = \mathbf{A_C + B_C}.$$

Proof. From elementary solid geometry the projections of equivalent di-rected segments are equivalent. Thus, if P^* denotes the projection of any point P on the line OC and $Q = \mathbf{V}(P)$, then $Q^* = \mathbf{V_C}(P^*)$; see Figure 3. (In the figure, the directed segment $\overrightarrow{PQ}$ is not necessarily in the plane OVC. The lines QQ^* and PP^* are not necessarily parallel,

†Recall that **O** is also said to be collinear with every vector. For **O** these state-ments are not in conflict since **O** has no definable direction.

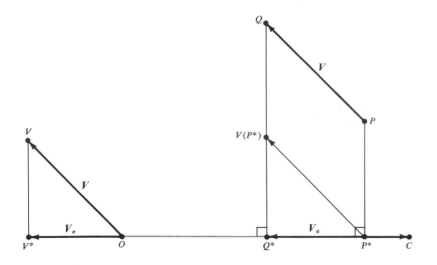

Figure 3

but lie in planes perpendicular to OVC seen end-on in perpendicular projection on that plane.) From

$$[\mathbf{A} + \mathbf{B}](O) = \mathbf{B}(A) = A + B \quad \text{and} \quad A = \mathbf{A}(O),$$

we then have

$$[\mathbf{A} + \mathbf{B}]_\mathbf{C}(O) = (A + B)^* = [\mathbf{B}(A)]^*$$
$$= \mathbf{B}_\mathbf{C}(A^*) = \mathbf{B}_\mathbf{C}\mathbf{A}_\mathbf{C}(O)$$
$$= [\mathbf{B}_\mathbf{C} + \mathbf{A}_\mathbf{C}](O) ;$$

hence,

$$[\mathbf{A} + \mathbf{B}]_\mathbf{C} = [\mathbf{A}_\mathbf{C} + \mathbf{B}_\mathbf{C}],$$

since the image of O is the same in both translations.   ⬜

The following basic properties of the dot products are easily derived.

(5) $$\mathbf{A} \cdot \mathbf{B} = \mathbf{B} \cdot \mathbf{A}.$$

(6) $$|\mathbf{A}|^2 = \mathbf{A} \cdot \mathbf{A}.$$

(7) $$|\mathbf{A} \cdot \mathbf{B}| \leq |\mathbf{A}|\,|\mathbf{B}|.$$

(8) $$(a\mathbf{A} + b\mathbf{B}) \cdot \mathbf{C} = a\mathbf{A} \cdot \mathbf{C} + b\mathbf{B} \cdot \mathbf{C}.$$

The derivations of (5) through (8) are left to Ex. 2.

From Properties (5) through (8) of dot products it follows that

$$|\mathbf{A} + \mathbf{B}|^2 = (\mathbf{A} + \mathbf{B}) \cdot (\mathbf{A} + \mathbf{B})$$
$$= |\mathbf{A}|^2 + 2\mathbf{A} \cdot \mathbf{B} + |\mathbf{B}|^2$$
$$\leq |\mathbf{A}|^2 + 2|\mathbf{A}|\,|\mathbf{B}| + |\mathbf{B}|^2$$
$$\leq (|\mathbf{A}| + |\mathbf{B}|)^2 ;$$

hence,

(9) $$|\mathbf{A} + \mathbf{B}| \leq |\mathbf{A}| + |\mathbf{B}| .$$

This inequality shows that length for vectors satisfies the same basic inequality as absolute value for numbers and justifies the use of the absolute value sign for length. Formula (9) is the vector expression of the geometrical theorem that the length of any side of a triangle is less than the sum of the lengths of the other two sides. Thus (9) is called the *triangle inequality*. From (9), in the same way as for the absolute values of numbers, A1.3(3), we obtain a lower estimate for the length of the sum of two vectors,

(10) $$\big||\mathbf{A}| - |\mathbf{B}|\big| \leq |\mathbf{A} + \mathbf{B}| .$$

Whenever a geometrical proposition involves the concept of perpendicularity the vector criterion $\mathbf{A} \cdot \mathbf{B} = 0$ for perpendicularity can likely be used to good advantage. Consider the following examples.

Example 1. The diagonals of a rhombus intersect at right angles.

Proof. Let the vertices of the rhombus be A, O, B, C, where

$$\mathbf{C} = \mathbf{A} + \mathbf{B} \quad \text{and} \quad |\mathbf{A}| = |\mathbf{B}| ;$$

see Figure 4. The diagonals $\overrightarrow{AB}$ and $\overrightarrow{OC}$ represent the vectors $\mathbf{B} - \mathbf{A}$ and $\mathbf{B} + \mathbf{A}$, respectively. The result is immediate from

$$(\mathbf{B} - \mathbf{A}) \cdot (\mathbf{B} + \mathbf{A}) = |\mathbf{B}|^2 - |\mathbf{A}|^2 = 0 . \qquad \square$$

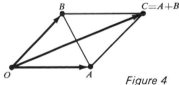

Figure 4

Example 2. The altitudes of a triangle are concurrent.

Proof. Let the vertices of the triangle be A, B, and C and let O be the intersection of the altitudes from A and B. Thus, $\mathbf{A}$ is perpendicular to $\mathbf{C} - \mathbf{B}$ and $\mathbf{B}$ is perpendicular to $\mathbf{A} - \mathbf{C}$; see Figure 5; hence,

$$\mathbf{A} \cdot (\mathbf{C} - \mathbf{B}) = \mathbf{A} \cdot \mathbf{C} - \mathbf{A} \cdot \mathbf{B} = 0 ,$$

$$\mathbf{B} \cdot (\mathbf{A} - \mathbf{C}) = \mathbf{B} \cdot \mathbf{A} - \mathbf{B} \cdot \mathbf{C} = 0 .$$

Adding, we obtain

$$\mathbf{A} \cdot \mathbf{C} - \mathbf{B} \cdot \mathbf{C} = \mathbf{C} \cdot (\mathbf{A} - \mathbf{B}) = 0 ,$$

thus the line OC is the altitude from C. $\square$

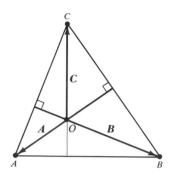 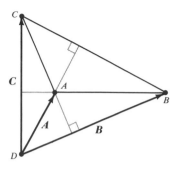

Figure 5

In 3.2 we showed that each vector in E^1 could be written as a multiple of any given nonnull vector. Similarly, each vector in E^2 can be written as a linear combination of any two given noncollinear vectors, and each vector in E^3 written as a linear combination of any three noncoplanar vectors. If each vector of a linear space can be written as a linear combination of the vectors in a certain set and no vector in the set can be written as a linear combination of the remaining vectors in the set, that set is called a *basis* for the linear vector space. In the chapter on linear algebra we shall prove that every basis of a given space has the same number of elements. Here, we make use of this assertion only for E^n, where $n = 1, 2, 3$ (see Ex. 3). The number of elements in a basis is called the *dimension* of the linear space. It is often desirable to fix a basis and to describe all other vectors as linear combinations of the vectors of that basis. In E^n, it is most convenient to choose a basis consisting of vectors of unit length in such a way that any two vectors of the basis are perpendicular.† We show how such a basis may be constructed for E^1, E^2, and E^3.

In E^1, given a nonnull vector $\mathbf{A}$, any vector $\mathbf{V} \in E^1$ can be written in the form $\mathbf{V} = \lambda\mathbf{A}$. Set

$$(11) \qquad\qquad \mathbf{i} = \frac{\mathbf{A}}{|\mathbf{A}|}.$$

The vector $\mathbf{i}$ has length 1 and $\mathbf{V}$ may then be written in the form

$$(12) \qquad\qquad \mathbf{V} = a\mathbf{i},$$

where $a = \lambda|\mathbf{A}|$. Thus $\{\mathbf{i}\}$ is a basis for E^1 (the criterion of perpendicularity is inapplicable here since a basis for E^1 contains only one element).

For E^2, if $\mathbf{A}$ and $\mathbf{B}$ are given noncollinear vectors, any vector $\mathbf{V} \in E^2$ can be written in the form

$$\mathbf{V} = \mu\mathbf{A} + \nu\mathbf{B}.$$

†Such a basis is called *orthonormal*.

First, we introduce the unit vector $\mathbf{i} = \dfrac{\mathbf{A}}{|\mathbf{A}|}$. Next, we subtract from $\mathbf{B}$ the component of $\mathbf{B}$ parallel to $\mathbf{i}$ to obtain from (4)

$$(13) \qquad \mathbf{J} = \mathbf{B} - \mathbf{B_i} = \mathbf{B} - (\mathbf{i} \cdot \mathbf{B})\mathbf{i} .$$

By taking the dot product with $\mathbf{i}$ in (13), we obtain

$$\mathbf{i} \cdot \mathbf{J} = \mathbf{i} \cdot \mathbf{B} - (\mathbf{i} \cdot \mathbf{B})(\mathbf{i} \cdot \mathbf{i}) = \mathbf{i} \cdot \mathbf{B} - \mathbf{i} \cdot \mathbf{B} = 0 ;$$

whence, the vector $\mathbf{J}$ is perpendicular to $\mathbf{i}$. Observe that $\mathbf{J} \neq \mathbf{O}$; otherwise, (12) would imply that $\mathbf{B}$ and $\mathbf{i}$, and hence $\mathbf{B}$ and $\mathbf{A}$, were collinear. Consequently, we may introduce the unit vector

$$(14) \qquad \mathbf{j} = \frac{\mathbf{J}}{|\mathbf{J}|} .$$

The vectors $\mathbf{i}$ and $\mathbf{j}$ are noncollinear and, therefore, constitute a basis of mutually perpendicular unit vectors for E^2. Any vector $\mathbf{X}$ in E^2 can, therefore, be written in the form

$$(15) \qquad \mathbf{X} = x\mathbf{i} + y\mathbf{j} .$$

Similarly, in E^3, if $\mathbf{A}$, $\mathbf{B}$, and $\mathbf{C}$ are noncoplanar, any vector $\mathbf{V} \in E^3$ can be written in the form

$$\mathbf{V} = \mu\mathbf{A} + \nu\mathbf{B} + \lambda\mathbf{C} .$$

We define $\mathbf{i}$ and $\mathbf{j}$ as in (11), (13), and (14) and set

$$(16) \qquad \mathbf{K} = \mathbf{C} - (\mathbf{i} \cdot \mathbf{C})\mathbf{i} - (\mathbf{j} \cdot \mathbf{C})\mathbf{j} .$$

Now, we observe that $\mathbf{K}$ is nonnull; otherwise $\mathbf{C}$ would be coplanar with $\mathbf{i}$ and $\mathbf{j}$, hence also with $\mathbf{A}$ and $\mathbf{B}$. Next, we set

$$(17) \qquad \mathbf{k} = \frac{\mathbf{K}}{|\mathbf{K}|}$$

and, on taking dot products with $\mathbf{i}$ and $\mathbf{j}$ in (16), verify that $\mathbf{k}$ is perpendicular to both $\mathbf{i}$ and $\mathbf{j}$. The three mutually perpendicular vectors $\mathbf{i}, \mathbf{j}, \mathbf{k}$ must be noncoplanar; otherwise there would exist a nontrivial linear combination of the three which satisfies

$$\alpha\mathbf{i} + \beta\mathbf{j} + \gamma\mathbf{k} = \mathbf{O} .$$

We take the dot product with $\mathbf{i}$ in this equation to obtain

$$\alpha\mathbf{i} \cdot \mathbf{i} + \beta\mathbf{i} \cdot \mathbf{j} + \gamma\mathbf{i} \cdot \mathbf{k} = \mathbf{i} \cdot \mathbf{O} ;$$

whence,

$$\alpha(\mathbf{i} \cdot \mathbf{i}) = \alpha = 0 .$$

Similarly, on taking the dot products with $\mathbf{j}$ and $\mathbf{k}$, we also find $\beta = 0$ and $\gamma = 0$; so no such nontrivial combination can exist. Thus, $\mathbf{i}, \mathbf{j}$, and $\mathbf{k}$ are noncoplanar, and any vector $\mathbf{X} \in E^3$ can be written in the form

(18) $$\mathbf{X} = x\mathbf{i} + y\mathbf{j} + z\mathbf{k} .$$

In the light of (12), (15), and (18), we shall treat E^2 as the subset of E^3 with $z = 0$ and E^1 as the subset of E^2 with $y = 0$. With this understanding, much that we say about E^3 can be carried over directly to E^1 and E^2 and, unless we specifically restrict the discussion to E^1 or E^2, it is to be assumed in the following that we are concerned with E^3.

On taking dot products with $\mathbf{i}, \mathbf{j}$, and $\mathbf{k}$ in (18), we find that the coefficients are

(19) $$x = \mathbf{i} \cdot \mathbf{X} , \quad y = \mathbf{j} \cdot \mathbf{X} , \quad z = \mathbf{k} \cdot \mathbf{X} ,$$

namely, the signed lengths of the projections of $\mathbf{X}$ on $\mathbf{i}, \mathbf{j}$, and $\mathbf{k}$, respectively; see Figure 6. Thus, (18) expresses $\mathbf{X}$ as the sum of its

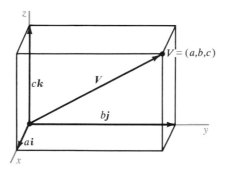

Figure 6

components in the directions of $\mathbf{i}, \mathbf{j}$, and $\mathbf{k}$,

(20) $$\mathbf{X} = (\mathbf{i} \cdot \mathbf{X})\mathbf{i} + (\mathbf{j} \cdot \mathbf{X})\mathbf{j} + (\mathbf{k} \cdot \mathbf{X})\mathbf{k} .$$

No such simple description of the representation of $\mathbf{X}$ exists if the basis vectors are not mutually perpendicular (see Ex. 4).

Given a basis $\{\mathbf{i}, \mathbf{j}, \mathbf{k}\}$ of mutually perpendicular unit vectors, we have established a one-to-one correspondence between position vectors $\mathbf{V}$ or points V and ordered triples of real numbers (a, b, c). This is true since there exists at least one representation of $\mathbf{V}$ in the form (18) and it must be unique, the coefficients in that representation being given by (19).

Thus, for a specific origin and fixed $\mathbf{i}, \mathbf{j}$, and $\mathbf{k}$, we may identify the point V by the ordered triple of real numbers (a, b, c) : we write $V = (a, b, c)$, and call a, b, and c the *coordinates* of V in the $\mathbf{ijk}$-system. Similarly, we may identify the vector $\mathbf{V}$ by the same ordered triple and write $\mathbf{V} = (a, b, c)$, but when we refer to the vector, we call a, b, and c the *components* of $\mathbf{V}$. (Note the distinction between the components of $\mathbf{V}$, the real numbers a, b, c, and the components of $\mathbf{V}$ in the directions $\mathbf{i}, \mathbf{j}, \mathbf{k}$, the vectors $a\mathbf{i}, b\mathbf{j}, c\mathbf{k}$, respectively.) The lines $\mathbf{X} = x\mathbf{i}$, $\mathbf{Y} = y\mathbf{j}$, and $\mathbf{Z} = z\mathbf{k}$ are called the x-, y-, and z- axes, respectively. Each coordinate of a point in space is then defined by the signed distance from the origin of its projection on the corresponding axis. Thus, we have obtained a vector description of the familiar concept of a rectangular coordinate system.

It is customary to depict E^1 on the page as a horizontal line; see Figure 7. There are two possible directions for $\mathbf{i}$ which can result from our method of construction (11): $\mathbf{i}$ may be directed to the right or to the left. Thus, there are two possible orientations of the coordinate line. It is conventional to orient E^1 with $\mathbf{i}$ directed to the right, as in Figure 7.

Figure 7

The plane E^2 is represented on the page with the x-axis horizontal and $\mathbf{i}$ directed to the right. Then, for $\mathbf{j}$ there are two possible directions, upward or downward. By convention we depict E^2 with $\mathbf{j}$ directed upward, as in Figure 8. There are two essentially distinct orientations of E^2, corresponding to $\mathbf{j}$ directed upward or downward for $\mathbf{i}$ directed to the right. By a rotation and translation within E^2 it is possible to bring any rectangular coordinate system into coincidence with one or the other of these choices, but not both. (See p. 386f.)

Three-dimensional space E^3 is represented conventionally with the z-axis vertical and with the orientation of the plane $z = 0$ seen from above as depicted in Figure 8. It is conventional to choose $\mathbf{k}$ directed upward, as in Figure 9. Again, there are two essentially distinct orientations corresponding to the two possibilities for choosing the direction of $\mathbf{k}$, upward or downward in Figure 9. Any rectangular coordinate system can be brought by a rotation and translation into coincidence with one of these two standard systems. We shall show (Chapter 11) that it is not possible by rotations and translations to bring one of these standard systems into coincidence with the other.

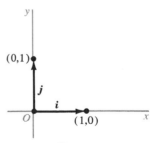

Figure 8

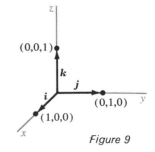

Figure 9

Once a coordinate system has been introduced, any vector concept can be expressed in terms of coordinates. For example, if $\mathbf{A} = (a_1, a_2, a_3)$ and $\mathbf{B} = (b_1, b_2, b_3)$, then

$$(21) \qquad \lambda \mathbf{A} = (\lambda a_1, \lambda a_2, \lambda a_3),$$

$$(22) \qquad \mathbf{A} + \mathbf{B} = (a_1 + b_1, a_2 + b_2, a_3 + b_3),$$

$$(23) \qquad \mathbf{A} \cdot \mathbf{B} = a_1 b_1 + a_2 b_2 + a_3 b_3,$$

and

$$(24) \qquad |\mathbf{A}| = \sqrt{\mathbf{A} \cdot \mathbf{A}} = \sqrt{a_1^2 + a_2^2 + a_3^2}.$$

These results are easily derived from the postulates for a linear space (p. 290), (5), (6), and (8); the derivations are left to Ex. 13. As an important consequence of (21) through (24), we observe that the distance between the points A and B is given by

$$(25) \quad |AB| = |\mathbf{A} - \mathbf{B}| = \sqrt{(a_1 - b_1)^2 + (a_2 - b_2)^2 + (a_3 - b_3)^2}.$$

This is the basic formula of analytic geometry. From it, although the demonstration would be somewhat lengthy, all of euclidean geometry can be derived.

We now have three ways of approaching a geometrical problem: we may use classical synthetic methods, vector methods, or we may transform the problem into a wholly numerical question by using coordinates. Each of these approaches may be valuable in an appropriate context and it is worthwhile to learn all three in order to take advantage of their different uses. The use of position vectors introduces an arbitrary element, a preferred origin. Coordinate geometry introduces further arbitrary elements, a preferred basis of mutually orthogonal unit vectors. Synthetic geometry at one extreme has no arbitrary elements, but is not easily adapted to quantitative investigation. Coordinate geometry, at the other extreme, is an ideal tool for quantitative description and study of geometrical objects, but the analysis rests on the choice of coordinates even when the results do not. Vector geometry combines some of the advantages of both synthetic and analytic geometry. Vector methods still contain an arbitrary element, and an analysis may be affected by the choice of an origin (see, for example, how the proof in Example 2 is affected if the origin is specified arbitrarily), but with vectors we can describe space independently of coordinates and still have the power of systematic algebraic operations.

Vector methods are useful for the investigation of properties of geometrical figures that do not depend on the choice of coordinates as we have seen in the examples of 3.1 and 3.2 and shall see again. Such properties are called *invariant* because they are not affected by a change of coordinate system. Thus, perpendicularity of two lines is invariant. There are other properties which are directly related to the coordinate system. For example, in 1.1 we attacked the problem of maximizing a real function by converting it into the geometrical problem of locating the highest point on its graph (1.1 Figure 1), that is, by maximizing the vertical coordinate. (The original problem bore no relation to geometry; it was purely numerical, and there is even no relation between the units of length on the two axes.) If the axes were rotated, or equivalently, if the curve were rotated oppositely with respect to the axes, the "highest" point on the curve would change; see Figure 10, and would no longer be meaningful for the original problem.

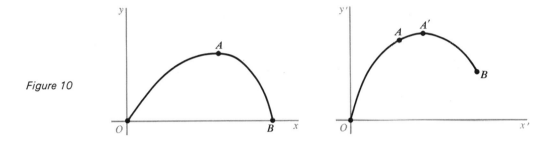

Figure 10

Thus, properties that are not invariant are just as important and fundamental as invariant properties, but they are used in different contexts.

We now have at our disposal three methods of attack on geometrical problems — synthetic, vectorial, and analytic. For the solution of any particular geometrical problem, we may try any method which seems most direct. Furthermore, there is no reason to restrict oneself purely to a single method in the solution of any problem, except perhaps as a textbook exercise. Frequently in the following sections, mixed methods will be used, and the reader should allow himself the same freedom.

A3.3 Exercises

1. Derive the law of cosines (1) from the Pythagorean Theorem. (Hint: construct a right triangle for which the hypotenuse is $[AB]$ and one leg lies on the line OA).

2. Derive properties (5) to (8) of dot products.

3. Show that every basis in E^n has n elements for $n = 1, 2, 3$.

4. Let $\{A, B\}$ be a basis for E^2. Without making any special assumptions about A and B express an arbitrary vector V as a linear combination of the basis vectors with coefficients given in terms of dot products.

5. Show that the vector $A^B = A - A_B$, where A_B is the component of A in the direction of B as defined by (4), is perpendicular to B. (The vector A^B is called the *component of* A *perpendicular to* B.)

6. Show, if θ is the angle between A and B that $|A^B| = |A| \sin \theta$.

7. Prove that any angle inscribed in a semicircle is a right angle.

8. Show that the perpendicular bisector of any chord of a circle passes through the center.

9. Show that all points of the perpendicular bisector of the segment $[PQ]$ are equidistant from P and Q.

10. Show that the sum of the squares of the sides of a parallelogram is equal to the sum of the squares of the diagonals.

11. Show for an arbitrary quadrilateral that the sum of the squares of the sides exceeds the sum of the squares of the diagonals by four times the square of the distance between the midpoints of the diagonals.

12. Let A and B be noncollinear vectors. Find the value of λ for which $|A - \lambda B|$ has its least value, and interpret the result geometrically.

13. Derive the coordinate representations in (21) through (24) of λA, $A + B$, $A \cdot B$, and $|A|$ from (5), (6), (8), and the postulates for a linear vector space given in A3.1.

14. a. Give the coordinates of the midpoint of the segment joining the points $(-1, 2, -3)$ and $(3, -6, -1)$.
    b. Derive the general formula for the coordinates of the midpoint of the segment joining two points $A = (a_1, a_2, a_3)$ and $B = (b_1, b_2, b_3)$.

15. Show that the points $(-3, 2, 4)$, $(-5, 1, 5)$, $(-2, 0, 1)$, and $(-4, -1, 2)$ are the vertices of a parallelogram.

16. Show that the triangle $[ABC]$ where $A = (2, 1, 2)$, $B = (-1, 2, 1)$, and $C = (1, 5, -2)$ is a right triangle.

17. What is the angle between the vectors $A = (5, 3, 4)$ and $i = (1, 0, 0)$?

18. Obtain a necessary and sufficient condition in terms of the components of the vector $A = (a, b, c)$ that A make an angle of $\frac{1}{4}\pi$ with the z-axis.

19. Prove that the null vector is the only vector perpendicular to every vector.

20. Construct a basis of mutually perpendicular unit vectors of E^3 for which one element of the basis lies in the direction of $U = (1, 1, 1)$.

21. Derive the formula for the coordinates of the point P which divides the segment joining the points $A = (a_1, a_2, a_3)$ and $B = (b_1, b_2, b_3)$ in the ratio $|AP|/|PB| = p/q$.

22. Find the equation of the line through the point $P = (1, 2, 1)$ parallel to the position vector $(0, 3, 4)$; then give the coordinates of a point on the line at distance 1 from P.

23. Is $D = (2, 1, 2)$ in the plane $\mathcal{P}$ containing $A = (1, 1, 3)$,

$$B = (1, 1, 2), \quad C = (1, 3, 3) ?$$

24. As a basis for E^2, take $\{u, v\}$ where u and v are unit vectors and the angle between the two vectors is θ. The generalized coordinates (a_1, a_2) of A and (b_1, b_2) of B in the $\{u, v\}$ system are defined by

$$A = a_1u + a_2v \quad \text{and} \quad B = b_1u + b_2v .$$

Obtain the distance between A and B in terms of their generalized coordinates.

25. Express (7) in terms of the components of A and B and identify the resultant inequality.

26. a. Show from formula (25) for the distance between two points, that distance is *least* distance; that is,

   (i) $$|AB| \leq |AC| + |CB| ,$$

   the direct distance from A to B is always less than or equal to the distance by way of a third point C.
   b. Show that equality holds in (i) if and only if C lies on the line AB between A and B.

27. Prove that if all the vertex angles of $[ABC]$ are acute, the intersection of the altitudes lies in the interior of the triangle. (See A3.2 Exercise 15.)

A3.4 LINES AND PLANES

For future reference, we give in this section the expressions, in terms of coordinates, of some useful properties of straight lines and planes. There are enough differences between the treatment of lines in the plane and the treatment of lines in space for us to consider the two separately.

A3.4a Lines in the plane

We shall use X to represent a point variable in E^2, and letters A, B, C, ... to represent specified points. In the coordinate representation of a point $X = (x, y)$, the first coordinate x is termed the *abscissa* of X, the second, y, the *ordinate*.

In the plane, a line may be described as in A3.2 (2) by giving one of its points $A = (a, b)$ and a nonnull vector $U = (u, v)$ parallel to the line:

(1) $$X = A + \lambda U , \qquad \lambda \text{ real.}$$

For the coordinates of X, we then have

(2)
$$\begin{cases} x = a + \lambda u\,, \\ y = b + \lambda v\,. \end{cases}$$

The equations (2) give x and y as functions of the independent variable λ. The variable λ is not something immediately associated with the line; λ depends on such extraneous matters as the choice of the point A on the line, and the length and orientation of $\mathbf{U}$. Such a variable of convenience is called a *parameter* to indicate its subordinate relation in a given discussion to variables such as x and y which are the center of attention.† The equations (2) are then called *parametric equations* of the line.

The purpose of the vector $\mathbf{U}$ in (1) is simply to fix the direction of the line. Any nonnull vector collinear with $\mathbf{U}$ would serve as well. Some of the arbitrariness in the parametric equations (2) can be eliminated if $\mathbf{U}$ is replaced by the *direction of* $\mathbf{U}$; that is, by the unit vector

(3a)
$$\mathbf{t} = \frac{\mathbf{U}}{|\mathbf{U}|}\,.$$

The direction of $\mathbf{U}$ may be specified by its components as in A3.3 (20); thus,

(3b)
$$\mathbf{t} = (\mathbf{i} \cdot \mathbf{t})\,\mathbf{i} + (\mathbf{j} \cdot \mathbf{t})\,\mathbf{j} = \cos \alpha\, \mathbf{i} + \cos \beta\, \mathbf{j}\,,$$

where α is the angle between $\mathbf{i}$ and $\mathbf{t}$, β between $\mathbf{j}$ and $\mathbf{t}$; see Figure 1. The components

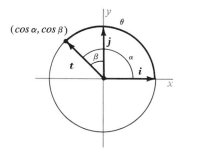 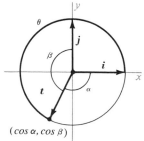

Figure 1

$$\cos \alpha = \mathbf{i} \cdot \mathbf{t} \quad \text{and} \quad \cos \beta = \mathbf{j} \cdot \mathbf{t}$$

of $\mathbf{t}$ are called the *direction cosines* of $\mathbf{U}$. In A3.3 the angle between two vectors was tacitly assumed not to exceed a straight angle so that

$$0 \le \alpha \le \pi \quad \text{and} \quad 0 \le \beta \le \pi\,.$$

---

†The concept of parameter is not very precise. It is necessary in any given context to specify which are the primary variables and which the parameters.

In E^2 it is convenient to determine the direction of any vector $\mathbf{U}$ by the angle between its direction $\mathbf{t}$ and the vector $\mathbf{i}$ given as the length of arc θ of the unit circle measured counterclockwise from $(1, 0)$ to the terminal point of $\mathbf{t}$. The arclength θ, is called the *direction angle* of the vector, and may take on any value in the interval $0 \leq \theta < 2\pi$. From the geometrical definition of the circular functions, $\mathbf{t} = (\cos \theta, \sin \theta)$. Since the components of a vector are uniquely determined, we have at once, $\cos \alpha = \cos \theta$, $\cos \beta = \sin \theta$. (See Ex. 1.) In E^2 it is convenient to define the direction of a vector in terms of its direction angle instead of the direction cosines. In E^3 the idea of direction angle cannot be utilized in such a simple way and it is preferable, in E^3, to express direction in terms of direction cosines.

The plane E^2 is divided into four *quadrants* defined in terms of direction angle. A point P is said to be in the k-th quadrant, for $k = 1, 2, 3, 4$, if the direction angle θ of its position vector satisfies $(k - 1)\dfrac{\pi}{2} < \theta < k\dfrac{\pi}{2}$. In Figures 1a and 1b, the terminal point of $\mathbf{t}$ lies in the second and third quadrants, respectively.

If $\mathbf{U}$ is replaced by its direction $\mathbf{t}$ in (1), the vector equation takes the form $\mathbf{X} = \mathbf{A} + \sigma\mathbf{t}$ and the parametric equations of the line become

$$(4) \qquad \begin{cases} x = a + \sigma \cos \theta, \\ y = b + \sigma \sin \theta. \end{cases}$$

In (4) the parameter σ is the signed distance from A to X, the sign being positive if X lies in the direction of $\mathbf{t}$ from A and negative if X lies on the opposite side of A.

The parameter λ may be eliminated from (2) to yield the nonparametric form of the equation of the line

$$(5) \qquad uy - vx = ub - va.$$

Conversely, it is easily shown that any linear equation

$$(6) \qquad px + qy = k,$$

where p and q are not both zero, is the nonparametric equation of a straight line. For, if $p \neq 0$, say, it can be shown that the set of solutions (x, y) of (6) is the same as the set of solutions $\mathbf{X} = (x, y)$ of (1) with

$$\mathbf{A} = \left(\frac{k}{p}, 0\right), \qquad \mathbf{U} = (q, -p),$$

and

$$\lambda = -\frac{y}{p}.$$

(See Ex. 2.)

If **U** is replaced by its direction $\mathbf{t} = (\cos\theta, \sin\theta)$, then the non-parametric equation (5) may be written

(7) $-x\sin\theta + y\cos\theta + d = 0$

where

$$d = a\sin\theta - b\cos\theta.$$

Let

$$\mathbf{n} = \left(\cos\left(\theta + \frac{\pi}{2}\right), \sin\left(\theta + \frac{\pi}{2}\right)\right) = (-\sin\theta, \cos\theta)$$

be the unit vector perpendicular to $\mathbf{t}$, so directed that the pair $(\mathbf{t}, \mathbf{n})$ has the same orientation as the pair $(\mathbf{i}, \mathbf{j})$; see Figure 2a, b. Then (7) can

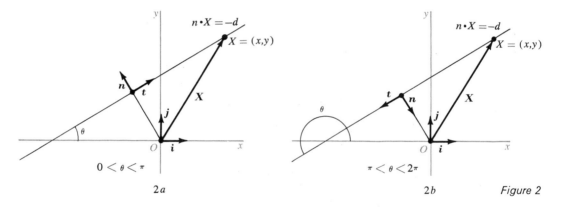

2a   2b   Figure 2

be written in the form

(8) $\mathbf{n} \cdot \mathbf{X} = -d.$

The vector $\mathbf{n}$ is called the *normal* to the line (with respect to the orientation $\mathbf{t}$) and (7) is called the *normal form* of the equation of the line. Any line given in the form (6) can be put into the normal form (7) by choosing θ so that

$$\sin\theta = \frac{-p}{\sqrt{p^2 + q^2}}, \quad \cos\theta = \frac{q}{\sqrt{p^2 + q^2}},$$

and, in that event,

$$d = -\frac{k}{\sqrt{p^2 + q^2}}.$$

Since **n** is a unit vector, $|\mathbf{n} \cdot \mathbf{X}|$ is the length of the projection of **X** on any perpendicular to the line, and, in particular, on the perpendicular through 0. Consequently, $|d| = |\mathbf{n} \cdot \mathbf{X}|$ is the distance from 0 to the line, the distance from any point to the line being defined as the distance along the perpendicular.

The sign of d in (7) depends upon which of the two possible orientations of the line is chosen; see Figures 2a and 2b. It is customary to orient the line by choosing the direction **t** so that the direction angle θ satisfies $0 \le \theta < \pi$, as in Figure 2a. If the line is not horizontal, this implies that the vertical component of **t** is positive, $\sin \theta > 0$. Under this convention, the normal **n** has a negative x-component. If the origin lies on the line, then $d = 0$. If the origin lies on the side of the line toward which **n** points, then $d > 0$, and if the origin lies on the opposite side of the line, then $d < 0$. In Figure 2a, for example, d would be negative, and in Figure 2b, positive.

Example 1. The normal form of the equation of the line given by

$$3x + 4y = 12$$

is

$$-\tfrac{3}{5}x - \tfrac{4}{5}y + \tfrac{12}{5} = 0 .$$

The chosen direction of the line is $\mathbf{t} = (-\tfrac{4}{5}, \tfrac{3}{5})$, and the direction angle θ satisfies $\cos \theta = -\tfrac{4}{5}$, $\sin \theta = \tfrac{3}{5}$. Thus, $\dfrac{\pi}{2} < \theta < \pi$. The distance of the origin from the line is $12/5$ and d is positive, $d = 12/5$; see Figure 3.

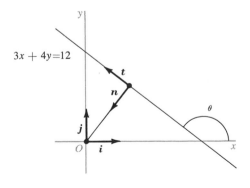

$3x + 4y = 12$

Figure 3

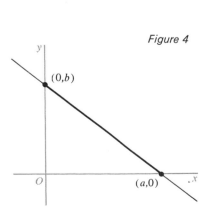

Figure 4

$(0,b)$

$(a,0)$

With each line in the plane, we have associated a unique direction angle θ subject to the restriction $0 \le \theta < \pi$. This angle is called the *inclination* of the line. If $\theta \ne \dfrac{\pi}{2}$, that is, $\cos\theta \ne 0$, we may solve for y in (7) to obtain the equation of the line in the form

$$(9) \qquad\qquad y = mx + b$$

where $m = \tan\theta$, $b = -\dfrac{d}{\cos\theta}$. Except for the vertical lines, then, a straight line is the graph of a linear function $x \to mx + b$. The coefficient m is called the *slope* of the line. The ordinate of the point $(0, b)$ where the line intersects the y-axis is called the *y-intercept* of the line (Figure 4). Similarly, if $m \ne 0$, the abscissa of the point $(a, 0)$ where the line meets the x-axis is called the *x-intercept*. Equation (9) is the *slope-intercept* form of the equation of the line; it is usually the most convenient form for the purposes of this text.

Example 2. We give a criterion for the perpendicularity of two lines in terms of their slopes.

Consider the lines $y = m_1 x + b_1$ and $y = m_2 x + b_2$. Putting these equations in the form of (6), we obtain

$$-m_1 x + y = b_1 \qquad\qquad (i = 1, 2).$$

For the respective cases we then obtain, as for (6), vectors parallel to the lines, namely

$$\mathbf{U}_1 = (1, m_1) \quad \text{and} \quad \mathbf{U}_2 = (1, m_2).$$

The condition $\mathbf{U}_1 \cdot \mathbf{U}_2 = 0$ for perpendicularity, yields

$$(10) \qquad\qquad m_1 m_2 = -1.$$

Example 3. We seek the intersection, if any, of two lines. The trivial case in which at least one of the lines is vertical is left as an exercise. (See Ex. 3.) Assuming that neither line is vertical, we write their equations in the slope-intercept form,

$$y = m_1 x + b_1 \quad \text{and} \quad y = m_2 x + b_2.$$

If (x, y) is a point common to both lines, on subtracting, we obtain

$$(11) \qquad\qquad (m_2 - m_1)x + b_2 - b_1 = 0;$$

whence,

$$(12) \qquad\qquad x = -\frac{b_2 - b_1}{m_2 - m_1}, \qquad y = \frac{m_2 b_1 - m_1 b_2}{m_2 - m_1}.$$

Thus, if $m_1 \neq m_2$ there is exactly one point of intersection with co-ordinates given by (12). If $m_1 = m_2$, then $b_1 \neq b_2$ (recall that a reference to "two" lines implies that the lines are distinct; see p. 246 footnote). If there were such a point then, from (12), we would have the contradictory result $b_1 = b_2$. Now, the two lines are parallel in the sense of having the same direction if and only if $m_1 = m_2$. Thus, we have come to the familiar result that distinct lines intersect in no more than one point, and that if they do not intersect they are parallel. In E^3 there is a third possibility, as we shall see.

Example 4. We determine the slope of a line in terms of any two of its points.

Let $X_1 = (x_1, y_1)$ and $X_2 = (x_2, y_2)$ be any two points of a nonvertical line $(x_1 \neq x_2)$. Since a line is determined by any two of its points, it is reasonable to expect that any property of the line can be ex-pressed in terms of the coordinates of those points. Thus, we seek an expres-sion for the slope m in terms of the coordinates of X_1 and X_2. First, we observe that $X_2 - X_1$ is a vector parallel to the line. Con-sequently, for some real λ, $X_2 - X_1 = \lambda t$, where $t = (\cos \theta, \sin \theta)$ is the direction of the line. Thus,

$$X_2 - X_1 = (\lambda \cos \theta, \lambda \sin \theta).$$

The slope $m = \tan \theta$ is, therefore, the ratio of the y-component to the x-component of $X_2 - X_1$; namely,

(13) $$m = \frac{y_2 - y_1}{x_2 - x_1}.$$

A3.4a Exercises

In the exercises of this section, assume throughout that the space is the plane E^2.

1. In E^2, let α and β be the angles made by a vector A with i and j, respectively. Express α and β in terms of the direction angle θ of A.

2. Prove the assertion of the text that the set of solutions (x, y) of (6) with $p \neq 0$ is the same as the set of solutions $X = (x, y)$ of (1) with

$$A = (k/p, 0), \quad U = (u, v), \quad \text{and} \quad \lambda = -y/p.$$

3. Determine the intersection of two lines if at least one of the lines is vertical.

4. Give the equations in any form you desire and sketch the graphs (on the same sheet of paper) of the straight lines parallel to the vector $U = (2, 3)$ which pass through the points

a. $(1, 1)$,   b. $(-3, 2)$,

c. $(4, -1)$,   d. $(-3, -5)$.

Is there any advantage, for the purposes of this problem, of any one form over another?

5. Given the inclination θ and the y-intercept b, obtain the equation of the line for each of the following. In each case, sketch the graph.

a. $\theta = \frac{1}{4}\pi$, $b = 1$.   b. $\theta = \frac{3}{4}\pi$, $b = 1$.

c. $\theta = 0$, $b = 1$.   d. $\theta = \frac{1}{3}\pi$, $b = -2$.

e. $\theta = \frac{5}{6}\pi$, $b = \frac{3}{2}$.   f. $\theta = \frac{2}{3}\pi$, $b = -3$.

6. Obtain nonparametric equations of the lines at unit distance from the origin and parallel to the vector $\mathbf{U} = (3, -4)$.

7. Each of the following sets of data uniquely determine a line. Derive nonparametric equations for the line in terms of the given data.

a. A point $X_0 = (x_0, y_0)$ on the line, and the slope m.
b. Two points $X_1 = (x_1, y_1)$ and $X_2 = (x_2, y_2)$ on the line.
c. The x-intercept a, and the y-intercept b, where $ab \neq 0$.

8. In each of the following cases, obtain the slope-intercept form of the equation of the line which passes through the given point A and has the slope m.

a. $A = (1, -2)$, $m = \frac{1}{2}$.   b. $A = (\pi, \sqrt{2})$, $m = 0$.

c. $A = (1, 1)$, $m = 1$.   d. $A = (-1, -1)$, $m = -1$.

e. $A = (0, 0)$, $m = 3$.

9. In each case, obtain a nonparametric equation for the line passing through the two given points.

a. $(0, 0)$, $(1, -1)$.   b. $(1, 2)$, $(3, 4)$.

c. $(-1, 2)$, $(5, -6)$.   d. (α, β), $(\alpha - \beta, \alpha + \beta)$.

e. $(\alpha \cos \theta, \alpha \sin \theta)$, $(\alpha \cos \phi, \alpha \sin \phi)$.

10. Find the equations of the two diagonals of the rectangle with sides given by the equations $x = x_1$, $x = x_2$, $y = y_1$, $y = y_2$.

11. Let $P = (p, q)$ be any point and let ℓ be any line. Find the foot of the perpendicular from P to ℓ and determine the length of the perpendicular.

12. Let θ be the inclination of line ℓ_2 with respect to line ℓ_1; that is, θ is the angle measured counterclockwise through which it is necessary to rotate ℓ_1 to bring ℓ_1 into parallelism with ℓ_2 $(0 \leq \theta < \pi)$. Prove that

$$\tan \theta = \frac{m_2 - m_1}{1 + m_1 m_2},$$

where m_k is the slope of ℓ_k $(k = 1, 2)$.

13. Let ℓ_1 and ℓ_2 be nonparallel lines with equations $p_1 x + q_1 y = k_1$, and $p_2 x + q_2 y = k_2$. Prove that the equation of any line passing through the intersection of ℓ_1 and ℓ_2 can be written in the form

(i) $\alpha(p_1 x + q_1 y - k_1) + \beta(p_2 x + q_2 y - k_2) = 0$,

where α and β are not both zero. Conversely, for each choice of α

and β, (i) is the equation of a straight line through the intersection of ℓ_1 and ℓ_2.

14. Let ℓ_1 and ℓ_2 be given as in Exercise 13. Show that the bisectors of the angles between ℓ_1 and ℓ_2 are given by (i) with

$$\alpha = 1/\sqrt{p_1^2 + q_1^2}, \qquad \beta = \pm 1/\sqrt{p_2^2 + q_2^2}.$$

15. Show that the lines ℓ_1 and ℓ_2 given by the nonparametric equations $A_1x + B_1y = C_1$ and $A_2x + B_2y = C_2$ are parallel if and only if $A_1B_2 = A_2B_1$. Thus, $A_1B_2 - A_2B_1 \neq 0$ is a sufficient condition that the lines intersect.

16. Let the direction $\mathbf{t}$ of a nonhorizontal line be chosen according to the convention that the y-component of $\mathbf{t}$ is positive. Let d be the constant term in the normal form (7) of the line and let a be the x-intercept. Prove that $\operatorname{sgn} d = \operatorname{sgn} a$.

A3.4b Lines and planes in space

Let us now extend the methods of A3.4a for treating lines in the plane to lines and planes in space. Some of the formal representations of lines in the plane will be seen to carry over to lines in space, others to planes. Some concepts, like inclination and slope, are primarily appropriate to E^2 and will not be directly generalized.

Again, we begin with the equation of a line ℓ in terms of one of its points $A = (a, b, c)$ and a nonnull vector $\mathbf{U} = (u, v, w)$ parallel to the line:

(1) $\mathbf{X} = \mathbf{A} + \lambda\mathbf{U}$ (λ real).

Equation (1) yields the parametric equations of the line ℓ in terms of the coordinates x, y, z of $\mathbf{X}$; namely,

(2)
$$\begin{cases} x = a + \lambda u, \\ y = b + \lambda v, \\ z = c + \lambda w. \end{cases}$$

Again, we may replace $\mathbf{U}$ in (2) by its direction $\mathbf{t}$, where

(3a) $\mathbf{t} = \dfrac{\mathbf{U}}{|\mathbf{U}|} = (\cos \theta, \cos \phi, \cos \psi).$

Here, θ, ϕ, ψ are the angles between $\mathbf{U}$ and the respective unit coordinate vectors $\mathbf{i}, \mathbf{j}, \mathbf{k}$. As before, the components of $\mathbf{t}$ are called the direction cosines of $\mathbf{U}$. The direction cosines are given explicitly by (3b).

(3b) $\cos\theta = \dfrac{u}{\sqrt{u^2+v^2+w^2}}$, $\cos\varphi = \dfrac{v}{\sqrt{u^2+v^2+w^2}}$,

$$\cos\psi = \dfrac{w}{\sqrt{u^2+v^2+w^2}}.$$

The direction cosines satisfy the equation

(3c) $\cos^2\theta + \cos^2\varphi + \cos^2\psi = 1$.

(This is a direct generalization of the trigonometric identity $\cos^2\theta + \sin^2\theta = 1$.) In terms of the direction cosines, the parametric equations (2) take the form

(4)
$$\begin{cases} x = a + s\cos\theta, \\ y = b + s\cos\phi, \\ z = c + s\cos\psi, \end{cases}$$

where the parameter s is now the signed distance between X and A.

Since U is nonnull, at least one of its components is not zero; say $u \neq 0$. In that case, we may replace λ in (2) by $\dfrac{x-a}{u}$ to obtain non-parametric equations for the line ℓ,

(5)
$$\begin{cases} y = \dfrac{v}{u}(x-a) + b = \mu_1 x + \beta_1, \\ z = \dfrac{w}{u}(x-a) + c = \mu_2 x + \beta. \end{cases}$$

Thus, a line in space may be defined by two linear equations.

The equations (5) may be given a geometrical interpretation. The equation $y = \mu_1 x + \beta_1$ imposes no restrictions on z. In E^3 it defines the set of points

$$\mathcal{P}_1 = \{(x, y, z): \ x, z \in \mathcal{R}, \ y = \mu_1 x + \beta_1\}.$$

This is the vertical plane that meets the xy-plane in the line

$$\ell_1 = \{(x, y, z): \ x \in \mathcal{R}, \ y = \mu_1 x + \beta_1, \ z = 0\}.$$

Similarly, the equation $z = \mu_2 x + \beta_2$ defines the plane $\mathcal{P}_2$ perpendicular to the xz-plane that meets the xz-plane in the line

$$\ell_2 = \{(x, y, z): \ x \in \mathcal{R}, \ z = \mu_2 x + \beta_2, \ y = 0\}.$$

The intersection of the planes $\mathcal{P}_1$ and $\mathcal{P}_2$ is the line ℓ, as depicted in Figure 1.

If none of the components of U vanish, (5) may be rewritten in the symmetric form

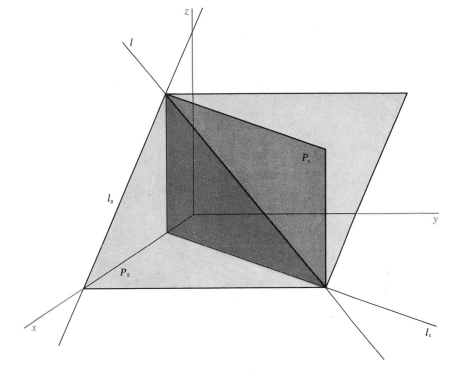

Figure 1

(6)
$$\frac{x-a}{u} = \frac{y-b}{v} = \frac{z-c}{w}$$

which merely expresses the collinearity of the vectors $\mathbf{X} - \mathbf{A}$ and $\mathbf{U}$.

Example 1. We apply these results to obtain nonparametric equations for the line through the points $A = (2, 3, 4)$ and $B = (4, 3, 2)$. Set

$$\mathbf{U} = \mathbf{B} - \mathbf{A} = (2, 0, -2).$$

Since the x-component of $\mathbf{U}$ is not zero, we may apply (5) directly to obtain

$$y = 3, \quad z = -x + 6.$$

Example 2. Let us find the equation of the line through the point $P = (-2, 2, 3)$ perpendicular to the line ℓ given by the equations $y = 1 + 2x$, $z = 3 - 4x$. The equations for ℓ may be put into the form (2), with x as the parameter; that is,

$$\begin{cases} x = \lambda, \\ y = 1 + 2\lambda, \\ z = 3 - 4\lambda. \end{cases}$$

Thus, the vector $\mathbf{U} = (1, 2, -4)$ is parallel to the line. Let A be the foot of the perpendicular from P to the line ℓ. Since A is a point of ℓ, if a is the x-coordinate of A, the other two coordinates are given by the equations for ℓ; hence $A = (a, 1 + 2a, 3 - 4a)$. Now, the condition for perpendicularity is

$$0 = (\mathbf{A} - \mathbf{P}) \cdot \mathbf{U} = (a + 2) + 2(2a - 1) - 4(-4a) = 21a.$$

Consequently, $a = 0$ and $\mathbf{A} = (0, 1, 3)$. The vector

$$\mathbf{A} - \mathbf{P} = (2, -1, 0)$$

is parallel to the desired perpendicular line, whose equation must then be

$$\mathbf{X} = \mathbf{A} + \lambda(\mathbf{A} - \mathbf{P}).$$

In the nonparametric form (5), the perpendicular has the equations

$$y = 1 - \tfrac{1}{2}x, \quad z = 3.$$

Notice that lines in space, in contrast to lines in the plane, if not parallel (that is, if not having the same direction) need not intersect. For example, the lines $\mathbf{X} = \lambda\mathbf{i}$ and $\mathbf{X} = \mathbf{k} + \lambda\mathbf{j}$ clearly do not intersect since the z-coordinate of a point on the former is always 0, and on the latter, 1. Lines that are not parallel and do not intersect are called *skew*.

We have already given a vector description of a plane, A3.2 (8), in terms of any noncollinear triple of its points. Equations A3.2 (8) may be more conveniently used in a form analogous to (1). Let $A = (a, b, c)$ be any point of the plane $\mathcal{P}$ and let $\mathbf{U}_1$ and $\mathbf{U}_2$ be any noncollinear vectors parallel to the plane. Then the equation of $\mathcal{P}$ may be written in the form

$$(7) \qquad\qquad \mathbf{X} = \mathbf{A} + \lambda_1\mathbf{U}_1 + \lambda_2\mathbf{U}_2 \qquad\qquad (\lambda_1, \lambda_2 \in \mathcal{R}).$$

Putting $\mathbf{U}_1 = (u_1, v_1, w_1)$, $\mathbf{U}_2 = (u_2, v_2, w_2)$, we obtain equations for the coordinates of any point $\mathbf{X} = (x, y, z)$ of $\mathcal{P}$ in terms of two parameters, λ_1 and λ_2:

$$(8) \qquad \begin{cases} x = a + \lambda_1 u_1 + \lambda_1 u_2, \\ y = b + \lambda_1 v_1 + \lambda_2 v_2, \\ z = c + \lambda_1 w_1 + \lambda_2 w_2. \end{cases}$$

It would be possible to eliminate λ_1 and λ_2 from the parametric equations (8) algebraically, but we proceed somewhat differently.

We shall characterize the plane as the union of all lines through the point A which are perpendicular to a given nonnull vector. For this purpose, we replace U_1 and U_2 by mutually perpendicular unit vectors e_1 and e_2, which may be constructed by the method of A3.3 :

$$e_1 = \frac{U_1}{|U_1|}, \qquad V = U_2 - (e_1 \cdot U_2) e_1, \qquad e_2 = \frac{V}{|V|}.$$

We may then replace U_1 and U_2 in (7) by means of

$$U_1 = |U_1| e_1, \qquad U_2 = (e_1 \cdot U_2) e_1 + (e_2 \cdot U_2) e_2$$

to put (7) in the form

(9) $$X = A + \sigma_1 e_1 + \sigma_2 e_2,$$

where $e_1 \cdot e_2 = 0$ and $|e_1| = |e_2| = 1$. Since there exists at least one point B not in the plane $\mathcal{P}$, the vector $W = B - A$ is noncoplanar with e_1 and e_2. Consequently, as in A3.3, we can construct a nonnull vector perpendicular to e_1 and e_2, namely,

$$N = W - (e_1 \cdot W) e_1 - (e_2 \cdot W) e_2.$$

Now, each line in $\mathcal{P}$ through A is defined by A and any other point X of the line. Since X is a point of the plane, it must be expressible in the form (9). The vector $X - A$, which defines the direction of the line, can then be written

$$X - A = \sigma_1 e_1 + \sigma_2 e_2 ;$$

hence, $X - A$ and the line are both perpendicular to N.

Conversely, if $\mathcal{S}$ is the union of all lines through the point A which are perpendicular to a given nonnull vector N, we have

$$\mathcal{S} = \{X : (X - A) \cdot N = 0\}.$$

If e_1 and e_2 are any perpendicular unit vectors which are also perpendicular to N (such vectors must exist; compare A3.3 Ex. 20), the plane $\mathcal{P}$ defined by the equation

$$X - A = \sigma_1 e_1 + \sigma_2 e_2$$

is contained in $\mathcal{S}$. Now, any set of three mutually perpendicular unit vectors constitute a basis for E^3. Thus, for $n = \dfrac{N}{|N|}$, $\{e_1, e_2, n\}$ is a basis. Therefore, given any vector $X \in \mathcal{S}$, we may express $X - A$ in the form

$$X - A = a_1 e_1 + a_2 e_2 + b n.$$

Consequently,

$$0 = (\mathbf{X} - \mathbf{A}) \cdot \mathbf{N} = b \mathbf{n} \cdot \mathbf{N} = b|\mathbf{N}| .$$

Since $\mathbf{N}$ is nonnull, $|\mathbf{N}| \neq 0$; hence we must have $b = 0$ and X must be a point of $\mathcal{P}$. We have shown that $\mathcal{S}$ contains $\mathcal{P}$ and that $\mathcal{P}$ contains $\mathcal{S}$; hence $\mathcal{P} = \mathcal{S}$. We have thereby justified the characterization of a plane as the union of the set of lines through a given point and perpendicular to a given nonnull vector.

We now have a nonparametric vector form of the equation of the plane in terms of any given point $A = (a, b, c)$ of the plane and any vector $\mathbf{N} = (p, q, r)$ perpendicular to the plane, namely

(10) $$(\mathbf{X} - \mathbf{A}) \cdot \mathbf{N} = 0 .$$

In terms of coordinates, (10) may be written in a form analogous to A3.4a (6),

(11) $$px + qy + rz = k ,$$

where $k = \mathbf{A} \cdot \mathbf{N} = pa + qb + rc$. Conversely, any linear equation in the three variables x, y, z whose coefficients p, q, r are not all zero can be written in the form (10) and is, therefore, the equation of a plane. In proof, simply observe that if $A = (a, b, c)$ is a point whose coordinates satisfy (11), then $pa + qb + rc = k$ and, hence, for any point $X = (x, y, z)$ with coordinates satisfying (11)

$$(\mathbf{X} - \mathbf{A}) \cdot \mathbf{N} = 0 ,$$

where $\mathbf{N} = (p, q, r)$.

The unit vectors $\pm \dfrac{\mathbf{N}}{|\mathbf{N}|}$ are called the *normals* to the plane. In terms of the normal

$$\mathbf{n} = \frac{\mathbf{N}}{|\mathbf{N}|} = (\cos \theta, \cos \phi, \cos \psi)$$

(11) may be put in the normal form

(12) $$x \cos \theta + y \cos \phi + z \cos \psi + d = 0 ,$$

where

$$\cos^2 \theta + \cos^2 \phi + \cos^2 \psi = 1 .$$

Here $|d|$ is the perpendicular distance of the origin from the plane, the sign of d being positive if the origin lies on the side of the plane toward which n points, negative if the origin lies on the opposite side, and zero if the origin lies on the plane. (See Ex. 1.)

The form (11) is completely general, but it is not unique, since we may multiply in (11) by any nonzero constant to obtain another equation for the same plane; that is, we may replace $\mathbf{N}$ in (10) by any nonnull vector $\lambda\mathbf{N}$ collinear with $\mathbf{N}$. To obtain (12), we choose

$$\lambda = \frac{1}{|\mathbf{N}|} = \frac{1}{\sqrt{p^2 + q^2 + r^2}}.$$

Another possibility is to choose λ as the reciprocal of any one of the coefficients which is not zero. Thus, if $r \neq 0$, say, we may choose $\lambda = \frac{1}{r}$ and solve for z to obtain the equation of the plane in the form

(13) $$z = \alpha x + \beta y + \gamma,$$

where $\alpha = -\frac{p}{r}$, $\beta = -\frac{q}{r}$, and $\gamma = \frac{k}{r}$. Thus, the plane is defined by giving z as a linear function of the two variables x and y.

Example 3. Let us find the various forms of the equation of the plane ABC where $A = (1, 2, 3)$, $B = (2, 3, 1)$, $C = (3, 1, 2)$. In (10), set

$$\mathbf{X} = \mathbf{B} \quad \text{and} \quad \mathbf{X} = \mathbf{C},$$

successively, to obtain $\mathbf{N} = (p, q, r)$, where $p = q = r$.

Apart from an irrelevant scalar factor, we find $\mathbf{N} = (1, 1, 1)$. In the form (11), the equation is

$$x + y + z = 6.$$

The normal form of the equation is

$$\frac{x}{\sqrt{3}} + \frac{y}{\sqrt{3}} + \frac{z}{\sqrt{3}} - 2\sqrt{3} = 0.$$

Example 4. Consider the plane $\mathscr{P}$ given by the equation $\mathbf{X} \cdot \mathbf{N} = k$ and a line ℓ, not parallel to $\mathscr{P}$ given by the equation

$$\mathbf{X} = \mathbf{P} + \lambda\mathbf{Q}.$$

Let us find the point of intersection of $\mathscr{P}$ and ℓ. If A is the point of intersection, A satisfies the equations for both $\mathscr{P}$ and ℓ:

$$\mathbf{A} \cdot \mathbf{N} = k, \quad \mathbf{A} = \mathbf{P} + \lambda\mathbf{Q}.$$

Take the dot product with $\mathbf{N}$ in the second equation to obtain

$$\lambda\mathbf{Q} \cdot \mathbf{N} = \mathbf{A} \cdot \mathbf{N} - \mathbf{P} \cdot \mathbf{N} = k - \mathbf{P} \cdot \mathbf{N}.$$

Since $\mathbf{Q}$ is not parallel to $\mathscr{P}$, we have $\mathbf{Q} \cdot \mathbf{N} \neq 0$. We may now solve the last equation for λ to obtain

$$\mathbf{A} = \mathbf{P} + \frac{k - \mathbf{P} \cdot \mathbf{N}}{\mathbf{Q} \cdot \mathbf{N}} \mathbf{Q} .$$

A3.4b Exercises

In these exercises, assume throughout that the space is E^3.

1. Let $\mathbf{U}_1$ and $\mathbf{U}_2$ be noncollinear vectors. Show that any two vectors perpendicular to both $\mathbf{U}_1$ and $\mathbf{U}_2$ must be collinear and, therefore, that the unit normals $\pm\mathbf{n}$ to the plane (7) are the only ones obtainable.

2. Find the coordinates of the foot of the perpendicular from the point $A = (a, b, c)$ to the plane $px + qy + rz = k$.

3. a. Consider the lines ℓ_1 and ℓ_2 given by the respective equations $\mathbf{X} = \mathbf{P} + \lambda\mathbf{U}$, and $\mathbf{X} = \mathbf{Q} + \lambda\mathbf{V}$, where $\mathbf{U}$ and $\mathbf{V}$ are noncollinear. Let $\mathbf{N}$ be any nonnull vector perpendicular to both $\mathbf{U}$ and $\mathbf{V}$. Prove that the condition

   (i) $$\mathbf{P} \cdot \mathbf{N} = \mathbf{Q} \cdot \mathbf{N}$$

   is both necessary and sufficient for ℓ_1 and ℓ_2 to intersect.

   b. Let the lines of Part a be skew; that is, assume that (i) is not satisfied. Show that there is exactly one line ℓ that meets both ℓ_1 and ℓ_2 perpendicularly, and give its equation.

4. Let $\mathscr{P}_1$ and $\mathscr{P}_2$ be planes with noncollinear normals $\mathbf{n}_1$ and $\mathbf{n}_2$, respectively. Prove that the intersection of the two planes is a line.

5. Let $\mathscr{P}_1$, $\mathscr{P}_2$, and $\mathscr{P}_3$ be planes with the noncoplanar normals $\mathbf{n}_1$, $\mathbf{n}_2$, $\mathbf{n}_3$, respectively. Prove that the intersection of the three planes is a point.

6. Obtain a formula for the distance of the point $A = (a, b, c)$ from the plane $px + qy + rz = k$.

7. The *perpendicular projection* of a point on a line or a plane is defined as the foot of the perpendicular from the point to the line or the plane. The perpendicular projection of a set S is the class of perpendicular projections of the points of S. The perpendicular projection of a vector $\mathbf{V}$ represented by a directed segment $\overrightarrow{PQ}$ is the vector $\mathbf{V}^*$ represented by the directed segment $\overrightarrow{P^*Q^*}$, where P^* and Q^* are the perpendicular projections of P and Q, respectively. Let the line ℓ be given by the equation

   (i) $$\mathbf{X} = \mathbf{A} + \lambda\mathbf{t},$$

   where $\mathbf{t}$ is a unit vector, and the plane $\mathscr{P}$ by

   (ii) $$\mathbf{X} \cdot \mathbf{n} = k,$$

where $\mathbf{n}$ is a normal to $\mathcal{P}$. Obtain expressions for the perpendicular projections of $\mathbf{V}$ on ℓ and $\mathcal{P}$, and prove that the projections are independent of the choice of representation $\overrightarrow{PQ}$ for $\mathbf{V}$.

8. The angle θ between a line ℓ and a vector $\mathbf{X}$, or a line parallel to $\mathbf{X}$, is defined by

$$\cos\theta = \frac{|\mathbf{t}\cdot\mathbf{X}|}{|\mathbf{X}|} \qquad (0 \le \theta \le \tfrac{1}{2}\pi),$$

where $\mathbf{t}$ is one of the two direction vectors of ℓ. The angle α between ℓ and a plane $\mathcal{P}$ with normal $\mathbf{n}$ is defined as the complement of the angle between ℓ and $\mathbf{n}$; thus, $\sin\alpha = |\mathbf{t}\cdot\mathbf{n}|$. (See figure.) Prove that

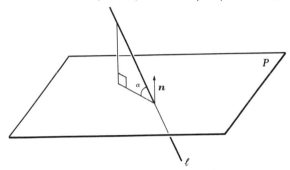

α is the minimum of all angles made by $\mathbf{t}$ with lines in the plane $\mathcal{P}$ and show that the minimum angle α is achieved only by lines parallel to the perpendicular projection of ℓ on $\mathcal{P}$.

9. The angle ψ between planes $\mathcal{P}_1$ and $\mathcal{P}_2$ is defined by

$$\cos\psi = |\mathbf{n}_1\cdot\mathbf{n}_2| \qquad (0 \le \psi \le \tfrac{1}{2}\pi).$$

Show that ψ is the angle between the lines of intersection of $\mathcal{P}_1$ and $\mathcal{P}_2$ with any plane $\mathcal{P}$ perpendicular to both $\mathcal{P}_1$ and $\mathcal{P}_2$.

A3.5 OTHER CURVES AND SURFACES

In a coordinate system curves and surfaces may be described by equations which generalize some of the basic forms used for lines and planes. Where linear functions describe lines and planes, the general equations of curves and surfaces employ functions from a class broad enough to represent any variety of object which we might willingly call a curve or surface.

A3.5a General description of curves and surfaces

For a curve in the plane we may employ a parametric representation in the form

(1a)
$$\begin{cases} x = \varphi(t) \\ y = \psi(t) \end{cases}$$

and, in space,

(1b)
$$\begin{cases} x = \varphi(t) \\ y = \psi(t) \\ z = \omega(t) \end{cases}$$

For a surface in space, the parametric equations have the general form

(2)
$$\begin{aligned} x &= \alpha(u, v) \\ y &= \beta(u, v) \\ z &= \gamma(u, v) \end{aligned}$$

For the parametric representations (1), it is assumed that the functions φ, ψ, ω have an interval of the t-axis as their common domain; for (2), the functions α, β, γ are assumed to have a region of the u, v-plane as their common domain. The parametric representations (1) and (2) may then be thought of as mappings that transform lines and planes into objects of the same dimension, that is, curves and surfaces, respectively.

The general concept of a dimension-preserving transformation is not needed in a calculus course where we deal with a much more restricted class of functions. The general treatment of dimension and dimension-preserving transformations is part of topology. It is quite easy to find a mapping of the form (1a) which is not dimension preserving. Here, except for linear spaces, we do not need a precise definition of "dimension." By any definition we might reasonably wish to adopt, however, a square should be a two-dimensional object and a segment, one-dimensional. As an example, consider the mapping of the interval $[0, 1]$ onto the square $\{(x, y) : x, y \in [0, 1]\}$. We represent each real number $t \in [0, 1]$ as an infinite decimal

$$t = .c_1 c_2 c_3 \dots$$

where the c_k are digits. Terminating decimals can be represented in two different ways as an infinite decimal, for example

$$\tfrac{3}{10} = .3000 \dots = .2999 \dots,$$

and except for $0 = .000 \dots$ we choose the form with the periodic repetition of nine rather than zero to represent such values of t. We then define φ and ψ in (1a) by

$$x = \varphi(t) = .c_1 c_3 c_5 \dots$$
$$y = \psi(t) = .c_2 c_4 c_6 \dots$$

Every point (x, y) of the square is covered in the mapping, for if $x = .a_1 a_2 a_3 \dots$ and $y = .b_1 b_2 b_3 \dots$ then $x = \varphi(t)$ and $y = \psi(t)$ where $t = .a_1 b_1 a_2 b_2 a_3 b_3 \dots$. (Some points will be covered more than once; for example, $(\frac{1}{2}, \frac{1}{2})$ has as antecedents in the mapping $.44999 \dots$, $.45909090 \dots$, and $.54090909 \dots$.) From the point of view of analysis, mappings that do not preserve dimension are considered oddities and are often called "badly behaved" or "pathological."

In (1a) and in (2) we may eliminate the parameters and represent the curve and the surface by nonparametric equations of the form

(3) $$\Phi(x, y) = 0$$

and

(4) $$\Gamma(x, y, z) = 0$$

Elimination of the parameter for the space curve (1b) will yield two equations

(5) $$\Phi(x, y, z) = 0 \quad \text{and} \quad \Psi(x, y, z) = 0 ;$$

thus any space curve may be represented nonparametrically as the intersection of two surfaces given in the form (4).

Finally, it may be possible to solve for one of the variables in (3) and (4). In that case, the plane curve (3) could be described by an equation of the form

(6) $$y = f(x) ;$$

that is, as the graph of a function. Similarly, the surface (4) could be described by an equation of the form

(7) $$z = F(x, y) ;$$

that is, as the graph of a function of two real variables. From the functional representation of a plane curve (6), a parametric form (1a) is easily obtained with $\varphi : t \rightarrow x$ and $\psi = f\varphi$. A nonparametric form (3) is obtained with $\Phi : (x, y) \rightarrow y - f(x)$. Similarly, (7) can be put into the parametric form (2) with $\alpha : u \rightarrow x$, $\beta : v \rightarrow y$ and $\gamma = \Gamma$, and into the nonparametric form (4) with $\Gamma : (x, y, z) \rightarrow z - F(x, y)$.

Example 1. Nonparametric equation for a circle.
A *circle* is defined as a set of points in the plane at a given distance (the

radius) from a given point (the center). Let the center be the point $A = (a, b)$ and let the radius be r. The vector equation for the circle is

(8) $$|\mathbf{X} - \mathbf{A}| = r,$$

where $X = (x, y)$ denotes any point on the circle. (See Ex. 7a.) Squaring in (8) and using the coordinate representation of the dot product

$$(\mathbf{X} - \mathbf{A}) \cdot (\mathbf{X} - \mathbf{A}),$$

we obtain

(9) $$(x - a)^2 + (y - b)^2 = r^2$$

which may be put in the form (3) with

$$\Phi(x, y) = (x - a)^2 + (y - b)^2 - r^2.$$

Example 2. *Nonparametric equation of a cone.*

We define a cone (more precisely, a right circular cone) in space as the union of all lines (*generators*) that pass through a given point A (the *vertex*) and make a given angle α with a given line (the *axis*) through A; see Figure 1. The vertex A separates the cone into two branches, called *nappes* of the cone. The angle α between the generators and the axis is defined uniquely by the requirement that it is acute,

$$0 < \alpha < \tfrac{1}{2}\pi,$$

(compare A3.4b Ex. 8).† If $\mathbf{U}$ is any nonnull vector parallel to the axis of the cone, and $\mathbf{X}$ any point on the cone, then

(10) $$|(\mathbf{X} - \mathbf{A}) \cdot \mathbf{U}| = |\mathbf{X} - \mathbf{A}| \, |\mathbf{U}| \cos \alpha.$$

Now let us put $X = (x, y, z)$, $A = (a, b, c)$, and $U = (u, v, w)$ in (10) and take squares to obtain the nonparametric equation

(11) $$(x - a)^2 + (y - b)^2 + (z - c)^2$$
$$= \kappa [u(x - a) + v(y - b) + w(z - c)]^2$$

where

Figure 1

$$\kappa = \frac{1}{(u^2 + v^2 + w^2) \cos^2 \alpha}.$$

Some additional interpretation is necessary if one of the

†The cases $\alpha = 0$ and $\alpha = \dfrac{\pi}{2}$ are degenerate.

variables does not appear explicitly in (3) or (4). Suppose, for example, that

$$\Gamma(x, y, z) = g(x, y)$$

in (4). The condition $g(x, y) = 0$ does not restrict z. In that case, if $g(a, b) = 0$ all points of the vertical line

$$\{(x, y, z) : x = a, \quad y = b, \quad z \in R\}$$

satisfy (4). Equation (4) defines a *cylinder* with the cross-section curve $g(x, y) = 0$ in the plane $z = 0$, and vertical lines as *generators*.

If two plane curves are given in the form (3) by equations

$$\Phi_1(x, y) = 0 \quad \text{and} \quad \Phi_2(x, y) = 0$$

their union has the nonparametric representation

$$(12) \qquad \Phi_1(x, y)\, \Phi_2(x, y) - 0.$$

If the product $\Phi_1(x, y)\, \Phi_2(x, y)$ is zero for any point (x, y), at least one of the factors is zero and (x, y) must be a point of the union. Conversely, if (x, y) is a point of the union, at least one of the factors vanishes and (12) is satisfied. The intersection of the two curves also has a simple nonparametric representation:

$$(13) \qquad \alpha^2 [\Phi_1(x, y)]^2 + \beta^2 [\Phi_2(x, y)]^2 = 0,$$

where α and β are not zero. Equation (13) is satisfied if and only if $\Phi_1(x, y) = \Phi_2(x, y) = 0$. Equations similar to (12) and (13) can be obtained for the union and intersection of two surfaces.

A3.5a Exercises

1. Consider the lines ℓ_1 and ℓ_2 in the plane and let their nonparametric equations be

$$A_1 x + B_1 y + C_1 = 0 \quad \text{and} \quad A_2 x + B_2 y + C_2 = 0.$$

   Obtain nonparametric quadratic equations for $\ell_1 \cup \ell_2$ and $\ell_1 \cap \ell_2$ by applying (12) and (13). Put these nonparametric equations in the form

   (i) $\qquad ax^2 + 2bxy + cy^2 + dx + ey + f = 0.$

   If ℓ_1 and ℓ_2 are not parallel show for $\ell_1 \cup \ell_2$ that $b^2 - ac > 0$ and for $\ell_1 \cap \ell_2$ that $b^2 - ac < 0$. If ℓ_1 and ℓ_2 are parallel, prove for both $\ell_1 \cup \ell_2$ and $\ell_1 \cap \ell_2$ that $b^2 - ac = 0$.

2. Consider a right circular cone with axis along the z-axis and vertex at the origin. Show that each nappe separately has an equation in the functional form (7).

3. Verify that each of the following sets of parametric equations define a circle.

a. $\quad x = a + r\cos\theta,\qquad y = b + r\sin\theta,\qquad\qquad (0 \le \theta < 2\pi).$

b. $\quad x = \cos\theta + \sin\theta,\qquad y = \cos\theta - \sin\theta,\qquad (0 \le \theta < 2\pi).$

c. $\quad x = \dfrac{1 - t^2}{1 + t^2},\qquad\qquad y = \dfrac{2t}{1 + t^2}.\qquad\qquad (t \in \mathcal{R}).$

4. A surface of revolution is the set of points obtained by rotation of a curve about a fixed line (the *axis*). Consider the plane curve given by the equations

$$x = f(z), \qquad y = 0.$$

Derive a nonparametric equation for the surface of revolution obtained by rotation of this curve about the z-axis.

5. Sketch the curves in the plane described by the following parametric equations.

a. $\quad x = 2u + 1,\qquad y = u - 2,\qquad\qquad\qquad (u \in \mathcal{R}).$

b. $\quad x = \cos\theta,\qquad y = |\sin\theta|,\qquad\qquad\qquad (0 \le \theta < 2\pi).$

c. $\quad x = a,\qquad y = b\cos\theta,\qquad\qquad\qquad\ (0 \le \theta \le \pi).$

d. $\quad x = t^3,\qquad y = t^2,\qquad\qquad\qquad\qquad\quad (t \in \mathcal{R}).$

e. $\quad x = |u| - u,\qquad y = |u| + u,\qquad\qquad\ (u \in \mathcal{R}).$

6. a. In general, a *cone* is defined as the union of lines (the *generators*) where each line passes through a point of a given plane curve and a given point A (the *vertex*) off the plane of the given curve. Let the curve be given by the parametric equations

$$x = \phi(t), \qquad y = \psi(t), \qquad z = 0$$

and set $A = (a, b, c)$ where $c \ne 0$. Obtain parametric equations for the cone.

b. Verify that the right circular cone of Example 2 is a cone in the sense defined by Part a, where the generating curve is a circle in a plane perpendicular to the axis and the center lies on the axis.

7. Given a quadratic equation in the form

$$x^2 + y^2 + \alpha x + \beta y + \gamma = 0,$$

show that it is the equation of a circle and determine the radius and the coordinates of the center.

A3.5b Circles and spheres

In A3.5a Example 1, we defined a circle and obtained a nonparametric equation for it. A sphere is similarly defined as a set of points in space at a given distance (the radius) from a given point (the center). If the center is the point $A = (a, b, c)$ and the radius is r, the vector equation of the sphere is

(1) $$|\mathbf{X} - \mathbf{A}| = r.$$

In terms of the coordinate representation $X = (x, y, z)$, Equation (1) becomes

(2) $$(x - a)^2 + (y - b)^2 + (z - c)^2 = r^2 .$$

This is the nonparametric equation of a surface (compare A3.5a (4)).

In the following discussion of circles it is to be assumed that we are restricting ourselves to plane geometry unless the context plainly indicates otherwise.

Example 1.

The intersection of a surface with a plane is called a *section* of that surface. We show that the section of a plane with a sphere must be a circle or a point or the empty set.

Let the sphere be given by (1) and P be the foot of the perpendicular from A to the plane; see Figure 1. Now set

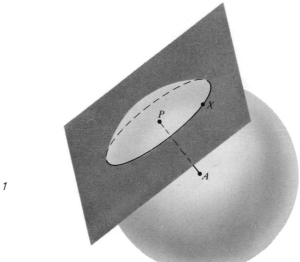

Figure 1

(3) $$|P - A| = d .$$

The equation of the plane is

(4) $$(X - P) \cdot (P - A) = 0$$

since $P - A$ is perpendicular to the plane. The intersection of plane and sphere must satisfy (1) and (4) simultaneously. We rewrite (1) in the form

(5) $$|X - A|^2 = |(X - P) + (P - A)|^2 = r^2$$

to obtain

$$|X - P|^2 + 2(X - P) \cdot (P - A) + |P - A|^2 = r^2 .$$

In this last equation we use (3) and (4) to obtain

(6) $$|X - P|^2 = r^2 - d^2 .$$

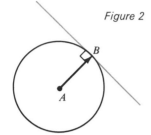

Figure 2

Here P and X are both points of the plane; hence if $d < r$, (6) is the equation of a circle in the plane; if $d = r$ then $X = P$ and (6) describes only the point P; if $d > r$ then no point X satisfies (6) and the section must be empty. We have seen that the section of the sphere must satisfy (4) and (6). Conversely, any point satisfying (4) and (6) must satisfy (5) and therefore lie on the sphere and be a point of the section. ⬜

Let B be any point of the circle or sphere $|X - A| = r$. A line through B is said to be *tangent* to the circle or sphere at B if it is perpendicular to the radius vector $B - A$; see Figure 2. Similarly, a plane through B is said to be tangent to the sphere at B if it is perpendicular to the radius vector $B - A$.

Figure 3

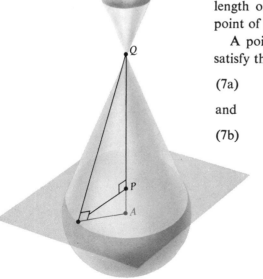

Example 2.

The set of all lines tangent to the sphere $|X - A| = r$ and passing through a point Q outside the sphere is a right circular cone with vertex Q and the line AQ as axis; see Figure 3. Furthermore, for every tangent line, the length of the segment with endpoints at Q and at the point of tangency is the same.

A point of tangency X of a line through Q must satisfy the conditions

(7a) $$|X - A| = r$$

and

(7b) $$(X - A) \cdot (X - Q) = 0 ,$$

namely, that X is a point of the sphere and that the line XQ is perpendicular to the radius vector $X - A$. For simplicity, let A be the origin O. Then (7a) and (7b) become, respectively,

(8a) $$|X| = r ,$$

(8b) $$\mathbf{X} \cdot (\mathbf{X} - \mathbf{Q}) = 0 .$$

Entering (8a) in (8b) we find

$$0 = |\mathbf{X}|^2 - \mathbf{X} \cdot \mathbf{Q} = r^2 - \mathbf{X} \cdot \mathbf{Q} .$$

Thus X satisfies

(9) $$\mathbf{X} \cdot \mathbf{Q} = r^2 .$$

Conversely, if $\mathbf{X}$ satisfies (9) and (8a) then (8b) is satisfied and X is the point of tangency of line XQ. Now set $d = |\mathbf{Q}|$; by assumption $d > r$. From (8a) and (9)

$$|\mathbf{Q} - \mathbf{X}|^2 = |\mathbf{Q}|^2 - 2\mathbf{Q} \cdot \mathbf{X} + |\mathbf{X}|^2 = d^2 - r^2 ;$$

hence,

$$|\mathbf{Q} - \mathbf{X}| = \sqrt{d^2 - r^2}$$

independently of the particular point of tangency X, as asserted. To show that the lines of tangency constitute a cone we show that the angle α between $\mathbf{Q} - \mathbf{X}$ and $\mathbf{Q}$ is independent of X. For this, observe that

$$\cos \alpha = \frac{(\mathbf{Q} - \mathbf{X}) \cdot \mathbf{Q}}{|\mathbf{Q} - \mathbf{X}| \, |\mathbf{Q}|} = \frac{|\mathbf{Q}|^2 - |\mathbf{X}|^2}{|\mathbf{Q} - \mathbf{X}| \, |\mathbf{Q}|} = \frac{d^2 - r^2}{d\sqrt{d^2 - r^2}} = \sqrt{1 - \frac{r^2}{d^2}} ,$$

independently of the choice of point of tangency X. ⬜

Equation (9) implies that X lies in a plane perpendicular to the vector $\mathbf{Q}$. Conversely, as we have noted, if X lies on the section of the plane and sphere, that is, if $\mathbf{X}$ satisfies (9) and (8a), then (8b) is satisfied.

It follows that the tangent lines from Q constitute the cone with vertex Q generated by the circle of points of tangency (see A3.5a Ex. 6a). From Example 1, the center P of the circular section is the foot of the perpendicular from Q to the plane. Consequently, P lies on the line OQ and $OQ = PQ$. (Compare A3.5a Ex. 6b.)

By reliance on diagrams, it would have been possible to arrive at the results of Examples 1 and 2 by means of simple synthetic arguments. The primary difficulty of diagrams is that each special case must be treated separately, and it is sometimes not obvious that all special cases have been considered. Analytical arguments have the virtue of generality, but an analytical sense takes practice to develop whereas the geometrical sense is close to our immediate perceptions. Of course, the purpose of this chapter is to develop an analytical sense, so we use analytical methods at times when a synthetic approach may be a bit simpler.

A3.5b Exercises

In these exercises, problems concerning circles are questions in plane geometry unless the context is clearly three-dimensional.

1. Find the equation of the circle centered at (a, b) and passing through the point (p, q).

2. Show if (a_1, b_1), (a_2, b_2) and (a_3, b_3) are noncollinear points, that there exists just one circle which passes through the three points. Find the coordinates of the center.

3. Let ℓ be any line and P, Q any two points such that $\mathbf{Q} - \mathbf{P}$ is not perpendicular to ℓ. Show that there exists exactly one circle with center on ℓ which passes through P and Q. When $\mathbf{Q} - \mathbf{P}$ is perpendicular to ℓ, discuss the possibility of drawing a circle through Q and P with center on ℓ.

4. Obtain the equation of the line tangent at the point $P = (p, q)$ to the circle with center $A = (a, b)$.

5. Show that two tangents to a circle pass through any point outside the circle.

6. Show that the intersection of two nonconcentric spheres is either empty, or a point, or a circle. Obtain a necessary and sufficient condition for each of these possibilities.

7. Prove that two chords of a circle (or sphere) are equal in length if and only if they subtend equal angles at the center.

8. Consider two intersecting circles (or spheres) of equal radius r and let P be any point of their intersection. Prove that the length of the segment intercepted by either circle (or sphere) on the line through P parallel to the line of centers is equal to the distance between the centers (see figure).

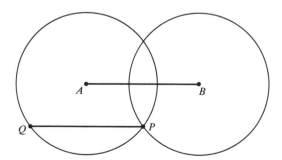

9. Given four points A, B, C, D on a circle there are three pairs of chords with A, B, C, D as endpoints, such that the two chords of a pair have no common endpoint, namely,

$$[AB], \quad [CD], \quad \text{and} \quad [AC], \quad [BD], \quad \text{and} \quad [AD], \quad [BC].$$

a. Show if the chords of one pair are parallel that the chords of each of the other pairs have the same length.

b. Show if the chords of one pair have the same length, that the chords of one of the other pairs are parallel and the chords of the remaining pair have the same length.

10. Prove that the larger of two chords of a circle (or sphere) is nearer the center.

11. Prove if two circles are both tangent to a given line at a given point that the common point of tangency lies on the line joining the centers. Circles having such a common point of tangency to a given line are said to be *tangent* to each other at that point.

12. Two circles (or spheres) are said to be *orthogonal* if they intersect at a point at which the radius vectors are perpendicular. Obtain necessary and sufficient conditions for orthogonality.

13. a. Prove if the circle (or sphere) $|X - A|^2 = r^2$ is orthogonal to the two circles (or spheres)

$$|X - A_1|^2 = r_1^2, \qquad |X - A_2|^2 = r_2^2$$

that it is orthogonal to every circle (or sphere) of the one-parameter family

(i) $$(1 - \lambda)(|X - A_1|^2 - r_1^2) + \lambda(|X - A_2|^2 - r_2^2) = 0.$$

b. For the sake of algebraic generality a straight line (or plane) is considered to be a degenerate circle (or sphere). Then the family (i) is extended to include all curves (or surfaces) with equations of the form

$$u_1(|X - A_1|^2 - r_2^2) + u_2(|X - A_2|^2 - r_2^2) = 0,$$

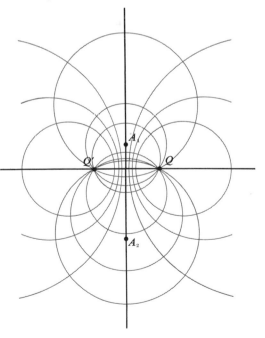

where $u_1^2 + u_2^2 \neq 0$. Show that the extended family consists of the family (i) and a straight line or plane through the center A of the circle or sphere $|X - A|^2 = r^2$ of Part a.

A circle and line, or sphere and plane, are said to be *orthogonal* if and only if the line passes through the center of the circle, or the plane through the center of the sphere. With these conventions, the circle, or sphere, $|X - A|^2 = r^2$ is orthogonal to all the members of the extended family.

c. By the conventions of Part b, the line of centers A_1A_2 is also orthogonal to the circles $|X - A_i|^2 = r_i^2$, for $i = 1, 2$. Represent the line of centers in the form $X \cdot N = k$ where N is a nonnull vector satisfying $N \cdot (A_2 - A_1) = 0$.

d. Show that every circle of the family

$$v_1(|X - A|^2 - r^2) + v_2(X \cdot N - k) = 0$$

is orthogonal to every circle of the family given in Part b; see figure. (Note that this is a problem in the plane.)

e. Assume the two circles $|\mathbf{X} - \mathbf{A}_i|^2 = r_i^2$, $(i = 1, 2)$ have a nonempty intersection. Show if P is not an intersection point of the two circles that exactly one circle from each of the families passes through P.

A3.5c Conic sections

A conic section, as its name implies, is the curve of intersection of a plane with a cone (a right circular cone). If the plane passes through the vertex the section is said to be *degenerate*. A degenerate conic section may be a point, or a line, or a pair of intersecting straight lines. Here we are concerned primarily with nondegenerate sections.

Let the cone be given, as in A3.5a (10), by

(1) $$|(\mathbf{X} - \mathbf{A}) \cdot \mathbf{U}| = |\mathbf{X} - \mathbf{A}| \, |\mathbf{U}| \cos \alpha$$

where A is the vertex of the cone, $\mathbf{U}$ is a vector in the direction of the axis, and α is the angle between the generators and the axis. Consider a plane that intersects the axis at a single point, not the vertex. Let $\mathbf{n}$ be the normal to the plane. If the angle θ between $\mathbf{n}$ and the axis is less than $\frac{\pi}{2} - \alpha$ the section of the cone is called an *ellipse*.† For such a section the

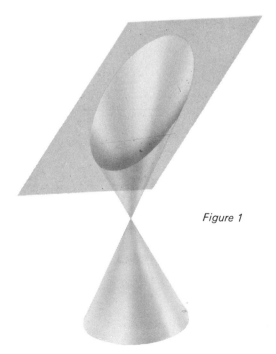

plane meets one nappe of the cone in a bounded curve; see Figure 1. If $\theta = 0$, in particular, the section is a circle (see A3.5a Ex. 6b). Thus a circle is a special kind of ellipse. The circle has so many exceptional properties, however, that, for the purposes of this section only, it will not be called an ellipse. If $\theta = \frac{\pi}{2} - \alpha$, the section is called a *parabola*.‡ For a parabolic section, the plane is parallel to one of the generators and meets one nappe of the cone in an unbounded curve; see Figure 2. If $\theta > \frac{\pi}{2} - \alpha$, the section is called a *hyperbola*.§ For a hyperbolic section, the plane meets both nappes of the cone in unbounded curves; see Figure 3.

Figure 1

†From Greek, ʼἔλλειψις, a deficiency.
‡From Greek, παραβολή, a likening.
§From Greek, ὑπερβολή, an excess.

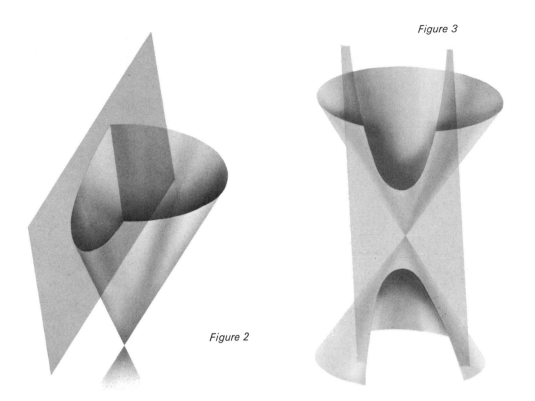

Figure 3

Figure 2

The properties of these curves are easily derived by a most elegant synthetic method of Dandelin and Quetelet.† The method is to introduce the tangent spheres common to the plane and the cone. Here, a sphere is said to be tangent to the cone if the cone is the union of all the lines through the vertex A which are tangent to the sphere (compare A3.5b Example 2). The points of tangency to the section plane of the Dandelin spheres are especially important; they are called the *foci* of the conic section. For the ellipse; see Figure 4, and the hyperbola there are two Dandelin spheres, hence two foci (F_1 and F_2 in Fig. 4); for the parabola there is one sphere and one focus. For the circle, both spheres are tangent to the section plane at the same point on the axis of the cone, the center of the circle.

Now, let S be a Dandelin sphere and let F be the point of tangency of S with the section plane. Let X be any point of the conic section. The generator AX is tangent to S at some point Q. The lines XF and XQ are both tangents to S from the same point X, with points

---

†Germinal Dandelin (1794–1847) and Adolphe Quetelet (1796–1874), Belgian geometers.

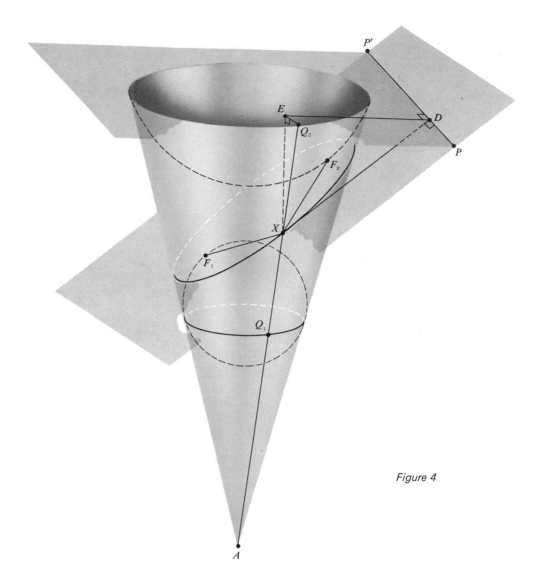

Figure 4

of tangency F and Q . From A3.5b Example 2, the segments $[XF]$ and $[XQ]$ have the same length; that is,

(2) $$|\mathbf{X} - \mathbf{F}| = |\mathbf{X} - \mathbf{Q}| .$$

Equation (2) yields very simple descriptions of the ellipse and the hyperbola. Let S_1 and S_2 be the two Dandelin spheres, F_1 and F_2 the respective foci, and Q_1 and Q_2 the respective points of tangency on the generator AX through the point X of the section. For the ellipse (Fig. 4) the point X lies between Q_1 and Q_2 on AX. Consequently (see A3.3 Exercise 26b),

$$|\mathbf{Q}_2 - \mathbf{Q}_1| = |\mathbf{Q}_2 - \mathbf{X}| + |\mathbf{X} - \mathbf{Q}_1|$$
$$= |\mathbf{X} - \mathbf{F}_2| + |\mathbf{X} - \mathbf{F}_1|,$$

by (2). In this $|\mathbf{Q}_2 - \mathbf{Q}_1|$ is constant, since $|\mathbf{Q}_2 - \mathbf{A}|$ and $|\mathbf{Q}_1 - \mathbf{A}|$ are the distances along the generator AX to the circles of tangency to S_2 and S_1, and therefore are the same for all generators. We put $|\mathbf{Q}_2 - \mathbf{Q}_1| = 2a$ and have

(3) $$|\mathbf{X} - \mathbf{F}_1| + |\mathbf{X} - \mathbf{F}_2| = 2a ;$$

that is, *an ellipse is a plane curve for which the sum of the distances of any point on the curve from two given points, the foci, is constant.* Conversely, if a curve has this property, it is an ellipse (see Exs. 15, 18). Note if $F_1 = F_2$ that (3) becomes the equation of a circle with radius a.

A point X of the hyperbola (Fig. 6) lies outside the segment $[Q_1Q_2]$. Consequently

$$|\mathbf{Q}_2 - \mathbf{Q}_1| = \big||\mathbf{X} - \mathbf{Q}_2| - |\mathbf{X} - \mathbf{Q}_1|\big|$$
$$= \big||\mathbf{X} - \mathbf{F}_2| - |\mathbf{X} - \mathbf{F}_1|\big|.$$

We then have

(4) $$\big||\mathbf{X} - \mathbf{F}_2| - |\mathbf{X} - \mathbf{F}_1|\big| = 2a ;$$

that is, *a hyperbola is a plane curve for which the absolute difference of the distances of any point on the curve from two given foci is constant.* The converse is also true; this property defines a hyperbola.

There is a simple general characterization of all the nondegenerate conic sections (except the circle) which we now obtain. Recall from A3.5b Example 2 that a sphere tangent to a cone meets the cone in a circle that consists of the points of tangency of the generators. The plane of the circle of tangency on a Dandelin sphere meets the section plane in a line called a *directrix* of the conic section. In Figure 4 we show the plane for S_2 ; the directrix is labeled PP'. Since the plane Q_2PP' of the circle is perpendicular to the axis, hence to $\mathbf{U}$, and the section plane XPP' is perpendicular to $\mathbf{n}$, the line PP' which lies in both planes is perpendicular to both $\mathbf{U}$ and $\mathbf{n}$.

We now introduce the plane through X which is parallel to both $\mathbf{U}$ and $\mathbf{n}$. This plane contains the foot E of the perpendicular from X onto the plane Q_2PP' of the circle, since the line XE is parallel to the axis and hence, to $\mathbf{U}$. This plane is perpendicular to PP' since

PP' is perpendicular to both U and n. Hence if D is the inter-section of this plane with PP' the lines ED and XD, as lines of the plane, must also be perpendicular to PP'. Since XE is parallel to the axis and the generator XQ_2 makes the angle α with the axis, we have in the right-triangle $[XEQ_2]$,

$$(5) \qquad \cos \alpha = \frac{|X - E|}{|X - Q_2|} = \frac{|X - E|}{|X - F_2|}$$

where we have used (2) at the last step. In the plane XED, the line ED is perpendicular to U and XD is perpendicular to n. Since the angle between U and n is θ, in the right-triangle $[XED]$ we find

$$(6) \qquad \sin \theta = \frac{|X - E|}{|X - D|}.$$

From (5) and (6) together,

$$(7) \qquad \frac{\sin \theta}{\cos \alpha} = \frac{|X - F_2|}{|X - D|}.$$

The quantity,

$$(8) \qquad e = \frac{\sin \theta}{\cos \alpha}$$

is called the *eccentricity* of the conic section. In the derivation of (7) we have used no specific property of the conic section, except that the section plane and the plane of the circle of tangency intersect. So (7) applies to any non-degenerate section provided that n is not parallel to the axis. If n is parallel to the axis, the section is a circle and no directrix exists, but the eccentricity as defined by (8) has the value $e = 0$. Equation (7) then states: with the exception of a circle, *a nondegenerate conic section is a plane curve for which the ratio of the distance of any point of the curve from a given point (the focus) to the distance from a given line (the directrix) is constant.*

For an ellipse $\theta < \dfrac{\pi}{2} - \alpha$, hence

$$\sin \theta < \sin \left(\frac{\pi}{2} - \alpha \right)$$

or $\sin \theta < \cos \alpha$. From (8) then, an ellipse is a conic section for which $0 < e < 1$. In the same way we see that a parabola has the eccentricity $e = 1$, and for a hyperbola, that $e > 1$.

We now obtain equations for the various conic sections in the section plane. The *axis* of the conic section is the line of intersection of the section plane and the plane that contains the foci and the axis of the cone. The *vertices* of the conic section are the intersections of the conic section with its axis. If the conic section has two foci, F_1 and F_2 , the midpoint of $[F_1F_2]$ is called the *center*.

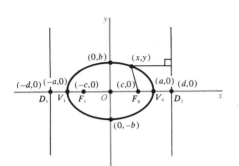 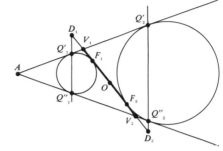

Figure 5

The ellipse. Figure 5a illustrates the ellipse as it appears in the section plane and Figure 5b shows the plane that contains the axis of the ellipse and the axis F_1F_2 of the cone. The points V_1 and V_2 are the vertices of the ellipse, and D_1 and D_2 , the points where the axis meets the directrices. The origin O in the section plane is taken at the center, $O = \frac{1}{2}(F_1 + F_2)$, and the x-axis is in the direction of F_2 , $i = F_2/|F_2|$. The coordinate representations of the foci are $F_1 = (-c, 0)$ and $F_2 = (c, 0)$, where $c - |F_1| = |F_2|$. For V_2 , we have

$$|V_2| = |V_2 - F_2| + |F_2|$$
$$= |V_2 - F_1| - |F_1| .$$

Taking the average of the two representations of $|V_2|$, we have from (3)

$$|V_2| = \tfrac{1}{2}(|V_2 - F_1| + |V_2 - F_2|) = a .$$

In the same way, it follows that $|V_1| = a$. Thus, $V_2 = (a, 0)$ and $V_1 = (-a, 0)$. The number a is called the *semi-major axis* of the ellipse. From (7) and (8), with $D_2 = (d, 0)$, we have

$$e = \frac{|V_2 - F_2|}{|V_2 - D_2|} = \frac{a - c}{d - a}$$

$$= \frac{|V_1 - F_2|}{|V_1 - D_2|} = \frac{a + c}{d + a} .$$

Equating the two expressions for e to solve for d , we find

(9) $$d = \frac{a^2}{c} ;$$

whence,

(10)
$$e = \frac{c}{a} \cdot$$

Now, if $X = (x, y)$ is any point of the ellipse,

$$\frac{|X - F_2|}{|x - d|} = e,$$

or

$$(x - c)^2 + y^2 = e^2(x - d)^2 = \frac{c^2}{a^2}\left(x - \frac{a^2}{c}\right)^2,$$

which yields

(11)
$$(a^2 - c^2)\, x^2 + a^2 y^2 = a^2(a^2 - c^2).$$

The y-intercepts of the curve (11) are $\pm \sqrt{a^2 - c^2}$. The number

$$b = \sqrt{a^2 - c^2}$$

is called the *semi-minor axis* of the ellipse. In terms of a and b the equation of the ellipse has the standard (or canonical) form

(12)
$$\frac{x^2}{a^2} + \frac{y^2}{b^2} = 1 \qquad\qquad (b < a).$$

We have shown only that all points of the ellipse satisfy (12). We have not proved the converse, that all points that satisfy (12) lie on the ellipse. Later (A3.5d) we shall prove the converse and give criteria for recognizing the equation of an ellipse when it is not in standard form.

The hyperbola. For the hyperbola we proceed in the same way as for the ellipse. We introduce the vertices V_1 and V_2, and the points D_1 and D_2 where the axis meets the directrices. We take the origin at the center, and take the x-axis in the direction of F_2; see Figure 6. With $c = |F_1| = |F_2|$ we have $F_1 = (-c, 0)$ and $F_2 = (c, 0)$. For V_2, we have

$$|V_2| = |F_2| - |V_2 - F_2| = |V_2 - F_1| - |F_1|.$$

Taking the average of the two representations of $|V_2|$, we obtain from (4)

$$|V_2| = \tfrac{1}{2}(|V_2 - F_1| - |V_2 - F_2|) = a.$$

In the same way, we can show $|V_1| = a$. Thus, $V_2 = (a, 0)$ and $V_1 = (-a, 0)$. We put $D_2 = (d, 0)$, and obtain exactly as before, $d = a^2/c$ and $e = c/a$, and from this, get the equation of the hyperbola in the form (11). For the hyperbola, however, $c > a$ since $e > 1$. We

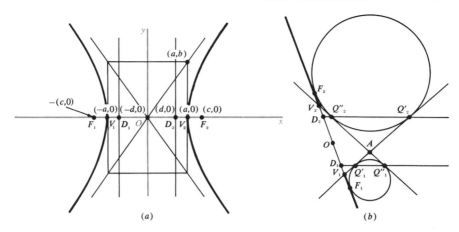

Figure 6

(a)   (b)

now put $b = \sqrt{c^2 - a^2}$ to obtain the equation of the hyperbola in the standard form

(13)
$$\frac{x^2}{a^2} - \frac{y^2}{b^2} = 1 .$$

The curve (13) has no y-intercepts, so b is not to be interpreted for the hyperbola as it is for the ellipse. Again, it has only been shown that the hyperbola is contained in the graph of (13). It remains to be shown that (13) contains no other points.

In contrast to the ellipse, the hyperbola is an unbounded figure. The two branches of the hyperbola are described by the equations

$$x = \pm \frac{a}{b} \sqrt{y^2 + b^2} .$$

Clearly, $|y|$ and hence $|x|$ can be taken larger than any given number. For large $|y|$ it is easily seen that the graph of the hyperbola approximates the two straight lines $x = \pm \frac{a}{b} y$. To show this, we estimate the distance for a given y of the points $\left(\pm \frac{a}{b} \sqrt{y^2 + b^2} , y \right)$ from the corresponding points of the straight lines $\left(\pm \frac{a}{b} |y|, y \right)$. For this, we use the estimates for $k > 0$

$$1 < \sqrt{1 + k} < \sqrt{1 + k + \frac{k^2}{4}} \le \sqrt{\left(1 + \frac{k}{2} \right)^2} \le 1 + \frac{k}{2} .$$

For the distance δ between a point on the hyperbola and the corresponding point on the straight lines

$$\delta = \frac{a}{b}\sqrt{y^2 + b^2} - \frac{a}{b}|y| = \frac{a}{b}|y|\left(\sqrt{1 + \frac{b^2}{y^2}} - 1\right).$$

Consequently, setting $k = \dfrac{b^2}{y^2}$ in the foregoing estimate we find for δ,

$$0 < \delta < \frac{ab}{2|y|}.$$

For $|y|$ large enough, the straight lines approximate the hyperbola within any prescribed error tolerance. For example, if we set an error tolerance ϵ, then for $|y| > \dfrac{ab}{2\epsilon}$, the distance δ between a point on the hyperbola and the corresponding point on the straight lines is less than ϵ. The two lines

(14) $$bx \pm ay = 0$$

are called the *asymptotes* of the hyperbola. The geometrical relation of the number b to the hyperbola can now be expressed simply: the asymptotes are extended diagonals of the rectangle with the four vertices $(\pm a, \pm b)$; see Figure 6a.

If the asymptotes are perpendicular $(a^2 = b^2)$ the hyperbola is said to be *rectangular*.

The parabola. In contrast to the ellipse and the hyperbola, the parabola has just one focus, one vertex, and one directrix. We take the origin at the vertex V and the y-axis in the direction of the focus F; see Figure 7. Since the eccentricity has the value $e = 1$, the vertex is equidistant from F

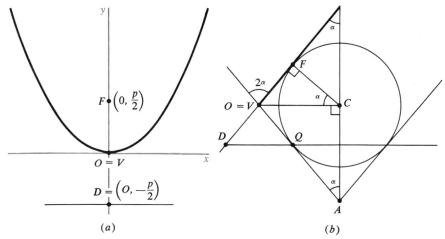

(a)   (b)   *Figure 7*

and the point D where the axis meets the directrix. If p is the distance between the focus and the directrix,

$$F = \left(0, \frac{p}{2}\right) \text{ and } D = \left(0, -\frac{p}{2}\right).$$

For every point $X = (x, y)$ of the parabola

$$e = \frac{|X - F|}{\left| y + \frac{p}{2} \right|} = 1.$$

Consequently,

$$x^2 + \left(y - \frac{p}{2}\right)^2 = \left(y + \frac{p}{2}\right)^2;$$

whence,

(15)
$$y = \frac{x^2}{2p}.$$

This is the standard form of the equation for a parabola.

With the conic sections we have completed a survey of those curves that may easily be studied without the help of the calculus. Even for the conic sections, there are many useful properties which are most easily investigated by the methods of calculus.

A3.5c Exercises

1. Let the distance between the focus and its associated directrix be p. For the ellipse let a and b be the numbers appearing in the standard equation (12).
   a. Express p in terms of a and b.
   b. Express a and b in terms of p and the eccentricity e.

2. The *interior* of the ellipse (12) is the set of points

   (i)
   $$S = \left\{ (x, y) : \frac{x^2}{a^2} + \frac{y^2}{b^2} < 1 \right\}.$$

   Prove that the set S is convex; that is, if P and Q are elements of S, the entire segment $[PQ]$ is contained in S. Show also that the union of the ellipse with its interior is convex.

3. Prove that any ray from the origin meets the ellipse (12) in exactly one point.

4. Prove that any ray from a point of the interior of the ellipse (12) meets the ellipse at exactly one point.

5. Prove that no line meets the ellipse in more than two points.

6. Prove that two ellipses with the same foci (*confocal* ellipses) cannot intersect.

7. Draftsmen construct ellipses by the following method. They draw chords perpendicular to the diameter of a circle and divide the half-chords between the diameter and the circle in a fixed ratio. (In the figure, the half-chords are divided in half.) The points of division are then joined to form the ellipse. Prove that this is a valid way to construct an ellipse. Calculate the eccentricity of the ellipse so constructed.

8. Show that the length s of any chord of the ellipse (12) satisfies $s \leq 2a$.

9. A chord through the center of the ellipse (12) is called a *diameter*. For the length s of any diameter obtain the lower estimate $2b \leq s$.

10. Show that the sum of the squares of the reciprocals of perpendicular diameters (see Exercise 9) of an ellipse is constant.

11. Prove that the midpoints of parallel chords of an ellipse lie on a straight line.

12. A line is called *tangent* to an ellipse if it is contained in the plane of the ellipse and intersects the ellipse at exactly one point. (The same definition could have been used for the circle.)

   a. Show for any family of all lines parallel to a given direction, that it contains two tangent lines to the ellipse (12). Give the coordinates of the points of tangency.

   b. Show that there is only one line tangent to the ellipse (12) at a given point, and find its equation.

13. Show that the ellipse does not cross its tangents; that is, the interior of the ellipse (see Exercise 2) lies entirely on one side of any tangent line.

14. The ellipse has the optical (or acoustical) property that any ray from one focus is reflected by the ellipse to the other focus. This property is used in "whispering galleries" where two people at the foci of an elliptical room or under an ellipsoidal dome can converse easily in quiet tones and yet be inaudible to anyone between them. Geometrically, this focal property of the ellipse means that the lines PF_1 and PF_2 which connect any point P of the ellipse to the foci make equal angles with the perpendicular to the tangent line at P. Demonstrate this property.

15. Derive (12) from the property (3) of the ellipse.

16. Demonstrate the converse to the result of Exercise 15: if $X = (x, y)$ satisfies (12) then X satisfies (3) for suitably chosen points F_1 and F_2.

17. Show that only one choice of F_1 and F_2 is possible in Exercise 16.

18. To show directly that (12) is the equation of the ellipse it is possible to proceed as follows. Choose a coordinate system for E^3 in which the origin is $\mathbf{O} = \frac{1}{2}(\mathbf{F}_1 + \mathbf{F}_2)$, and the unit coordinate vectors are $\mathbf{i}, \mathbf{j}, \mathbf{k}$, where $\mathbf{i} = \mathbf{F}_2/|\mathbf{F}_2|$, $\mathbf{j}$ is perpendicular to $\mathbf{i}$ in the section, and $\mathbf{k} = \mathbf{n}$, is the normal to the section plane. The section plane then has the equation $z = 0$. To obtain the equation of the ellipse express a vector $\mathbf{U}$ in the direction of the axis in terms of its components and A in terms of its coordinates, then put $z = 0$ in (1). Carry out this approach.

19. For each of the preceding problems determine whether the stated result holds

for the hyperbola (13). If it does not, state a corresponding result for the hyperbola. Prove your assertions.

20. Show that the foot of the perpendicular from a focus of the hyperbola (13) on an asymptote is a point of the directrix associated with the given focus.

21. For a rectangular hyperbola show that the area of the triangle formed by any tangent line with the asymptotes is constant.

22. Determine whether the parabola (15) satisfies each of the results stated for the ellipse in Exercise 1 through 18. If not, try to find an analogous result.

EA3.5d The General Quadratic Equation

Among the conic sections we have found certain properties which we have used to derive standard equations of the plane curves having them. One small nagging doubt must yet be resolved. We have not shown that the sets consisting of all points that satisfy the standard equations are conic sections; all we know is that the conic sections satisfy the equations. In principle, there could be other points which satisfy a standard equation but do not lie on the corresponding conic section. We could attack the issue directly and prove that a point lies on the conic section if its coordinates satisfy the standard equation (see A3.5c Ex. 18). We did not do so because we shall now show for a more general class of equations that they are equations of conic sections, and we shall be able to classify these equations by the kinds of conic sections they define.

The more general approach is not only more informative, but it is also in some respects simpler. Recall that the standard equation does not involve all the data connected with the definition of the conic section. The angles α and θ are not recoverable from the standard equation; only the ratio $e = \sin\theta/\cos\alpha$ can be retrieved. A given ellipse or parabola can be obtained as a section of any cone. For a hyperbola, the condition $\sin\theta \leq 1$ yields the restriction $\cos\alpha \leq 1/e$. From

$$e = \frac{c}{a} = \frac{\sqrt{a^2 + b^2}}{a},$$

the condition on α becomes $\tan\alpha \geq b/a$; hence α must not be less than the angle made by an asymptote with the axis of the hyperbola. If this condition is satisfied, the hyperbola can be obtained as a section of the cone. A conic section may then be obtained as a section of any one of infinitely many geometrically distinct cones (that is, cones with different vertex angles). Here, by choosing a cone with no criterion in mind except algebraic convenience, we show that any equation of a certain general class describes a conic section.

Each of the standard equations in A3.5c is a quadratic equation in two variables. The general form of a quadratic equation in two variables† is

(1) $ax^2 + 2bxy + cy^2 + 2dx + 2ey + f = 0$ $(a^2 + b^2 + c^2 \neq 0)$.

Theorem 1. For any coordinate system in the section plane, the equation of a conic section is quadratic.

Proof. Let the section plane be given by $z = 0$. By putting $z = 0$ in Equation A3.5a (11), we get the equation of the conic section and that equation is easily seen to be quadratic (Ex. 1).   ☐

The converse, with minor exceptions, is also true.

Theorem 2. Any quadratic equation (1) is the equation of a conic section, or of two parallel straight lines, or of the empty set.

Proof. Take $X = (x_0, y_0, z_0)$ as the vertex of the cone, $U = (u, v, w)$ as a vector in the direction of the axis, and let α be the vertex angle. The equation of the cone is

(2) $[(X - X_0) \cdot U]^2 = \lambda^2 |X - X_0|^2$,

where $\lambda^2 = |U|^2 \cos^2 \alpha = (u^2 + v^2 + w^2) \cos^2 \alpha$. Rewrite (2) in the form

(3) $[\lambda^2 |X|^2 - (X \cdot U)^2]$

$+ 2[(X \cdot U)(X_0 \cdot U) - \lambda^2 (X \cdot X_0]$

$+ [\lambda^2 |X_0|^2 - (X_0 \cdot U)^2] = 0$.

In (3), we have bracketed together, successively, the quadratic terms, the linear terms, and the constant terms.

Now, we take the section of the cone (3) by the plane $z = 0$; that is, we set $X = (x, y, 0)$. Next we obtain formulas for the coefficients of the resultant quadratic equation in terms of λ, X_0, and U. Finally, we show how to choose λ, X_0 and U so that the coefficients take on any pre-assigned values.

---

† A polynomial $P(x, y)$ in two variables is a sum of terms of the form $a_{mn} x^m y^n$ where m and n are nonnegative integers. If $a_{mn} \neq 0$ the degree of $a_{mn} x^m y^n$ is defined to be $m + n$. The degree of the polynomial $P(x, y)$ is

$$\deg P = \max \{m + n : a_{mn} \neq 0\}.$$

A quadratic equation in two variables is an equation of the form $P(x, y) = 0$ where $\deg P = 2$.

Comparing (1) and (3), we obtain for the quadratic terms

(4a)
$$\lambda^2 - u^2 = a ,$$

(4b)
$$-uv = b ,$$

(4c)
$$\lambda^2 - v^2 = c .$$

From (4a) and (4c) we have

$$u^2 v^2 = \lambda^4 - (a + c)\lambda^2 + ac .$$

Applying (4b) in this result, we obtain

$$\lambda^4 - (a + c)\lambda^2 + ac - b^2 = 0 .$$

This is a quadratic equation for λ^2 and has the roots

$$\lambda^2 = \tfrac{1}{2}[a + c + \epsilon \sqrt{(a + c)^2 - 4(ac - b^2)}] ,$$

where $\epsilon = \pm 1$. Since $0 < \alpha < \dfrac{\pi}{2}$ we must require

$$\lambda^2 = |U|^2 \cos^2 \alpha \neq 0 ;$$

that is, $\lambda^2 > 0$. To achieve this when $ac - b^2 \geq 0$ we take $\epsilon = 1$ and $a + c \geq 0$ in (1) — if $a + c < 0$, we may multiply in (1) by -1. When $ac - b^2 < 0$ we only require $\epsilon = 1$. Now, λ^2 is always real, since

(5a)
$$\lambda^2 = \tfrac{1}{2}[a + c + \sqrt{(a + c)^2 - 4(ac - b)^2}]$$
$$= \tfrac{1}{2}[a + c + \sqrt{(a - c)^2 + 4b^2}] ,$$

so that the number under the square root sign is nonnegative. We use (5a) in (4a) and (4c) to obtain

(5b)
$$u^2 = \tfrac{1}{2}[c - a + \sqrt{(a - c)^2 + 4b^2}] ,$$

(5c)
$$v^2 = \tfrac{1}{2}[a - c + \sqrt{(a - c)^2 + 4b^2}] ,$$

and observe that these equations for u and v always have solutions since the expressions on the right are nonnegative. These expressions for u^2 and v^2 must be supplemented by the condition on the signs of u and v imposed by (4b):

$$\text{sgn } u \text{ sgn } v = -\text{sgn } b ;$$

if $b > 0$, for example, u and v have opposite signs. Note that there could be a restriction on w in the form of an inequality since $\lambda^2 / (u^2 + v^2 + w^2) = \cos^2 \alpha < 1$ requires that $\lambda^2 - u^2 - v^2 < w^2 ,$

or

$$w^2 > \tfrac{1}{2}[(a + c) - \sqrt{(a + c)^2 - 4(ac - b^2)}] \, .$$

If $ac - b^2 \geq 0$ we shall satisfy this condition by taking $w^2 = \lambda^2$. If $ac - b^2 < 0$, the expression on the right is negative and there is no restriction on w.

Identifying the remaining terms in (1) and (3), we have for the linear terms

(6a) $$u(X_0 \cdot U) - \lambda^2 x_0 = d \, ,$$

(6b) $$v(X_0 \cdot U) - \lambda^2 y_0 = e \, ,$$

and for the constant term

(7) $$\lambda^2 |X_0|^2 - (X_0 \cdot U)^2 = f \, .$$

From (6) we obtain linear equations for x_0 and y_0 in terms of z_0, u, v, w and the coefficients in (1); namely,

(8a) $$ax_0 + by_0 = z_0 uw - d \, ,$$

(8b) $$bx_0 + cy_0 = z_0 vw - e \, ,$$

where we have used (4) in getting the coefficients of x_0 and y_0. The linear system (8) always has a unique solution unless $ac - b^2 = 0$ (see A3.4a Ex. 15), a special situation which we shall investigate later. From (7), by similar means, we obtain

(9) $$(ax_0^2 + 2bx_0 y_0 + cy_0^2 - f)$$
$$- 2z_0 w(x_0 u + y_0 v) + (\lambda^2 - w^2)z_0^2 = 0 \, . \qquad \Box$$

The preceding results are quite general, but to complete the proof we must now consider special cases. In the preceding analysis the sign of the number $ac - b^2$ has entered the discussion at several places. We shall have to treat the three different possibilities for $\operatorname{sgn}(ac - b^2)$ as separate cases. The number

(10) $$\Delta = ac - b^2$$

is called the *discriminant* of the *quadratic form*

(11) $$Q(x, y) = ax^2 + 2bxy + cy^2 \qquad (a^2 + b^2 + c^2 \neq 0) \, .$$

The equation A3.5c (13) of the hyperbola in standard form has a positive discriminant; the parabola A3.5c (15), a zero discriminant; and the ellipse A3.5c (12), a negative discriminant. We shall see that this result is general.

Now, let us suppose only that $\Delta \neq 0$; we shall separate the positive and negative cases later. If $\Delta \neq 0$ we can rewrite (1) in the form

(12a) $a(x - p)^2 + 2b(x - p)(y - q) + c(y - q)^2 = k$;

that is, we can find an origin (p, q) in the x, y plane for which the linear terms in (1) do not appear. Comparing (1) and (12a), we obtain for the conditions on p and q

(12b)
$$ap + bq = -d,$$
$$bp + cq = -e.$$

If $\Delta = ac - b^2 \neq 0$, these equations have the unique solution

(12c) $$p = \frac{eb - cd}{\Delta}, \quad q = \frac{bd - ae}{\Delta}.$$

For k we have simply

(12d) $$k = ap^2 + 2bpq + cq^2 - f = Q(p, q) - f.$$

If $\Delta \neq 0$, then, we set $x - p = \xi$ and $y - q = \eta$ and rewrite (1) in the form

(13) $$Q(\xi, \eta) = a\xi^2 + 2b\xi\eta + c\eta^2 = k.$$

Correspondingly, in the ξ, η, ζ system we set $A = (\xi_0, \eta_0, \zeta_0)$, where $\xi_0 = x_0 - p$, $\eta_0 = y_0 - q$, $\zeta_0 = z_0$. In this coordinate system, the quadratic conditions (4) are not affected, the conditions (8) on the linear terms are replaced by

(14a) $a\xi_0 + b\eta_0 = uw\zeta_0,$

(14b) $b\xi_0 + c\eta_0 = vw\zeta_0,$

and the condition (9) on the constant term becomes

(15) $$k + a\xi_0^2 + 2b\xi_0\eta_0 + c\eta_0^2 - 2\zeta_0 w(\xi_0 u + \eta_0 v)$$
$$+ (\lambda^2 - w^2)\zeta_0^2 = 0.$$

In (15), we replace the linear term in ζ_0, taking the expressions for $uw\zeta_0$ and $vw\zeta_0$ from (14a) and (14b) respectively:

(16) $$2\zeta_0 w(\xi_0 u + \eta_0 v) = 2(\xi_0 uw\zeta_0 + \eta_0 vw\zeta_0)$$
$$= 2(a\xi_0^2 + 2b\xi_0\eta_0 + c\eta_0^2) = 2Q(\xi_0, \eta_0).$$

This yields the equation

(17) $$(\lambda^2 - w^2)\zeta_0^2 - Q(\xi_0, \eta_0) + k = 0.$$

We are now ready to treat the separate cases.

   Case 1. $ac - b^2 > 0$. We know the ellipse A3.5c (12) has a positive discriminant so we anticipate that this condition will yield ellipses, and perhaps some degenerate cases. As we have remarked, when the discriminant is nonnegative there is no restriction on w. We simplify matters by setting $w^2 = \lambda^2$ to obtain from (17),

(18) $$Q(\xi_0, \eta_0) = k.$$

Since the discriminant is positive, and $a + c > 0$ both a and c must be positive. It follows that $Q(\xi, \eta)$ is positive definite (see Ex. 2). Therefore, solutions of (18) exist if and only if $k \geq 0$; the cases $k \leq 0$ are unimportant. If $k < 0$ the quadratic equation (13) is the equation of the empty set; if $k = 0$ it is the equation of the one point $(0, 0)$. For $k > 0$, we seek a solution (ξ_0, η_0, ζ_0) of (14) and (18). We use (16) to replace (18) by

(19) $$w\zeta_0(u\xi_0 + v\eta_0) = k.$$

From (14)

(20a) $$\xi_0 = w\zeta_0(cu - bv)/\Delta,$$
(20b) $$\eta_0 = w\zeta_0(av - bu)/\Delta.$$

Enter these values for ξ_0 and η_0 in (19c), and recall that $w^2 = \lambda^2$ to get

$$\frac{\lambda^2 \zeta_0^2}{\Delta}(av^2 - 2buv + cu^2) = k,$$

or

(20c) $$\zeta_0^2 = \frac{k\Delta}{\lambda^2 Q(v, -u)}.$$

From 5(a) $\lambda^2 > 0$ and from 5(b, c), at least one of u, v is positive so that $Q(v, -u) > 0$. Consequently (20c) does have a solution ζ_0. In terms of $\zeta_0, u, v,$ and λ we then find ξ_0 and η_0. We leave it as an exercise to verify that we have determined the vertex (ξ_0, η_0, ζ_0), direction of the axis (u, v, w), and vertex angle α of a cone for which (13) is a section, and that the section is an ellipse (Exs. 3, 4). To do the same for (1) we have only to refer back to the original origin; that is, to set $\xi = x - p$, $\eta = y - q$, $\zeta = z$ and take p, q and k from (12c, d). Observe too that the conic section defined by (13) for $\Delta > 0$ and $k > 0$ must be an ellipse since the set of solutions (x, y) of (13) is bounded (Ex. 2c) and the only unbounded nondegenerate conic sections are ellipses.

Case 2. $ac - b^2 < 0$. The hyperbola A3.5c (13) has a negative discriminant so we expect that this condition will yield hyperbolas and some degenerate cases. In this case, we are free to choose w as we please. We take $w = 0$. The equations (14) then have only the trivial solution $\xi_0 = \eta_0 = 0$. Equation (15) then reduces to $\zeta_0^2 \lambda^2 = -k$. We require $k \le 0$, as we may, since we could always multiply by -1 in (13) if $k > 0$. Then $\zeta_0 = \sqrt{-k}/\lambda$. With the values of λ, u, v given by (5), $w = 0$, $\xi_0 = \eta_0 = 0$ and $\zeta_0 = \sqrt{-k}/\lambda$ we have determined a cone for which (13) is the equation of a section.

If $\Delta < 0$ the quadratic form $Q(\xi, \eta)$ can be factored into relatively prime linear polynomials (Ex. 5).† We may then rewrite (13) in the form

(21) $$(\alpha_1\xi + \beta_1\eta)(\alpha_2\xi + \beta_2\eta) = k,$$

where the coefficient vectors (α_1, β_1) and (α_2, β_2) are noncollinear. If $k = 0$, the vertex of the cone lies on the section plane and (21) is the equation of two intersecting straight lines. If $k < 0$, the conic section is nondegenerate. Furthermore, we now verify that the solution set of (21) consists of two separated branches, and must, therefore, be a hyperbola (also see Ex. 6). The lines $\alpha_1\xi + \beta_1\eta = 0$ and $\alpha_2 x + \beta_2 y = 0$ divide the plane into four angles defined by the signs of the expressions $d_i = \alpha_i\xi + \beta_i\eta$, $(i = 1, 2)$. With $k < 0$ we see that $d_1 d_2 < 0$ so that d_1 and d_2 have opposite signs. The solution set must lie in the interior of one pair of vertical angles formed by the two lines. Furthermore, if (ξ, η) is a solution of (21), so is $(-\xi, -\eta)$ and therefore the solution set cannot lie wholly in one of the two angles (the solution set is easily shown to be nonempty).

Case 3. $ac - b^2 = 0$. The parabola A3.5c (15) has discriminant zero. We expect, then, that the condition $\Delta = 0$ will yield parabolas and degenerate cases. If $\Delta = 0$ we cannot expect to reduce (1) to the form (13), since the equations (12b) may represent parallel noncoincident lines and therefore have no solution. We now have $ac = b^2$ and may put

(22) $$Q(x, y) = ax^2 + 2\epsilon\sqrt{ac}\, xy + cy^2,$$

where $\epsilon = \mathrm{sgn}\, b$. Since at least one of the coefficients must be nonzero, a and c are not both zero. Say $a \ne 0$. Recall that we have required that $a + c \ge 0$ when $\Delta \ge 0$. Since $ac = b^2 \ge 0$ it follows that $a > 0$ and $c \ge 0$. We may then rewrite (22) in the form

$$Q(x, y) = (\sqrt{a}\, x + \epsilon\sqrt{c}\, y)^2.$$

†Two linear polynomials $\alpha_1 x + \beta_1 y$ and $\alpha_2 x + \beta_2 y$ are relatively prime if and only if they are not proportional; that is, the vectors (α_1, β_1) and (α_2, β_2) are noncollinear.

With $p = \sqrt{a}$ and $q = \epsilon\sqrt{c}$ we then put (1) in the form

(23) $\qquad p^2 x^2 + 2pqxy + q^2 y^2 + 2dx + 2ey + f = 0 .$

In (23) we use $p^2 x^2 + 2dx = [p(x - \mu)]^2 - p^2\mu^2$, where $\mu = -\dfrac{d}{p^2}$,

to obtain

$$[p(x - \mu) + qy]^2 + 2\left(e - \frac{qd}{p}\right) y + f - \frac{d^2}{p^2} = 0 .$$

In the nondegenerate case, $e \neq \dfrac{qd}{p}$ and the equation can be put in the form

(24) $\qquad (p\xi + q\eta)^2 + 2\gamma(\eta - \beta) = 0$

where $\xi = x - \mu$ and $\eta = y$ are coordinates referred to the origin $(\mu, 0)$ with $\gamma = e - \dfrac{qd}{p} \neq 0$, and $\beta = \dfrac{1}{2\gamma}\left(\dfrac{d^2}{p^2} - f\right)$. It is now easy to represent (24) as a conic section. From (5) we may take

$$\lambda^2 = p^2 + q^2 , \quad u = q , \quad v = -p$$

The equations (8) become

(25a) $\qquad\qquad p^2\xi_0 + pq\eta_0 = \zeta_0 wq$

(25b) $\qquad\qquad pq\xi_0 + q^2\eta_0 = -\zeta_0 wp - \gamma ,$

and (9) becomes

(26) $\qquad 2\beta\gamma + (p\xi_0 + q\eta_0)^2 - 2\zeta_0 w(q\xi_0 - p\eta_0)$
$$+ [(p^2 + q^2) - w^2]\zeta_0^2 = 0 .$$

The restriction $w^2 > \lambda^2 - u^2 - v^2$ requires only that $w \neq 0$ in this case; we choose $w^2 = p^2 + q^2$ to simplify (26). Equations (25a, b) can be written

$$p(p\xi_0 + q\eta_0) = \zeta_0 qw \quad \text{and} \quad q(p\xi_0 + q\eta_0) = -\zeta_0 pw - \gamma .$$

We may therefore eliminate $p\xi_0 + q\eta_0$ in (25a, b) to obtain $\zeta_0 q^2 w + \zeta_0 p^2 w + p\gamma = 0$; hence,

(27) $\qquad\qquad \zeta_0 w(p^2 + q^2) = -p\gamma .$

With $w^2 = p^2 + q^2$, this yields

$$\zeta_0 = -p\gamma/(p^2 + q^2)^{3/2} .$$

Now, from (25a), $p\xi_0 + q\eta_0 = \zeta_0 wq/p$; hence with $w^2 = p^2 + q^2$ we have from (25a) and (26)

(28a) $$q\xi_0 - p\eta_0 = \frac{\beta_0\gamma}{\varsigma_0 w} + \frac{(\varsigma_0 wq)^2}{2p^2}.$$

Couple this equation with (25a) in the form

(28b) $$p\xi_0 + q\eta_0 = \varsigma_0 wq/p.$$

Recall that $\varsigma_0 w$ is already given by (27). In (28) we then have a pair of simultaneous linear equations for ξ_0 and η_0 and these equations have a solution (see A3.4a Ex. 15). It is easily verified that the solution of (28), with ς_0 and w^2 as given, do satisfy (25) and (26).

Finally, we note that the conic section (24) must be a parabola, since for any η on the side of the line $\eta = \beta$ for which $\gamma(\eta - \beta) > 0$ we can solve (24) for ξ, and no solution exists if $\gamma(\eta - \beta) < 0$. Thus (24) is the equation of a conic section which is unbounded, hence it is not an ellipse; it lies entirely on one side of a line $(\eta = \beta)$, hence is not a hyperbola; it is not degenerate $(\varsigma_0 \neq 0)$, hence must be a parabola. (See Ex. 7 as well.)

In the degenerate cases, $\gamma = 0$, and we have not (24) but

(29) $$(p\xi + q\eta)^2 = k,$$

where $k = d^2 - f$. If $k < 0$, equation (29) describes the empty set. If $k = 0$, then (29) is the equation of the union of the line $p\xi + q\eta = 0$ with itself $\big($see A3.5a (12)$\big)$; therefore it only defines the line $p\xi + q\eta = 0$ redundantly. In this case, $\xi_0 = \eta_0 = \varsigma_0 = 0$ will define a cone for which the line is a section. If $k > 0$ then (29) is the equation of the two parallel lines $p\xi + q\eta = \pm \sqrt{k}$ and cannot therefore be a section of the cone.† ☐

In A3.5c we proved that any nondegenerate conic section satisfies a standard quadratic equation in some coordinate system. Here we have shown how to represent the solution set of a quadratic equation, if it is non-empty, as the equation of a conic section or of two parallel straight lines. In particular, we may now satisfy ourselves directly that the standard equations A3.5c (12, 13, 15) satisfy the conditions for nondegenerate conic sections (Ex. 9). Thus we have eliminated the possibility that there may be extra points which satisfy the standard equations and do not lie on a conic section. In addition, we have obtained a classification of quadratic equations according to the nature of the geometrical figures they describe. Furthermore, we have defined the classes algebraically in terms of the coefficients in (1).

---

†In most texts every quadratic equation is called a conic section although the empty set and the union of two parallel lines cannot be obtained as the section of a cone with any plane.

A3.5d Exercises

1. Put $z = 0$ in the equation of a cone A3.5a (11) and verify that the resulting equation is quadratic.

2. a. A quadratic form

$$Q(x, y) = ax^2 + 2bxy + cy^2 \qquad (a^2 + b^2 + c^2 \neq 0).$$

   is said to be *positive definite* if $Q(x, y) > 0$ for all x and y except when $x = y = 0$. If $Q(x, y) \geq 0$ for all x and y, but

$$Q(x, y) = 0$$

   for at least two distinct pairs (x, y) then $Q(x, y)$ is called *positive indefinite*. Prove if $Q(x, y)$ is positive definite that a, c and the discriminant $\Delta = ac - b^2$ are all positive. Prove conversely, if $a > 0$ and $\Delta > 0$ that $Q(x, y)$ is positive definite. Show further if $Q(x, y)$ is positive indefinite that $\Delta = 0$ and either a or c is positive; conversely, if either a or c is positive and $\Delta = 0$, then $Q(x, y)$ is positive indefinite.

   b. Show for a positive quadratic form (definite or indefinite) that the equation

   (i) $$Q(x, y) = k$$

   has a solution for each nonnegative k.

   c. If $Q(x, y)$ is positive definite, show for $k \geq 0$ that the solution set of (i) is bounded; that is, show that the x-coordinates and the y-coordinates of the points of the solution set are bounded.

3. Verify that (13) is the section of the plane $z = 0$ with the cone (2) for data defined by (5), (20) and $w^2 = \lambda^2$.

4. Calculate the eccentricity in terms of the coefficients of (13) to show that the section in Exercise 3 is an ellipse.

5. a. Let $Q(x, y)$ be a quadratic form with a negative discriminant. Prove that $Q(x, y)$ can be factored into relatively prime linear polynomials:

$$Q(x, y) = (\alpha_1 x + \beta_1 y)(\alpha_2 x + \beta_2 y).$$

   b. Show in this case that the solution set of $Q(x, y) = k$, $(k > 0)$ is unbounded.

   c. Show that the lines $\alpha_i x + \beta_i y = 0$ are asymptotes of the curve

$$Q(x, y) = k.$$

6. Calculate the eccentricity of the conic section (13) if $\Delta < 0$ and $k < 0$ and verify that $e > 1$ so that the section must be a hyperbola.

7. When $\gamma \neq 0$ verify that the conic section (24) is a parabola by calculating its eccentricity.

8. Show that a degenerate conic section may also be defined as the set of points for which the ratio of the distances to a given point and given line is constant, but the given point lies on the given line.

9. Verify that the standard equations A3.5c (12, 13, 15) satisfy the conditions obtained in this section that they are nondegenerate conic sections.

10. Prove the assertions of the text that
    a. A given ellipse can be obtained as a section of any cone.
    b. A given parabola can be obtained as a section of any cone.
    c. A given hyperbola of eccentricity e can be obtained as the section of any cone with vertex angle α restricted to satisfy $\cos \alpha \leq \dfrac{1}{e}$, where e is the eccentricity of the hyperbola.

11. Determine the direction of the axis for a conic section given in the form (1).

12. Show that the center of an ellipse or hyperbola is the only point which has the property that it bisects every chord on the lines through it.

13. Locate the vertices of the conic section (13).

A3.6 TRANSFORMATIONS AND SYMMETRIES

A *transformation of a set* is a one-to-one mapping of the set onto itself. We have already examined one class of transformations of euclidean space, the translations. Although we could have developed geometry without this concept, clearly, the notion of translation has greatly enriched and extended our appreciation of geometry. The modern approach to the study of any space is through its transformations; here we treat certain classes of transformations of euclidean space in detail since this attack has proved most fruitful.

It is easy to overlook the simplest of all transformations, the *identity transformation*†

$$I : P \to P$$

that maps each point of space onto itself. Since the domain and range of the transformations of space both consist of all points in space, compositions of transformations may be formed freely and again are mappings of space onto itself. The component transformations of such a mapping are one-to-one; hence their composition is one-to-one and is also a transformation. Thus, if T_1 and T_2 are transformations, so also are the compositions $T_1 T_2$ and $T_2 T_1$. This property is called *closure* with respect to composition. Since transformations are mappings, we already know that they satisfy the associative law of composition

$$T_3(T_2 T_1) = (T_3 T_2)T_1 .$$

†The identity transformation I is, of course, the same as the translation $\mathbf{O}$.

(See A2.3, p. 265f.) If T is any transformation,

$$IT = TI = T .$$

Since T is one-to-one, we conclude further that T has an inverse T^{-1}, also a transformation, where

$$TT^{-1} = T^{-1}T = I .$$

The four properties of a binary operation,† *closure, associativity, existence of an identity*, and *existence of an inverse* appear in many important contexts — for example, addition of integers, multiplication of real numbers (except zero), and composition of translations. In general, we say a set $\mathcal{G}$ is a *group* with respect to a binary operation $\otimes$ if, for any $a , b , c \in \mathcal{G}$ the four properties are satisfied.

a. *Closure:*

$$a \otimes b \in \mathcal{G} .$$

b. *Associativity:*

$$(a \otimes b) \otimes c = a \otimes (b \otimes c) .$$

c. *Identity:*
There exists an element e in $\mathcal{G}$, the *identity*, such that for every $a \in \mathcal{G}$,

$$a \otimes e = e \otimes a = a .$$

d. *Inverse:*
For each $a \in \mathcal{G}$ there exists an element a^{-1}, the *inverse* of a, such that

$$a \otimes a^{-1} = a^{-1} \otimes a = e .$$

We have seen that the transformations of space form a group with respect to composition. The subset of the full transformation group consisting of the translations alone is also a group with respect to the same operation. Such a subset is called a *subgroup*. We shall study only certain subgroups of the transformation group, principally the *isometries*,‡ the subgroup consisting of those transformations which preserve lengths. A property that is not changed in a transformation is called an *invariant* of the transformation. Since length is an invariant under an isometry T, we must have

$$|T(A) - T(B)| = |A - B| .$$

---

†A binary operation is simply a function $(a, b) \to c$ on an ordered pair of elements. Thus, addition of real numbers is the mapping $(a, b) \to a + b$.

‡From Greek *isos* (equal) + *metron* (measure).

(Recall that addition of points is defined by the one-to-one correspondence of points and position vectors.) In particular, if $\mathbf{U}$ is the position vector of the point U, the translation $\mathbf{U}$ satisfies

$$\mathbf{U}(A) - \mathbf{U}(B) = (U + A) - (U + B)$$
$$= A - B \,;$$

consequently, a translation is an isometry. The set of isometries is easily shown to be a subgroup of the transformation group (see Exercise 1).

A3.6a Rotations and reflections of the plane

We shall consider isometries of the plane only. When we have introduced the techniques of linear algebra (Chapter 15) we shall be able to extend the ideas of this section to transformations of space.

With the sole exception of the identity, translations leave no point of the plane invariant. Now, we investigate isometries that do have fixed points.

We make use of the conventions which enable us to represent points by position vectors; namely, upon choosing an origin O, we write $\alpha\mathbf{A} + \beta\mathbf{B}$ to represent both a translation and the image of O in the translation. In particular, we shall write transformations of the plane in the form of mappings of position vectors onto position vectors.

Let T be an isometry with fixed points and choose the origin $\mathbf{O}$ as one of the fixed points. For this choice of origin, we shall prove that the isometry T is a *linear transformation;* that is

(1) $$T(a\mathbf{U} + b\mathbf{V}) = aT(\mathbf{U}) + bT(\mathbf{V}) \,.$$

First, we observe that the defining property of an isometry is

(2) $$|\mathbf{U}' - \mathbf{V}'| = |\mathbf{U} - \mathbf{V}|$$

where $\mathbf{U}' = T(\mathbf{U})$ and $\mathbf{V}' = T(\mathbf{V})$. If $\mathbf{O}$ is a fixed point of T, $T(\mathbf{O}) = \mathbf{O}$, we may set $\mathbf{V} = \mathbf{O}$ in (2) to obtain

(3) $$|\mathbf{U}'| = |\mathbf{U}| \,.$$

Lemma 1. If $\mathbf{O}$ is a fixed point of the isometry T then dot products are invariant under T.

Proof. Since dot products can be expressed in terms of absolute values, and absolute values are invariant by (3), it follows that dot products are invariant; thus,

$$\mathbf{U}' \cdot \mathbf{V}' = \tfrac{1}{2}\{|\mathbf{U}'|^2 + |\mathbf{V}'|^2 - |\mathbf{U}' - \mathbf{V}'|^2\}$$
$$= \tfrac{1}{2}\{|\mathbf{U}|^2 + |\mathbf{V}|^2 - |\mathbf{U} - \mathbf{V}|^2\} = \mathbf{U} \cdot \mathbf{V} \,. \qquad \square$$

Since dot products and length are both invariants under an isometry with a fixed point, it follows that angle measure is also invariant. In A3.6b we shall prove that any isometry can be represented as the composition of isometries with fixed points. Thus, in general, length and angle are invariants under isometry, isometry preserves size and shape. Two figures are congruent (have the same size and shape) if and only if one can be mapped onto the other by an isometry.

Theorem 1. If T is an isometry with the fixed point $\mathbf{O}$, then T is a linear transformation.

Proof. In order to show that T satisfies (1) it is sufficient to establish separately that

$$(4) \qquad\qquad T(\lambda \mathbf{U}) = \lambda T(\mathbf{U})$$

and

$$(5) \qquad\qquad T(\mathbf{U} + \mathbf{V}) = T(\mathbf{U}) + T(\mathbf{V}).$$

To prove (4), we set $\mathbf{W} = \lambda \mathbf{U}$ and use primes to denote images under T, getting from (2) and Lemma 1

$$
\begin{aligned}
|\mathbf{W}' - \lambda \mathbf{U}'|^2 &= |\mathbf{W}'|^2 - 2\lambda \mathbf{W}' \cdot \mathbf{U}' + \lambda^2 |\mathbf{U}'|^2 \\
&= |\mathbf{W}|^2 - 2\lambda \mathbf{W} \cdot \mathbf{U} + \lambda^2 |\mathbf{U}|^2 \\
&= \lambda^2 |\mathbf{U}|^2 - 2\lambda^2 \mathbf{U} \cdot \mathbf{U} + \lambda^2 |\mathbf{U}|^2 \\
&= 0 .
\end{aligned}
$$

Since $|\mathbf{W}' - \lambda \mathbf{U}'| = 0$, we must have $\mathbf{W}' = \lambda \mathbf{U}'$; that is, $T(\lambda \mathbf{U}) = \lambda T(\mathbf{U})$ as we sought to prove.

The proof of (5) is obtained by the same method (see Exercise 2).   □

We now introduce perpendicular unit coordinate vectors $\mathbf{i} = (1, 0)$ and $\mathbf{j} = (0, 1)$. Under the isometry T the images $\mathbf{i}'$ and $\mathbf{j}'$ of $\mathbf{i}$ and $\mathbf{j}$ are also perpendicular unit vectors, for (2) implies

$$|\mathbf{i}'| = |\mathbf{i}| = 1, \qquad |\mathbf{j}'| = |\mathbf{j}| = 1,$$

and Lemma 1 yields

$$\mathbf{i}' \cdot \mathbf{j}' = \mathbf{i} \cdot \mathbf{j} = 0.$$

If θ is the direction angle of $\mathbf{i}'$ with respect to $\mathbf{i}$, the coordinate representation is

$$(6) \qquad\qquad \mathbf{i}' = (\cos \theta, \sin \theta).$$

For $\mathbf{j}'$ we then have two possibilities; namely, that the rotation through a right angle which maps $\mathbf{i}'$ onto $\mathbf{j}'$ is either counterclockwise or clockwise. In the former event,

$$(7) \qquad \mathbf{j}' = \left(\cos \left(\theta + \frac{\pi}{2} \right), \ \sin \left(\theta + \frac{\pi}{2} \right) \right)$$
$$= (-\sin \theta, \cos \theta) \, ;$$

in the latter,

$$(8) \qquad \mathbf{j}' = \left(\cos \left(\theta - \frac{\pi}{2} \right), \ \sin \left(\theta - \frac{\pi}{2} \right) \right)$$
$$= (\sin \theta, -\cos \theta) \, .$$

First, we suppose that the isometry T maps the coordinate vectors by the rules (6) and (7). Let $\mathbf{X} = (x, y)$ be any vector, α its direction angle with respect to $\mathbf{i}$, and r its length. Thus,

$$(9) \qquad x = r \cos \alpha \, , \qquad y = r \sin \alpha \, .$$

Since T is a linear transformation, the image $\mathbf{X}' = (x', y')$ of $\mathbf{X}$ under T satisfies

$$\mathbf{X}' = T(\mathbf{X}) = T(x\mathbf{i} + y\mathbf{j})$$
$$= xT(\mathbf{i}) + yT(\mathbf{j}) = x\mathbf{i}' + y\mathbf{j}' \, .$$

Hence, from (6), (7), and (9),

$$\begin{cases} x' = r \left(\cos \alpha \cos \theta - \sin \alpha \sin \theta \right) = r \cos \left(\alpha + \theta \right), \\ y' = r \left(\cos \alpha \sin \theta + \sin \alpha \cos \theta \right) = r \sin \left(\alpha + \theta \right). \end{cases}$$

Thus, the effect of T is simply a rotation of $\mathbf{X}$ about O through the angle θ. Using (9), we may rewrite the equations for x' and y' in the form

$$(10) \qquad \begin{cases} x' = x \cos \theta - y \sin \theta \, , \\ y' = x \sin \theta + y \cos \theta \, . \end{cases}$$

Equation (10) gives the coordinates (x', y') of the point upon which a rotation about O through the angle θ maps (x, y).

Example 1. Upon what point does a rotation about O through the angle $\pi/6$ map the point $(3, 4)$? Applying (10), we find the image point $(\frac{3}{2} \sqrt{3} - 2, \ \frac{3}{2} + 2 \sqrt{3})$.

The rotations of the plane with the identity transformation given by $\theta = 0$ in (10) form a group. To prove this, we need only verify that the composition consisting of a rotation through the angle θ_1, followed by one through the angle θ_2, is a rotation through $\theta_1 + \theta_2$ (see Exercise 5). The inverse of a rotation through the angle θ is then a rotation through $-\theta$. Thus, the inverse of the mapping $(x, y) \to (x', y')$ given by (10) is defined by

(11)
$$\begin{cases} x = x' \cos \theta + y' \sin \theta, \\ y = -x' \sin \theta + y' \cos \theta. \end{cases}$$

Example 2. Let us find the equation of the image of the hyperbola

$$x^2 - y^2 = 1$$

under a rotation through the angle $\pi/4$. Using (11) with $\theta = \pi/4$, we have

$$x = \frac{1}{\sqrt{2}}(x' + y'), \qquad y = \frac{1}{\sqrt{2}}(-x' + y').$$

Hence,

$$1 = x^2 - y^2 = \tfrac{1}{2}(x' + y')^2 - \tfrac{1}{2}(-x' + y')^2,$$

and the desired equation is

$$2x'y' = 1.$$

Here, x' and y' are variables representing image points under the transformation. If we have no further need for a reference to the transformation, we may drop the primes in writing the equation for the image curve since the expression "the curve $2x'y' = 1$" is meant to represent the set $\{(x', y') : 2x'y' = 1\}$ and it does not matter what two names we give the variables. Thus, we may say that a rotation through $\pi/4$ radians maps the curve $x^2 - y^2 = 1$ onto the curve $2xy = 1$.

Rotations of space are more complicated than plane rotations. For example, the two compositions of a pair of space rotations are generally different, but composition of plane rotations is commutative. (See Exercise 6).

Now, we consider the remaining possibility, that the isometry T maps **i** and **j** by the rules (6) and (8). Then, if $X = (x, y)$, where $x = r \cos \alpha$, $y = r \sin \alpha$, and $T(X) = X' = (x', y')$,

$$x' = r (\cos \alpha \cos \theta + \sin \alpha \sin \theta) = r \cos (\theta - \alpha)$$
$$y' = r (\cos \alpha \sin \theta - \sin \alpha \cos \theta) = r \sin (\theta - \alpha).$$

Thus, if $\alpha = \theta - \alpha$, or, equivalently, if $\alpha = \tfrac{1}{2}\theta$, the point X is invariant. The result remains true if θ is replaced by $\theta + 2\pi$ and

$\alpha = \frac{1}{2}\theta + \pi$. Consequently, all points of the line

(12) $$\mathbf{X} = \left(\lambda \cos\frac{\theta}{2}, \lambda \sin\frac{\theta}{2}\right) \qquad (\lambda \quad \text{real})$$

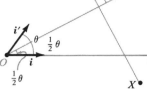

are fixed. The isometry T is a *reflection* in the line (12); that is, the line is the perpendicular bisector of the segment $[XX']$; see Figure 1. The proof is left to Exercise 7. The equations of the reflection are

(13) $$\begin{cases} x' = x \cos\theta + y \sin\theta, \\ y' = x \sin\theta - y \cos\theta. \end{cases}$$

Example 3. To find the reflection in the line $y = 2x$ of the point $(1, 1)$, we employ the direction vector of the line $(\cos\frac{1}{2}\theta, \sin\frac{1}{2}\theta) = \left(\dfrac{1}{\sqrt{5}}, \dfrac{2}{\sqrt{5}}\right)$. From (13), with

Figure 1

$$\cos\theta = 1 - 2\sin^2\frac{1}{2}\theta = -\tfrac{3}{5} \quad \text{and} \quad \sin\theta = 2\sin\frac{1}{2}\theta\cos\frac{1}{2}\theta = \tfrac{4}{5},$$

we find

$$x' = -\tfrac{3}{5} + \tfrac{4}{5} = \tfrac{1}{5}, \qquad y' = \tfrac{4}{5} + \tfrac{3}{5} = \tfrac{7}{5}.$$

A reflection is its own inverse; that is, the composition of a reflection with itself is the identity transformation. It leaves the plane unchanged. (See Exercise 8.)

Example 4. We find the reflection in the line $y = x$ of the curve given by an equation $\varphi(x, y) = 0$. The inclination of the line is $\pi/4$, thus $\theta = \pi/2$ in (13). Furthermore, the equations of the inverse have the same form as (13); hence,

$$x = x' \cos\theta + y' \sin\theta = y', \qquad y = x' \sin\theta - y' \cos\theta = x'.$$

The desired curve is given by the equation

$$\varphi(y', x') = 0.$$

Thus we see that the effect of such a reflection is to interchange the roles of the x and y coordinates.

We have classified isometries with fixed points. If just one point is fixed, the isometry is a rotation; if more than one point, but not every point, is fixed the points of an entire line are fixed and the isometry is a reflection; if all points are fixed, the isometry is the identity.

A3.6a Exercises

1. Show that the set of all transformations with a given invariant is a group.

2. Complete the proof of Theorem 1 by deriving (5).

3. If T is a transformation for which $\mathbf{O}$ is not a fixed point, $T(\mathbf{O}) \neq \mathbf{O}$, show that T is not linear.

4. a. Upon what point does a rotation through the angle $\frac{1}{6}\pi$ about the point $(1, 2)$ map the point $(3, 4)$?
   b. Give the general expression for the coordinates of the image of the point $X = (x, y)$ in a rotation through the angle θ about any point

$$A = (a, b).$$

5. Show that the composition formed by plane rotation through the angle θ_1 followed by plane rotation through the angle θ_2 is a plane rotation through the angle $\theta_1 + \theta_2$.

6. Demonstrate that composition of space rotations is not commutative.

7. Prove that the isometry satisfying rules (6) and (8) is a reflection in the line (12), namely; if $X' = T(X)$, that the line is the perpendicular bisector of the segment $[XX']$.

8. Prove that the reflection T given by (13) is its own inverse; that is $TT = I$ where I is the identity transformation.

9. What is the image of the curve $\varphi(x, y) = 0$ under a reflection
   a. in the x-axis,
   b. in the y-axis?

10. What is the reflection of the point $(1, 1)$ in the line $y = 2x + 1$? (Compare Example 3.)

11. Let R be a rotation other than the identity and T any translation. Show that RT and TR are rotations. (Hint: Use the result of A3.4a Exercise 15.)

12. Determine the reflection $P' = (p', q')$ of $P = (p, q)$ in the line $y = mx + b$.

13. Let $P_1, P_2, \ldots, P_n$ be the consecutive vertices of a regular polygon of n sides. Show that $\mathbf{P}_1 + \mathbf{P}_2 + \cdots + \mathbf{P}_n = \mathbf{O}$ where O is the center of the polygon. Is this result independent of origin?

14. Let (x, y) be a point of the quadratic curve

(i) $$ax^2 + 2bxy + cy^2 + 2dx + 2ey + f = 0.$$

Show that the image (ξ, η) of (x, y) under a rotation satisfies the equation

(ii) $$\alpha\xi^2 + 2\beta\xi\eta + \gamma\eta^2 + 2\delta\xi + 2\epsilon\eta + \kappa = 0$$

where $ac - b^2 = \alpha\gamma - \beta^2$.

15. Rotate the curve given by the general quadratic equation

(i) $$ax^2 + 2bxy + cy^2 + 2dx + 2ey + f = 0,$$

where at least one of the coefficients a, b, c is nonzero, in such a way that the equation of the rotated curve takes the form

(ii) $$\alpha x^2 + \gamma y^2 + 2\delta x + 2\epsilon y + \kappa = 0$$

in which the xy-term is missing. Show further how to map the curve so that it has an equation in standard form (see A3.4c).

E A3.6b Representation of Isometries by Reflections

In this section, we prove that any isometry can be expressed as a composition of reflections. For this we first describe an isometry in terms of the way it maps the origin and the unit coordinate vectors.

Let T be an isometry and let A', B', C', ... represent the respective images of the points A, B, C, ... under T. The defining property of an isometry, given in A3.6a (2), states that for any points A and B

(1) $$|\mathbf{A}' - \mathbf{B}'| = |\mathbf{A} - \mathbf{B}|.$$

From (1) it follows, as A3.6a Lemma 1 follows from A3.6a (3), that dot products of differences are invariant; that is

$$(\mathbf{A}' - \mathbf{B}') \cdot (\mathbf{C}' - \mathbf{D}') = (\mathbf{A} - \mathbf{B}) \cdot (\mathbf{C} - \mathbf{D}).$$

(For the proof, substitute $\mathbf{A}' - \mathbf{B}' = \mathbf{U}$ and $\mathbf{C}' - \mathbf{D}' = \mathbf{V}$ in the argument of A3.6a Lemma 1.) This result leads, in the same way as the proof of A3.6a Theorem 1, to the generalization

(2) $$(a\mathbf{A} + b\mathbf{B})' - \mathbf{O}' = a(\mathbf{A}' - \mathbf{O}') + b(\mathbf{B}' - \mathbf{O}').$$

Note that (2) is not linear unless O is a fixed point, $O' = O$. (See A3.6a Exercise 3.) From (2), knowing how O and the points $i = (1, 0)$ and $j = (0, 1)$ are mapped by T, we know the mapping of any point $P = (a, b)$; namely,

(3) $$T(\mathbf{P}) = \mathbf{P}' = (a\mathbf{i} + b\mathbf{j})' = \mathbf{O}' + a(\mathbf{i}' - \mathbf{O}') + b(\mathbf{j}' - \mathbf{O}').$$

Equation (3) shows that T is uniquely defined in terms of the mapping of O and the points i and j.

Next we prove that if $\mathbf{i}' - \mathbf{O}'$ and $\mathbf{j}' - \mathbf{O}'$ are any perpendicular unit vectors, there is a composition of three reflections or less which maps O, i, and j onto O', i' and j' respectively. Any composition of isometries is an isometry; therefore, this composition of reflections is also one. Any isometry is uniquely determined by the mapping of these three points.

Theorem 1. Any isometry can be represented as a composition of no more than three reflections.

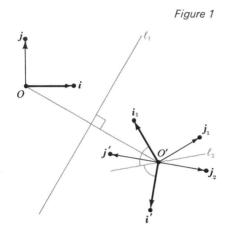

Figure 1

Proof. First, we use a reflection L_1 in the perpendicular bisector ℓ_1 of OO' to map O onto O'; see Figure 1. We set $i_1 = L_1(i)$ and $j_1 = L_1(j)$. Hereafter we keep O' fixed. Second, we use a reflection L_2 in the bisector ℓ_2 of $\angle i_1 O'i'$ to map i_1 onto i', and set $j_2 = L_2(j_1)$. The directed segments $\overrightarrow{O'j'}$ and $\overrightarrow{O'j_2}$ are unit perpendiculars to $\overrightarrow{O'i'}$. If they have the same direction, $j' = j_2$ and the desired composition is L_2L_1; if they do not, the reflection L_3 in the line $O'i'$ maps j_2 on j' and the desired composition is $L_3L_2L_1$. ⬜

A3.6b Exercises

1. a. Show that the composition L_2L_1 of reflections L_1 and L_2 in the respective lines ℓ_1 and ℓ_2 is a translation if ℓ_1 and ℓ_2 are parallel and a rotation if not.

   b. Show conversely that any translation can be represented as the composition L_2L_1 of reflections L_1 and L_2 in parallel lines ℓ_1 and ℓ_2 respectively, and any rotation as the composition for intersecting lines.

2. For an isometry T without fixed points, prove if T is not a translation that it is the composition of a reflection in a line ℓ and a translation in the direction of ℓ. Such an isometry is called a *glide-reflection* and the line ℓ, its *axis*. (Hint: If T is a glide-reflection and $X' = T(X)$, the midpoint of $[XX']$ lies on the axis of T.)

3. Let A_1, A_2, A_3 be vertices of a triangle and L_1, L_2, L_3 be reflections in the extended opposite sides ℓ_1, ℓ_2, ℓ_3, respectively. Show that $T = L_3L_2L_1$ is a glide-reflection with axis passing through the feet of the altitudes on ℓ_1 and ℓ_3.

4. In space, a point A' is said to be the *reflection of A in the plane* $\mathcal{P}$ if and only if $\mathcal{P}$ is the perpendicular bisector of $[AA']$. Show that any isometry in space can be expressed as the composition of five reflections in planes.

A3.6c Symmetries

Symmetry implies a balance or equality of proportions.† The predominant

†From the Greek *symmetria, syn* (like) + *metron* (measure).

bilateral symmetry of the higher animals is the most striking example. A plane figure has *bilateral* or *mirror* symmetry if there is a line ℓ which bisects the figure in the sense that the figure contains with each of its points the reflection of the point in ℓ; see Figure 1. We also say a set of points is *symmetric to the line* ℓ when reflection in ℓ maps the set onto itself. In general, we give the idea of symmetry precision by defining a *symmetry* of a figure as any isometry that maps the figure onto itself. This definition may seem a trifle too broad since even an irregular figure has the identity as a symmetry. In compensation, under the given definition, the set of all symmetries of a figure is a group with respect to composition.

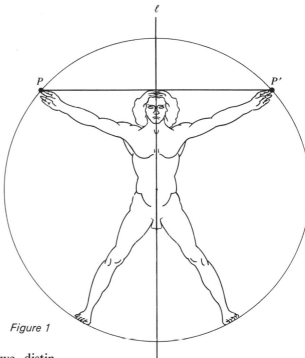

Figure 1

In addition to mirror symmetry, we distinguish the following plane symmetries:

Central Symmetry in which the isometry is a rotation through π (also called a *half-turn about* C or a *reflection in* C); see Figure 2. In this

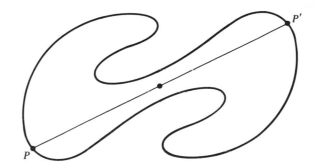

Figure 2

symmetry, the fixed point C of the rotation is called the *center* of the figure. In a centrally symmetric figure each point P has an *image* P' in C such that C bisects $[PP']$. (In space, this last property defines central symmetry and a central symmetry in space is *not* a rotation.)

Rotational Symmetry in which the isometry is a rotation through an angle θ. (Central symmetry is the special case $\theta = \pi$.) An equilateral triangle (see Figure 3) has a rotation through the angle $\frac{2}{3}\pi$ as a rotational symmetry. A circle is symmetric with respect to all rotations about its center.

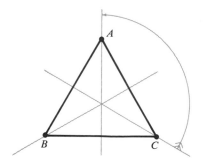

Figure 3

Example 1. There are two basic symmetries of an equilateral triangle, a reflection in a median and a rotation through $\frac{2}{3}\pi$; from these we can construct all the others. Let L_1, L_2, and L_3 be the reflections in the medians through vertices A, B, and C, respectively, and R the rotation through $\frac{2}{3}\pi$ about the centroid; see Figure 3. Any symmetry of the triangle can be described by the mapping of the vertices, for example,

$$R : (A, B, C) \rightarrow (B, C, A),$$
$$L_1 : (A, B, C) \rightarrow (A, C, B).$$

We form the composition $R^2 = RR$, a rotation through $\frac{4}{3}\pi$, and obtain

$$R^2 : (A, B, C) \rightarrow (C, A, B).$$

It is easily verified (Ex. 2) that

(1)
$$L_1 R = L_2, \qquad RL_1 = L_3,$$
$$R^3 = L_1^2 = L_2^2 = L_3^2 = I;$$

thus the six isometries

$$I, L_1, L_2, L_3, R, R^2$$

can be constructed from R and L_1. These six isometries constitute the symmetry group of the equilateral triangle. We may easily write down a table of all possible compositions of two symmetries. (See Exercise 3.) In the group table, look up the first isometry of the composition in the top

	I	R	R^2	L_1	L_2	L_3
I	I	R	R^2	L_1	L_2	L_3
R	R	R^2	I	L_3	L_1	L_2
R^2	R^2	I	R	L_2	L_3	L_1
L_1	L_1	L_2	L_3	I	R	R^2
L_2	L_2	L_3	L_1	R^2	I	R
L_3	L_3	L_1	L_2	R	R^2	I

row, the second in the leftmost column, and locate the composition directly below the first entry and to the right of the second, as is shown for

$$L_1 R = L_2.$$

Since composition is not commutative, it is necessary to be consistent about the order of the constituent transformations.

Symmetry of a plane curve

$$(2) \qquad\qquad g(x, y) = 0$$

is sometimes easily recognizable from the invariance of the form of $g(x, y)$ under an isometry. For example, in mirror symmetry to the y-axis, when (x, y) is a point of the curve (2), so is the point $(x', y') = (-x, y)$. A sufficient condition for symmetry to the y-axis is, therefore,

$$(3) \qquad\qquad g(-x, y) = g(x, y)$$

for all points (x, y) in the domain of g. So, for example, the horizontal line $y = c$, the parabola $y = ax^2$, the ellipse $\dfrac{x^2}{a^2} + \dfrac{y^2}{b^2} = 1$, the hyperbola $\dfrac{x^2}{a^2} - \dfrac{y^2}{b^2} = 1$, the graph of the absolute value function $y = |x|$, and the graph $y = \cos x$, are all symmetric to the y-axis.

The test (3), although sufficient, is not a necessary condition for symmetry to the y-axis. In other words, the test may fail and the curve (2) may yet have the symmetry.

Example 2. Consider the curve defined by (2) where

$$g(x, y) = x^2 y - x^2 + xy - x + y - 1.$$

Since $g(1, 0) = -3$ and $g(-1, 0) = -1$, the test (3) does not reveal symmetry to the y-axis. Nonetheless, $g(x, y)$ can be written as the product

$$g(x, y) = (y - 1)(x^2 + x + 1)$$

in which the second factor is never zero. The equation $g(x, y) = 0$, therefore, describes the line $y = 1$ which does have the symmetry undetected by the test.

Also useful are the tests for symmetry to the x-axis,

$$(4) \qquad\qquad g(x, -y) = g(x, y),$$

and central symmetry with respect to the origin (briefly called *symmetry to the origin*),

$$(5) \qquad\qquad g(-x, -y) = g(x, y).$$

A curve that satisfies any two of the tests (3), (4), (5) must satisfy the third (see Exercise 5). Among curves having symmetry to both axes, hence the origin, are the ellipse $\dfrac{x^2}{a^2} + \dfrac{y^2}{b^2} = 1$ and the hyperbola $\dfrac{x^2}{a^2} - \dfrac{y^2}{b^2} = 1$.

Symmetry to the line $y = x$ exists if

(6) $g(x, y) = g(y, x)$,

and this test is occasionally useful. Examples of curves having this symmetry are $x + y = 1$ (a line), $x^2 + y^2 = 1$ (a circle), $|x| + |y| = 1$ (a square) .

In space, a geometrical configuration is said to have bilateral or mirror symmetry if it is invariant under reflection in a plane. A surface

(7) $\varphi(x, y, z) = 0$

is symmetric to the yz-plane, $x = 0$, if

(8) $\varphi(-x, y, z) = \varphi(x, y, z)$.

Similar sufficient conditions hold for symmetry to the other coordinate planes.

A central symmetry in space, unlike the plane, cannot be expressed as a rotation. Symmetry to a point P implies that with each point Q of the configuration, the point Q' with position vector

$$\mathbf{Q'} = 2\mathbf{P} - \mathbf{Q}$$

belongs to the configuration; that is, P is the midpoint of $[QQ']$. The point Q' is called the reflection of Q in P. A sufficient condition for symmetry of a surface (7) to the origin is

(9) $\varphi(-x, -y, -z) = \varphi(x, y, z)$.

An important symmetry in space is *axial symmetry*, invariance with respect to all rotations about a given line. For example, axial symmetry about the z-axis implies that a configuration containing a point (x, y, z) must contain the points (x', y', z') with

(10) $\begin{cases} x' = x \cos \theta - y \sin \theta , \\ y' = x \sin \theta + y \cos \theta , \\ z' = z , \end{cases}$

for all values of θ (compare A3.6a (10)). A sufficient condition for this symmetry is that φ can be given in the special form

(11) $\varphi(x, y, z) = \psi(x^2 + y^2, z)$.

An example of a surface having all the foregoing space symmetries is the right circular cone

$$x^2 + y^2 - a^2z^2 = 0$$

with axial symmetry to the z-axis, mirror symmetry to all three coordinate planes, and central symmetry to the origin.

A3.6c Exercises

1. What are the symmetries of these figures?

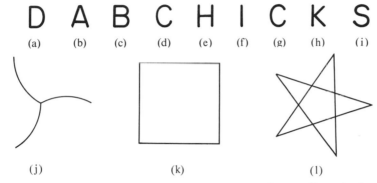

D A B C H I C K S
(a)   (b)   (c)   (d)   (e)   (f)   (g)   (h)   (i)

(j)   (k)   (l)

2. Derive the relations (1) for the symmetry group of an equilateral triangle.

3. Obtain the group table of Example 1 for the symmetries of an equilateral triangle from the relations (1). (Hint: The inverse of the composition T_1T_2 of two transformations is $T_2^{-1}T_1^{-1}$.)

4. Describe the symmetries of a rhombus. Write out the group table.

5. Show that a curve (2) that satisfies any two of the conditions (3), (4), (5) must satisfy the third.

6. Can a set have more than one center?

7. a. Are any straight lines symmetric to both axes? If so, which?
   b. Apart from hyperbolas and ellipses (including circles) are there any quadratic graphs symmetric to both axes? If so describe.

8. Which of the following are symmetric to the x-axis, the y-axis, the origin, the line $y = x$, none of these?

   a. $x = 2$.   b. $x^2 = 2$.

   c. $y = 1 - x$.   d. $y = 1 - x^2$.

   e. $x^2 + y^2 = 1$.

   f. $x^n + y^n = 1$ (n, a natural number).

   g. $x^2 + xy + y^2 = 1$.   h. $y^3 = 3xy^2 - 4x^2y$.

   i. $y = \dfrac{x + a}{bx + 1}$.   j. $y = \dfrac{x + a}{bx - 1}$.

9. Show that (11) is a sufficient condition for invariance of the surface (7) under the isometry (10).

10. A *surface of revolution* is defined as the union of all possible images obtained by rotation of a given plane curve about a given axis in the plane.

   a. Find an equation of the surface of revolution obtained by rotation of the curve $g(x, y) = 0$ about the x-axis and show that the surface has axial symmetry.

   b. What kinds of surfaces of revolution are obtained by the rotation of straight lines?

A3.6d Linear Transformations of the Plane.†

Any isometry of the plane

$$(x, y) \rightarrow (x', y')$$

can be described by special equations of the form

(1) $$\begin{cases} x' = ax + by + x_0, \\ y' = cx + dy + y_0. \end{cases}$$

(See Exercise 1.) Any mapping defined by equations of the form (1) is called a *generalized linear mapping*. Note that a generalized linear mapping is not linear unless $x_0 = y_0 = 0$. (See A3.6a Exercise 3.) The mapping (1) can be described as the composition TL of the linear mapping

$$L : (x, y) \rightarrow (ax + by, cx + dy)$$

and the translation

$$T : (x, y) \rightarrow (x + x_0, y + y_0).$$

Since translations leave all basic geometrical properties unchanged, we may study the geometrical properties of the generalized linear mapping (1) through the linear mapping

(2) $$\begin{cases} x' = ax + by, \\ y' = cx + dy. \end{cases}$$

Often, it is convenient to rewrite (2) in the vector form

(3) $$\mathbf{X'} = (\mathbf{X} \cdot \mathbf{P})\mathbf{i} + (\mathbf{X} \cdot \mathbf{Q})\mathbf{j}$$

where $\mathbf{X} = (x, y)$, $\mathbf{X'} = (x', y')$, $\mathbf{P} = (a, b)$, and $\mathbf{Q} = (c, d)$. From (3), the linearity of (2) is immediate:

$$\begin{aligned} (\alpha\mathbf{X} + \beta\mathbf{Y})' &= [(\alpha\mathbf{X} + \beta\mathbf{Y}) \cdot \mathbf{P}]\mathbf{i} + [(\alpha\mathbf{X} + \beta\mathbf{Y}) \cdot \mathbf{Q}]\mathbf{j} \\ &= \alpha[(\mathbf{X} \cdot \mathbf{P})\mathbf{i} + (\mathbf{X} \cdot \mathbf{Q})\mathbf{j}] + \beta[(\mathbf{Y} \cdot \mathbf{P})\mathbf{i} + (\mathbf{Y} \cdot \mathbf{Q})\mathbf{j}] \\ &= \alpha\mathbf{X'} + \beta\mathbf{Y'}. \end{aligned}$$

†These results can and will be extended to space in the chapter on linear algebra.

We shall not study mappings for which $\mathbf{i}'$ and $\mathbf{j}'$ are collinear, these being degenerate cases for which the entire plane is mapped onto a line or point (see Exercise 2). If $\mathbf{i}'$ and $\mathbf{j}'$ are not collinear, the linear mapping is a transformation, that is, a one-to-one mapping of the plane onto itself.† To see that the mapping is a transformation, we must prove that every point of the plane is covered in the mapping and covered only once. From A3.2 (8), if $\mathbf{i}'$ and $\mathbf{j}'$ are noncollinear, any point x' of the plane can be expressed in the form

$$(4) \qquad\qquad \mathbf{X}' = \alpha\mathbf{i}' + \beta\mathbf{j}' .$$

Consequently, $\mathbf{X}' = (\alpha\mathbf{i} + \beta\mathbf{j})'$ and is covered in the mapping. Since the representation (4) is unique (see A3.2 Exercise 2), it follows that $\mathbf{X}'$ has only the one antecedent $\alpha\mathbf{i} + \beta\mathbf{j}$ in the mapping.

Linear transformations need not be isometries, but they leave many useful geometrical properties invariant. If $\mathbf{X} = (1 - \lambda)\mathbf{P} + \lambda\mathbf{Q}$, then $\mathbf{X}' = (1 - \lambda)\mathbf{P}' + \lambda\mathbf{Q}'$; hence linear transformations map lines onto lines, rays onto rays, and segments onto segments. If X divides the segment $[PQ]$ in a given proportion, its image X' divides $[P'Q']$ in the same proportion; thus the midpoint of a segment maps onto the midpoint of the image segment. Furthermore, the proportions of lengths on parallel lines are invariant: if X_1 and Y_1 are points on line ℓ_1, X_2 and Y_2 points on ℓ_2, where ℓ_1 and ℓ_2 both lie in the direction of $\mathbf{U}$, there are scalars λ_1 and λ_2 for which $\mathbf{X}_1 - \mathbf{Y}_1 = \lambda_1\mathbf{U}$ and $\mathbf{X}_2 - \mathbf{Y}_2 = \lambda_2\mathbf{U}$; hence, $\mathbf{X}_1' - \mathbf{Y}_1' = \lambda_1\mathbf{U}_1'$ and $\mathbf{X}_2' - \mathbf{Y}_2' = \lambda_2\mathbf{U}_2'$. From this we see that not only the proportions of lengths on parallel lines are invariant, but so are the relative directions, same or opposite, of directed segments on such lines.

Example 1. If C is the centroid of the three points P_1, P_2, P_3, the image of C in a linear transformation is the centroid of their images. This follows from the definition of centroid (p. 296),

$$\mathbf{C} = \tfrac{1}{3}(\mathbf{P}_1 + \mathbf{P}_2 + \mathbf{P}_3)$$

and the linearity of the transformation. Alternatively, if $P_1, P_2,$ and P_3 are noncollinear, we observe that the midpoints of the side of the triangle $[P_1P_2P_3]$ map onto the midpoints of the sides of $[P_1'P_2'P_3']$; hence the medians map onto the medians. The centroid C which is the intersection of the medians, must map onto the intersection of the images of the medians, that is, the centroid of $[P_1'P_2'P_3']$.

---

†A linear transformation is sometimes called an *affine* transformation; sometimes the term affine denotes a generalized linear transformation.

Any linear transformation can be expressed as the composition of certain basic simple types. These include a rotation, perhaps a reflection, and some nonisometric transformations which we now describe.

The *uniaxial magnifications*

$$(5) \qquad\qquad (x, y) \rightarrow (\alpha x, y) \qquad\qquad (\alpha > 0),$$

and

$$(6) \qquad\qquad (x, y) \rightarrow (x, \beta y) \qquad\qquad (\beta > 0),$$

multiply lengths in the directions **i** and **j** by α and β, respectively, whereas lengths in the corresponding perpendicular directions are invariant. The numbers α and β are called the *scale factors* of their respective transformations.

Example 2. A uniaxial magnification maps a circle onto an ellipse.

Let the circle be given by the equation

$$(7) \qquad\qquad x^2 + y^2 = r^2$$

and consider the effect of the transformation (6). The transformation is described by equations

$$x' = x, \quad y' = \beta y$$

and the inverse transformation by

$$x = x', \quad y = \frac{y'}{\beta}.$$

In (7), enter the expressions for x and y in terms of x' and y' to obtain for the image curve

$$(x')^2 + \frac{(y')^2}{\beta^2} = r^2,$$

which may be written in a standard form of the equation for an ellipse,

$$\frac{(x')^2}{r^2} + \frac{(y')^2}{\beta^2 r^2} = 1.$$

This result is the basis for the construction of A3.5c Exercise 7.

In most applications of real functions, there is no intrinsic geometrical relation between the units of the independent and dependent variables. For example, in 1.1 we studied the total working time T of a committee as a function of the number x of its members. In representing the function $f : x \rightarrow T$ by a graph, there is no reason to represent one hour of time by the same length along the T-axis as one person is represented along the x-axis. If we are to draw conclusions about the function from geometrical properties of its graph, it can only be that these properties are invariant under uniaxial magnifications. In 1.1 we infer that the graph of the function f is horizontal at a maximum of T. For a line, horizontality is invariant under uniaxial magnifications and we shall not be surprised to find that this invariance holds for curves, in general. At a point where the graph $T = f(x)$ is horizontal, the derivative vanishes, $f'(x) = 0$. The invariance of horizontality under uniaxial magnification, therefore, has some bearing on this application of calculus. To see what it may be, consider a cartesian coordinate system $\{(\xi, \eta)\}$ with equal scales on the two axes. Let the unit in x be represented by the length α on the ξ-axis and the unit in T by the length β on the y-axis, where α and β may be any positive numbers. In the cartesian system, the point corresponding to $T_0 = f(x_0)$ is then (ξ_0, η_0), where $\xi_0 = \alpha x_0$, $\eta_0 = \beta T_0$. Thus, the cartesian equation of the graph is

$$\eta = \beta f\left(\frac{\xi}{\alpha}\right) = g(\xi).$$

For invariance of horizontality under uniaxial magnification, if the derivative with respect to ξ of the function $g : \xi \to \beta f(\xi/\alpha)$ has a zero at $\xi = \xi_0$, the derivative with respect to x of the function $f : x \to T$ should have a zero at $x_0 = \alpha \xi_0$. This will be seen to be true in Chapter 4.

The *linear shear* defined by

(8) $$x' = x + \gamma y, \quad y' = y$$

leaves points on the x-axis fixed, and displaces any other point horizontally in proportion to its distance from the x-axis, see Figure 1. Within a given

$$T : (x,y) \to (x + \gamma y, y)$$

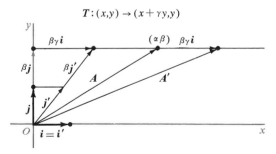

Figure 1

horizontal line $y = \beta$, the effect of (8) is that of the translation $\beta \gamma i$. A linear shear maps the unit square with vertices $0, i, j$ and $i + j$ onto

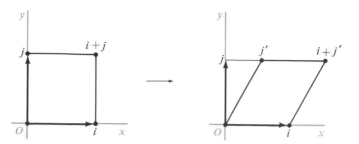

Figure 2

a parallelogram that has the same base and altitude, hence the same area; see Figure 2.

Theorem 1. A linear transformation can be expressed as the composition of no more than a shear, a reflection, two uniaxial magnifications, and a rotation.

Proof. To construct the composition, it will be convenient to work backwards and construct the inverse transformation. We need only map i' and j' back onto i and j, respectively, to determine the entire mapping. From (2) or (3),

$$\mathbf{i}' = a\mathbf{i} + c\mathbf{j},$$
$$\mathbf{j}' = b\mathbf{i} + d\mathbf{j};$$

see Figure 3a. Let R be a rotation through the angle θ equal to the inclination of $\mathbf{i}'$ to the x-axis, where $0 \leq \theta < 2\pi$. The inverse rotation R^{-1} maps $\mathbf{i}'$ onto the point $i_1 = (|\mathbf{i}'|, 0)$ of the x-axis. Now, let us apply A3.6a (11) with

$$\cos \theta = \frac{a}{\sqrt{a^2 + c^2}}, \quad \sin \theta = \frac{c}{\sqrt{a^2 + c^2}}$$

to obtain

$$j_1 = R^{-1}(j') = \left(\frac{ab + cd}{\sqrt{a^2 + c^2}}, \frac{ad - bc}{\sqrt{a^2 + c^2}} \right);$$

see Figure 3b.

Figure 3

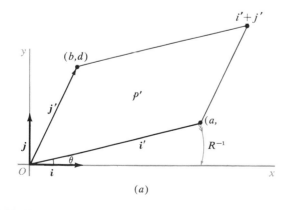

(a)

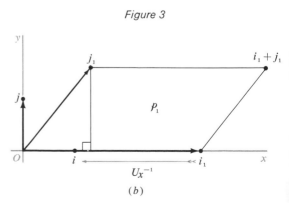

(b)

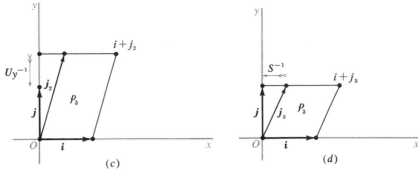

Figure 3

(c)   (d)

The parallelogram p' with vertices $0, i', j'$, and $i' + j'$ is congruent to the parallelogram p_1 with vertices $0, i_1, j_1$, and $i_1 + j_1$; therefore, the two have the same area. This area may easily be computed since we have the length of one side, $|i'| = |i_1| = \sqrt{a^2 + b^2}$ and the length of the altitude to that side, the absolute value of the y coordinate of j_1, namely $\dfrac{|ad - bc|}{\sqrt{a^2 + b^2}}$. Taking the product of the two, we have the area $|ad - bc|$. The requirement that i' and j' are noncollinear is equivalent to the condition that $|ad - bc| \neq 0$. As we shall see, the sign of $ad - bc$ also has a useful geometrical interpretation. The number $ad - bc$ is called the *determinant* of the transformation.

We let U_x represent the uniaxial magnification that maps i onto i_1. The scale factor of U_x is $\sqrt{a^2 + c^2}$. The inverse U_x^{-1} has the reciprocal $1/\sqrt{a^2 + c^2}$ as scale factor. Consequently,

$$j_2 = U_x^{-1}(j_1) = \left(\frac{ab + cd}{a^2 + c^2}, \frac{ad - bc}{\sqrt{a^2 + c^2}} \right).$$

Thus, U_x^{-1} maps p_1 onto a parallelogram p_2 with unit base; see Figure 3c. Next, let U_y be the uniaxial magnification (6) with scale factor $\beta = \dfrac{|ad - bc|}{\sqrt{a^2 + c^2}}$. The inverse transformation U_y^{-1} maps p_2 onto a parallelogram p_3 with unit altitude; see Figure 3d. We have $U^{-1}(i) = i$ and

$$j_3 = U_y^{-1}(j_2) = \left(\frac{ab + cd}{a^2 + c^2}, \operatorname{sgn} D \right)$$

where $D = ad - bc$.

Two cases remain. If $\operatorname{sgn} D = -1$, we employ a reflection L in the x-axis to obtain $L(i) = i$ and

$$j_4 = L(j_3) = \left(\frac{ab + cd}{a^2 + c^2}, 1 \right).$$

If sgn $D = 1$, we set $j_4 = j_3$ to obtain the same coordinate representation of j_4. In either case, we can map j onto j_4 and leave i fixed by means of the shear S given by (8) with $\gamma = \dfrac{ab + cd}{a^2 + c^2}$. Thus, the inverse of the linear transformation (2) is

$$T^{-1} = S^{-1} K U_y^{-1} U_x^{-1} R^{-1}$$

where K is the identity transformation if the determinant is positive, and is a reflection in the x-axis if negative. Inverting, we find

$$T = R U_x U_y K S,$$

as claimed.   □

The meaning of the sign of the determinant D is clear from the foregoing proof. Let ϕ be the angle of inclination of j' with respect to i' (see Figure 3a). In Figure 3b, $j_1 = (|\mathbf{j}'| \cos \phi, |\mathbf{j}'| \sin \phi)$, since the y-coordinate of j_1 was found to be

$$\frac{D}{\sqrt{a^2 + b^2}} = \frac{D}{|\mathbf{i}'|},$$

(9) $$\sin \phi = \frac{ad - bc}{\sqrt{a^2 + b^2} \sqrt{c^2 + d^2}} = \frac{D}{|\mathbf{i}'| \, |\mathbf{j}'|}.$$

If $\phi = 0$ or π, the vectors $\mathbf{i}'$ and $\mathbf{j}'$ are collinear and $D = 0$. If $D > 0$, then $0 < \phi < \pi$ and the point j' lies on the left of the line $0i'$, as viewed in the direction $\mathbf{i}'$; if $D < 0$, then $\pi < \phi < 2\pi$ and j' appears on the right. We say that the ordered pair $(\mathbf{i}', \mathbf{j}')$ is *positively oriented* if $D > 0$, *negatively oriented* if $D < 0$.

Given any two vectors $\mathbf{U} = (u_1, u_2)$ and $\mathbf{V} = (v_1, v_2)$, we introduce the function

$$\Phi(\mathbf{U}, \mathbf{V}) = (u_1 v_2 - v_2 u_1).$$

If ϕ is the angle of inclination of $\mathbf{V}$ with respect to $\mathbf{U}$, where $0 < \phi < 2\pi$, the inclination of $\mathbf{U}$ with respect to $\mathbf{V}$ is $2\pi - \phi$. Recall that inclination is measured counterclockwise; see Figure 4. From (9),

$$\sin \phi = \frac{\Phi(\mathbf{U}, \mathbf{V})}{|\mathbf{U}| \, |\mathbf{V}|}$$

and the relation between the relative inclinations of the two vectors corresponds to the property of Φ,

$$\Phi(\mathbf{U}, \mathbf{V}) = -\Phi(\mathbf{V}, \mathbf{U}).$$

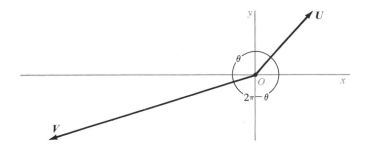

Figure 4

The number $\Phi(\mathbf{U}, \mathbf{V})$ is sometimes called the *cross product* of two vectors $\mathbf{U}$ and $\mathbf{V}$ in E^2 and written $\mathbf{U} \times \mathbf{V}$. If $\mathbf{U}$ and $\mathbf{V}$ are non-collinear, $\mathbf{U} \times \mathbf{V}$ represents the signed area of the parallelogram with adjacent sides $[0U]$ and $[0V]$. A necessary and sufficient condition that $\mathbf{U}$ and $\mathbf{V}$ are collinear is that $\Phi(\mathbf{U}, \mathbf{V}) = \mathbf{U} \times \mathbf{V} = 0$.

The determinant D of the linear transformation (2) can be given a broad interpretation in terms of area. In the proof of Theorem 1, we have seen that the linear transformation maps the unit square with adjacent sides $[0i]$ and $[0j]$ onto a parallelogram p' with area $|D|$. Since the transformation maps parallel lines onto parallel lines and retains the proportions of length on parallel lines, it maps any square with horizontal and vertical sides and area A onto a parallelogram similar to p' with area $|D|A$. (See Exercise 13.) We may estimate the area of a region R as a sum of areas of squares in the following way. We first rule off the plane in squares. We take the sum of the areas of all the squares that lie wholly within R as a lower estimate for the area, and the sum of areas of these and all squares that meet R at any point as an upper estimate; see Figure 5a. We thus obtain approximations to the area of R by areas of rectangular polygons through a slightly different method from that of 1.2 (the two methods can be shown to be equivalent). Now, let the sidelength of the squares be s.

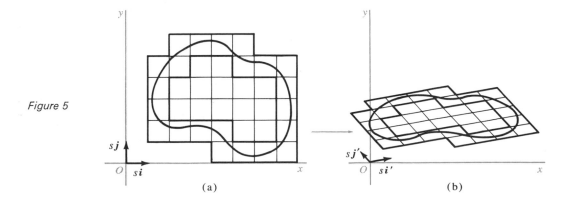

Figure 5

(a)   (b)

The smaller we take s the better the approximation of the polygons to the boundary of R and we expect their areas to better approximate the area of R. Let us suppose that by taking s small enough, we may make the errors in the upper and lower estimates for the area α of R less than any fixed tolerance; namely, in the language of 1.1 and 1.2, that α is the limit of such approximations. If R' is the image of R in the linear transformation, any square that consists wholly of points of R maps onto a parallelogram consisting wholly of points of R', and any square that contains at least one point of R maps onto a parallelogram containing at least one point of R'. Thus, the area of R' is approximated from above and below by sums of areas of parallelograms that are the images of the squares under the transformation; see Figure 5b. Consequently, if m and M are the lower and upper estimates, respectively, of the area α of R, we obtain the lower and upper estimates $m' = m|D|$ and $M' = M|D|$, respectively, for the area of α' of R'. Furthermore, if the difference $M - m$ is less than some given tolerance $\epsilon > 0$, the difference $M' - m'$ between the estimates for α' is less than $\epsilon|D|$. We see then that α' is the limit of approximations by the sums of areas of such parallelograms. We infer further that $\alpha' = \alpha|D|$. In words, an effect of a linear transformation is to multiply all areas by the absolute value of its determinant.†

If a linear transformation multiplies areas by the absolute value of its determinant, the composition $T_2 T_1$ of linear transformations T_1 and T_2 with determinants D_1 and D_2, respectively, multiplies areas by $|D_2 D_1|$. This is a consequence of a sharper result: the determinant of $T_2 T_1$ is the product $D_2 D_1$ of the determinants of the constituent transformations (see Exercise 15).

From the foregoing property of determinants, we can prove the assertion of A3.3 (p. 311) that any rectangular coordinate system can be mapped by translation and rotation into either the coordinate system with basis $\{\mathbf{i}, \mathbf{j}\}$ or basis $\{\mathbf{i}, -\mathbf{j}\}$, but not into both. A translation, except for the identity, is not a linear transformation, and to cover translations, we extend the definition of determinant to the generalized linear transformation (1); namely, the determinant is the signed area $ad - bc$ of the parallelogram onto which the generalized linear transformation maps the unit square with adjacent sides $[0i]$ and $[0j]$. Translations and rotations both have determinant 1; hence, any composition formed with them must also have determinant 1. (See Exercise 14.) If there were compositions of translations and rotations T_1 and T_2 that mapped the unit coordinate vectors $\mathbf{i}^*, \mathbf{j}^*$ of a rectangular coordinate system so that $T_1(\mathbf{i}^*) =$

†In Chapters 6 and 11 we develop the means to prove this result rigorously.

$T_2(\mathbf{i}^*) = \mathbf{i}$ and $T_1(\mathbf{j}^*) = -T_2(\mathbf{j}^*) = \mathbf{j}$, the linear transformation $T_2T_1^{-1}$ would map $\mathbf{i}$ and $\mathbf{j}$ onto $\mathbf{i}$ and $-\mathbf{j}$, respectively. Thus, $T_2T_1^{-1}$ would be a reflection in the x-axis and have determinant -1, an impossibility, since $T_2T_1^{-1}$ is composed of rotations and reflections.

A3.6d Exercises

1. Verify that any isometry $(x, y) \rightarrow (x', y')$ can be expressed by generalized linear equations (1).

2. Let $\mathbf{i}'$ and $\mathbf{j}'$ be the images under the linear mapping (3) of the unit coordinate vectors $\mathbf{i}$ and $\mathbf{j}$. Prove that $\mathbf{i}'$ and $\mathbf{j}'$ are collinear if and only if the entire plane is mapped on a line or point.

3. Show that any linear transformation can be described in the form (2).

4. Prove that a linear transformation maps a center of symmetry of a set onto a center of symmetry of the image set.

5. Prove that the inverse of a linear transformation is linear.

6. Verify that under a linear transformation the image S' of any convex set S is a convex set.

7. Prove that a composition of linear transformations is linear.

8. Show that a linear transformation maps quadratic curves onto quadratic curves of the same type; that is, ellipses (including circles) onto ellipses, parabolas onto parabolas, and hyperbolas onto hyperbolas.

9. Show that the midpoints of parallel chords of an ellipse lie on a diameter of the ellipse. (Compare A3.5c Exercise 11.)

10. Show that the linear transformation

$$(x, y) \rightarrow (ax, ay), \qquad\qquad a > 0,$$

multiplies all lengths by a and preserves angles. Such a transformation is called a *similarity*.

11. Show that only horizontal and vertical directions are invariant under a uniaxial magnification with a scale factor other than one.

12. Interpret the result of A3.4a Exercise 15 in terms of (9).

13. Show that a linear transformation maps all squares with horizontal and vertical sides onto similar parallelograms. If the area of such a square is A and the determinant of the transformation is D show further that the area of the image parallelogram is $|D|A$.

14. Prove that rotations and translations have determinant 1 and reflections have determinant -1.

15. Let T_1 and T_2 be linear transformations, D_1 and D_2, their respective determinants. Prove that the determinant of T_2T_1 is the product D_2D_1.

16. Given a quadratic curve

(i) $$\alpha x^2 + 2\beta xy + \gamma y^2 + 2\delta x + 2\epsilon y + \kappa = 0,$$

let $\Delta = \alpha\gamma - \beta^2$ be its discriminant. If D is the determinant of the linear transformation T, show that T maps the curve (i) onto a quadratic curve whose equation has the discriminant Δ/D^2.

A3.7 POLAR COORDINATES

The cartesian description of a point by its coordinates in a rectangular coordinate frame is the one most generally useful, but often other coordinate systems are better adapted to some special purpose. Descartes commonly used, but did not entirely restrict himself to perpendicular axes and equal scales on them; cartesian systems should include those with oblique axes and unequal scales, the generalized coordinates of A3.2 (p. 298). After rectangular coordinates, the ones most commonly used are polar.

A3.7a Polar coordinates in the plane

In our work with polar coordinates and other coordinate systems, we assume an underlying rectangular cartesian coordinate system in the plane. Let P be any point of the plane with abscissa x and ordinate y.† We may fix the location of P by giving x and y, but we may also do it by giving other numerical data. For example, if $r = |OP|$ and θ is the inclination of $\mathbf{P}$ to the x-axis,

(1) $$x = r\cos\theta, \quad y = r\sin\theta;$$

see Figure 1. The ordered pair (r, θ) is a *polar coordinate* representation

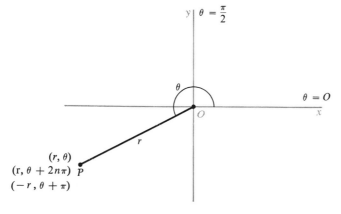

Figure 1

†In this section parentheses are reserved for use with noncartesian coordinates, as (r, θ) for the polar system in the plane.

of P. The origin is defined by $r = 0$ with no restriction on θ, and is represented by $(0, \theta)$ for any value of θ.

Given the polar coordinates of P, the point is fixed uniquely by (1). The converse is not true. If the cartesian coordinates x and y are given, then, from (1), if $x \neq 0$,

$$(2) \qquad\qquad \tan \theta = \frac{y}{x}.$$

Since tan is periodic with period π (see A2.6 Exercise 4c), if θ is any solution of (2), so is $\theta + n\pi$ where n is any integer. If (r, θ) is any pair that satisfies (1), so do all the pairs $(r, \theta + n\pi)$ for n even, and $(-r, \theta + n\pi)$ for n odd; any of these is a representation of P in polar coordinates. In contrast to a cartesian system, in a polar system every point has infinitely many representations.

In order to plot the point $(-r, \theta)$ for $r > 0$ without obtaining its cartesian representation, we observe that the point is the reflection in the origin of the point (r, θ), or that it has the alternative representation $(r, \theta + \pi)$; see Figure 2.

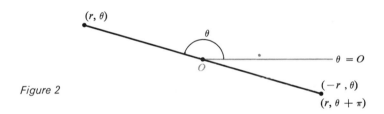

Figure 2

The graph in polar coordinates of a relation between two real variables r and θ is the set of points (r, θ) that satisfy the relation. A point lies on the graph if and only if it has at least one polar coordinate representation for which r and θ satisfy the given relation. The graph in polar coordinates of a function $f: \theta \to r$ does not define the function as would the cartesian graph. If (r, θ) is a point of the graph, all we can conclude is that either $f(\theta + 2k\pi) = r$ or $f(\theta + [2k - 1]\pi) = -r$ for some integral value k.

Example 1. The graph of $f: \theta \to r$ where f is a constant function, $\theta \to r_0$, consists of all points (r_0, θ) where θ is any real number. It is the circle of radius $|r_0|$ with center at the origin. The graph of $\theta \to -r_0$ is the same circle.

Example 2. The graph of $g: r \to \theta$, where g is the constant function

$r \to \theta_0$, consists of all points (r, θ_0) where $r \in \mathcal{R}$. For the part of the domain where r is positive the graph consists of the open ray from the origin with inclination θ_0 to the x-axis, for r negative, the ray with inclination $\theta_0 + \pi$, and for r zero, the origin. The graph is the line through the origin at inclination θ_0 to the x-axis. Note that the graph is described by any of the functions $r \to \theta_0 + n\pi$ where n is an integer.

In polar coordinates, as we see from the preceding examples, the co-ordinate grid of curves $r = r_0$ and $\theta = \theta_0$ consists of circles centered at the origin and lines through the origin. Polar coordinate paper is ruled in circles with equal increments in r and lines with equal increments in θ; see Figure 3. Polar coordinate paper is generally available from sources for

Figure 3

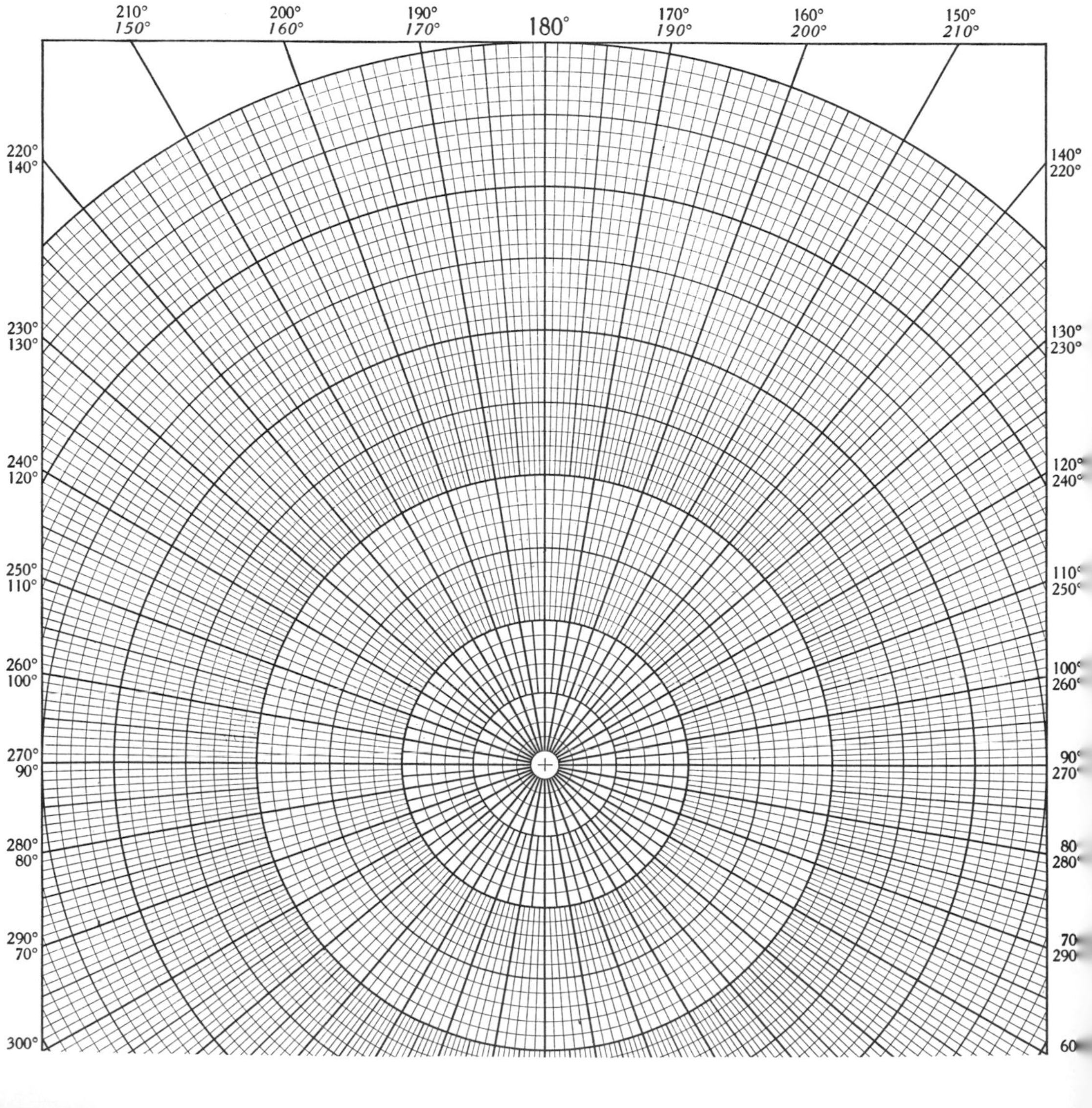

draftsmen's supplies and offers the same convenience for plots in polar coordinates as square-ruled paper for cartesian coordinates. Polar coordinates are especially convenient for the representation of the circular functions of θ because the entire graph is traced out in one period.

Example 3. We sketch the graph of the function defined by

$$(3) \qquad\qquad r = \cos\theta .$$

The cosine increases from the value 0 at $\theta = -\tfrac{1}{2}\pi$ to 1 at $\theta = 0$ and then decreases to 0 at $\theta = \tfrac{1}{2}\pi$. Since $\cos(\theta + \pi) = -\cos\theta$, the point $\left(\cos(\theta + \pi), \theta + \pi\right)$ is the same as $(\cos\theta, \theta)$, and the curve for $-\tfrac{1}{2}\pi \leq \theta \leq \tfrac{1}{2}\pi$ is the entire graph.

To sketch the graph of the function, we calculate r for a few convenient values of θ, particularly $\tfrac{1}{6}\pi, \tfrac{1}{4}\pi$, and their multiples. We then locate the corresponding points on polar coordinate paper, and sketch the graph as in Figure 4; it appears to be a circle and we shall presently verify that it is.

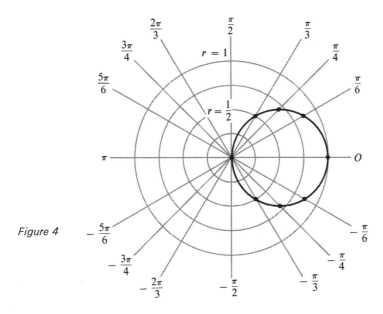

Figure 4

In order to identify the curve of the preceding example, it is convenient to obtain the cartesian representation of the curve. From (1),

$$(4) \qquad\qquad r^2 = x^2 + y^2 .$$

We multiply by r in (3) to obtain

(5) $r^2 = r \cos \theta$,

an equation that has the same graph as (3) because if $r \neq 0$, we may divide both members of the equation by r to obtain the given equation; and the origin $r = 0$ is on both graphs. It may not be immediately obvious that the origin is on both graphs since some polar representations of the origin will not satisfy the equation $r = \cos \theta$. For example, both $(0, 0)$ and $(0, \frac{1}{2}\pi)$ represent the origin, but only the latter satisfies

$$r = \cos \theta .$$

We use (1) and (4) in (5) to obtain

$$x^2 + y^2 = x$$

or,

$$(x - \tfrac{1}{2})^2 + y^2 = \tfrac{1}{4} ,$$

an equation for the graph in rectangular coordinates. We recognize this as an equation of the circle with center at $(\frac{1}{2}, 0)$ and radius $\frac{1}{2}$, in agreement with Figure 4.

Example 4. We seek an equation in polar coordinates for the curve whose equation in cartesian coordinates is

$$(x^2 + y^2)^2 = a^2(x^2 - y^2) .$$

Equations (1) and (4) yield

$$r^4 = a^2 r^2 (\cos^2 \theta - \sin^2 \theta) = a^2 r^2 \cos 2\theta .$$

This is equivalent to

$$r^2 = 0 \quad \text{(the origin)} \quad \text{and} \quad r^2 = a^2 \cos 2\theta .$$

Since $r^2 = a^2 \cos 2\theta$ is satisfied by $(0, \frac{1}{4}\pi)$, a set of polar coordinates for the pole, we see that $r^2 = 0$ adds no points to the graph of $r^2 = a^2 \cos 2\theta$. Hence, the latter is an equation in polar form equivalent to the cartesian one. The graph of this equation is the *lemniscate of Bernoulli*;† see 4.8 Figure 1.

Conic sections. The nondegenerate conic sections have a very simple representation in polar coordinates. From A3.5c, we recall that a conic

---

†Jacques Bernoulli (1654–1705), Swiss, one of a remarkable family; nine Bernoullis became eminent in mathematics and physics. His lemniscate is defined geometrically as the set of points P for which the product of the distances from P to two fixed points equals one-fourth the square of the distance between the fixed points.

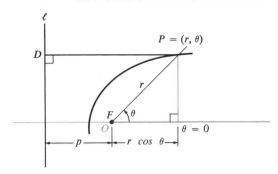

Figure 5

section may be defined as the set of all points P such that the ratio of the distance between P and a fixed point F (the focus) to the distance between P and a fixed line ℓ (the directrix) is a positive constant e (the eccentricity). If $e = 1$, the conic section is a parabola, if

$$0 < e < 1$$

an ellipse, and if $e > 1$, a hyperbola.

We take the focus F at the origin and the directrix ℓ as the vertical line at the distance $p > 0$ to the left of the origin; see Figure 5. Let $P = (r, \theta)$ be any point of the conic section. Since the section is non-degenerate, $r \neq 0$ and we may suppose $r > 0$. By definition, $e = |PF|/|PD|$ where D is the foot of the perpendicular from P on the directrix. From $|PF| = r$ and $|PD| = p + r\cos\theta$, we find

$$e = \frac{r}{p + r\cos\theta},$$

which yields the expression for r as a function of θ,

(6)
$$r = \frac{ep}{1 - e\cos\theta}.$$

This is the standard form of the equation for a nondegenerate conic section in polar coordinates.

The derivation of (6) assumes that the expression $p + r\cos\theta$ for $|PD|$ was positive. This poses no restriction for the ellipse and the parabola, but for the hyperbola, the derivation is valid only for the right branch, which is described by values of θ satisfying $\cos\theta < \dfrac{1}{e}$. For $\cos\theta > \dfrac{1}{e}$, Equation (6) yields negative values of r and describes the left branch of the hyperbola. We leave to Exercise 10 the problem of showing that (6) describes the entire hyperbola.

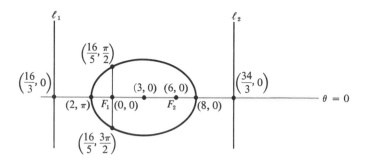

Figure 6

Example 5. We describe and sketch the graph of the equation

$$r = \frac{16}{5 - 3\cos\theta}.$$

In the standard form (6), this equation becomes

$$r = \frac{\frac{16}{5}}{1 - \frac{3}{5}\cos\theta} = \frac{\frac{3}{5}\cdot\frac{16}{3}}{1 - \frac{3}{5}\cos\theta},$$

from which $e = \frac{3}{5}$ and $p = \frac{16}{3}$. Since $e < 1$, the graph is an ellipse with focus F_1 at the pole and major axis on the polar axis. By giving θ the values 0 and π, we find the ends of the major axis to be $(8, 0)$ and $(2, \pi)$. Thus the length of the major axis is 10, the center of the ellipse is the point $(3, 0)$, and the other focus is the point $F_2 = (6, 0)$. Since $p = \frac{16}{3}$ (the distance between a focus and corresponding directrix of the ellipse), the equation of the directrix ℓ_1 corresponding to the focus at the pole is $r\cos\theta = -\frac{16}{3}$ (see Exercise 6a), and the equation of the directrix ℓ_2 corresponding to the focus F_2 is $r\cos\theta = \frac{34}{3}$. We employ the point $(\frac{16}{5}, \frac{1}{2}\pi)$ at one end of the vertical chord through F_1 and the other endpoint $(\frac{16}{5}, \frac{3}{2}\pi)$ to help us to sketch the ellipse, as shown in Figure 6.

Symmetries. If the origin is a fixed point of an isometry which maps a curve C given by

(7) $$g(r, \theta) = 0$$

onto itself, we have simple tests akin to those of A3.6c for the symmetry. If the symmetry is a rotation through the angle α, then for any point (r, θ) of C, the point $(r, \theta + \alpha)$ is also on C. Thus, a sufficient condition for this symmetry is $g(r, \theta + \alpha) = g(r, \theta)$. More generally, any condition,

(8a) $$g(r, \alpha + \theta + 2k\pi) = g(r, \theta),$$

or

(8b) $$g(-r, \alpha + \theta + [2k - 1]\pi) = g(r, \theta),$$

where k is an integer, is sufficient for a rotation through the angle α to be a symmetry.

If the symmetry is a reflection in the line $\theta = \frac{1}{2}\alpha$, and the point (r, θ) lies on C, so does the point $(r, \alpha - \theta)$. We conclude that any of the conditions

(9a) $$g(r, \alpha - \theta + 2k\pi) = g(r, \theta),$$

or

(9b) $$g(-r, \alpha - \theta + [2k - 1]\pi) = g(r, \theta),$$

where k is an integer, is a sufficient condition for symmetry to the line $\theta = \frac{1}{2}\alpha$.

Example 6. The curve
$$r^2 \sin 2\theta = 1$$
can be described in the form (7) with
$$g(r, \theta) = r^2 \sin 2\theta - 1.$$
Since $g(r, \theta) = g(r, \theta + \pi)$, Equation (8a) yields a half-turn or reflection in the origin as a symmetry. In addition, $g(r, \theta) = g(r, \frac{1}{2}\pi - \theta)$; hence, by (9a), the curve is symmetric to the line $\theta = \frac{1}{4}\pi$. Furthermore,
$$g(r, \tfrac{1}{2}\pi - \theta) = g(-r, \tfrac{1}{2}\pi - \theta) = g(-r, -\tfrac{1}{2}\pi - \theta + \pi);$$
hence, by (9b), the curve is symmetric to the line $\theta = -\frac{1}{4}\pi$.

Multiplication of complex numbers. The idea of imaginary numbers was adopted by mathematicians with great reluctance. For a long time imaginary numbers were considered to be meaningless and were used only for algebraic consistency. Negative numbers have a somewhat similar history, but nowadays we see negative numbers and their representation as points on a line at such an early age that they no longer seem unnatural. Imaginary numbers also lose their mystery if we represent them geometrically. Without any such representation of imaginary numbers mathematicians, particularly Euler,† were able to reason about them abstractly and make significant contributions to a theory of imaginaries. The theory

---

†Leonhard Euler (1707–1783), Swiss. A great versatile and prolific mathematician. There is scarcely a field of mathematics which lacks an Euler's Equation, Euler's Formula, and Euler's Theorem.

grew out of the impulse to develop the elegant formalism of imaginary numbers long before mathematicians were willing to credit them with any meaning.

In order to solve the general quadratic equation with real coefficients,

$$ax^2 + 2bx + c = 0 \qquad\qquad (a \neq 0),$$

when $b^2 - ac < 0$, it is necessary to introduce the imaginary number $i = \sqrt{-1}$ and complex numbers $\alpha + \beta i$ where α and β are real. Addition and multiplication of complex numbers are defined by the ordinary rules of algebra, coupled with the rule $i^2 = -1$ for reducing powers of i to degree one or zero. Thus, the sum of $z = x + iy$ and $w = u + iv$ is

$$z + w = (x + u) + i(y + v).$$

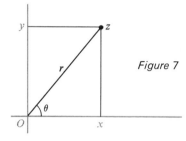

Figure 7

Addition of complex numbers is formally identical with addition of vectors in their cartesian representation. We may, therefore, represent complex numbers as vectors interpreted as translations or as points. In the latter interpretation, the complex number $z = x + iy$ is thought of as the point of the cartesian plane with abscissa x and ordinate y; see Figure 7.

Although addition of complex numbers is a new guise for a familiar idea, multiplication in the cartesian representation,

(10) $$zw = (xu - yv) + i(xv + yu)$$

may not seem so. We can better interpret multiplication in a polar coordinate representation. Let $\mathbf{z}$ and $\mathbf{w}$ be the position vectors of z and w, respectively, and θ and φ their respective inclinations. In polar coordinates,

$$z = (|\mathbf{z}|, \theta) \text{ and } w = (|\mathbf{w}|, \varphi).$$

Now we may employ (1) to get the representations

(11a) $$z = |\mathbf{z}| (\cos \theta + i \sin \theta)$$

and

(11b) $$w = |\mathbf{w}| (\cos \varphi + i \sin \varphi).$$

Entering (11) in (10) and simplifying, we get

(12) $$zw = |\mathbf{z}| |\mathbf{w}| \{\cos (\theta + \varphi) + i \sin (\theta + \varphi)\}.$$

Thus the effect of multiplying a complex number by z is that of a rotation through the angle θ followed by a similarity transformation with the scale factor $|z|$ (see A3.6d, Exercise 10). Again, we have an interpretation in terms of familiar concepts.

A3.7a Exercises

1. Find all the polar coordinate representations of each of the following points:

   a. $\left(6, \dfrac{\pi}{4}\right)$.   b. $\left(-6, \dfrac{\pi}{4}\right)$.

   c. $\left(6, -\dfrac{\pi}{4}\right)$.   d. $\left(-6, -\dfrac{\pi}{4}\right)$.

2. Find rectangular coordinates of the points in Exercise 1.

3. Find polar coordinates of each of the following points whose rectangular coordinates are given.

   a. $x = 4$, $y = -4$.   b. $x = -\frac{3}{2}\sqrt{3}$, $y = \frac{3}{2}$.
   c. $x = -2$, $y = -2\sqrt{3}$.   d. $x = 0$, $y = -10$.
   e. $x = -3$, $y = 0$.   f. $x = -3$, $y = 4$.
   g. $x = -\sqrt{3}$, $y = 1$.   h. $x = \sqrt{2}$, $y = -\sqrt{2}$.

4. Given the cartesian coordinates x and y of a point, obtain its polar coordinates (r, θ) for $0 \le \theta \le \pi$.

5. Determine the polar coordinates of the 3 vertices of an equilateral triangle if the triangle has sides of length L, the centroid of the triangle coincides with the pole, and the angular coordinate of one vertex is θ_1 radians.

6. Find equations, in polar coordinates, of the following curves:

   a. $x = c$, c a constant.   b. $y = c$, c a constant.
   c. $ax + by = c$.   d. $x^2 + (y - k)^2 = k^2$.
   e. $y^2 = 4ax$.   f. $x^2 - y^2 = a^2$.

7. Find equations, in rectangular coordinates, of the following curves:

   a. $r = a$.   b. $r \sin \theta = -5$.

   c. $r = 2a \sin \theta$.   d. $r = \dfrac{1}{1 - \cos \theta}$.

   e. $r = 2 \tan \theta$.

8. a. Derive an equation in polar coordinates for conic sections with a focus at the origin and directrix perpendicular to the x-axis and p units to the right of the origin.
   b. Do the same if the directrix is parallel to the x-axis and p units above the focus at the origin.
   c. Do the same if the directrix is parallel to the x-axis and p units below the focus at the origin.

9. Discuss and sketch each of the following curves in polar coordinates.

   a. $r = \dfrac{8}{1 - \cos \theta}$.   b. $r = \dfrac{12}{1 - 3 \cos \theta}$.

c. $r = \dfrac{36}{5 - 4 \sin \theta}$.   d. $r = \dfrac{16}{5 + 3 \sin \theta}$.

e. $r \sin \theta = 1 - r$.

10. Show for $e > 1$ that (6) is an equation for the entire hyperbola with eccentricity e, focus at the origin, and vertical directrix at distance $p > 0$ to the left of the origin.

11. Certain types of symmetry of curves in polar coordinates are readily detected. For example, a curve is symmetric to the origin if the equation is unchanged when r is replaced by $-r$. What kind of symmetry occurs if an equation is unchanged when

a. θ is replaced by $-\theta$?
b. θ is replaced by $\pi - \theta$?
c. r and θ are replaced by $-r$ and $-\theta$, respectively?
d. θ is replaced by $\pi + \theta$?

12. Without actually sketching the graphs, describe the symmetries of the graphs of the following equations.

a. $r(1 - \cos \theta) = 10$.   b. $r = \cos^2 2\theta$.

13. Sketch the following curves in polar coordinates.

a. $r = a\theta$.   b. $r = a(1 - \cos \theta)$.
c. $r = a \sin 2\theta$.   d. $r = a^2 \sin^2\theta \cos^2\theta$.
e. $r\theta = a$.

14. In each of the following, find all points of intersection of the given pairs of curves. (Recall that the polar representation of a point is not unique.)

a. $r = 2 - 2 \sin \theta$, $r = 2 - 2 \cos \theta$.
b. $r = -2 \sin 2\theta$, $r = 2 \cos \theta$.
c. $r = 4(1 + \cos \theta)$, $r(1 - \cos \theta) = 3$.

15. If $z = |z|(\cos \theta + i \sin \theta)$ find a complex number w such that $zw = 1$.

16. Show for $z = |z|(\cos \theta + i \sin \theta)$ and $w = |w|(\cos \phi + i \sin \phi)$, that

$$\frac{z}{w} = \frac{|z|}{|w|} \{\cos(\theta - \phi) + i \sin(\theta - \phi)\} .$$

⋏17. Prove for any rational number r and complex number

$$z = |z|(\cos \phi + i \sin \phi)$$

that the equation $w = z^r$ has the solution

$$w_1 = |z|^r(\cos r\phi + i \sin r\phi)$$

and find all other solutions of the equation if there are others.

A3.7b Polar coordinate systems in space

In three-dimensional space two polar coordinate systems are in common use. For a problem with axial symmetry it is usually convenient to take the z-axis as the axis of symmetry and to use the *cylindrical coordinate system* in which the point P with rectangular coordinates x, y, and z is fixed by the data in Figure 1:

    r, the distance of P from the z-axis,

    θ, the inclination with respect to the x-axis of the projection of P on the xy-plane as seen from above,

    z, the height of P above the xy-plane.

The position of P defined by its rectangular coordinates is determined

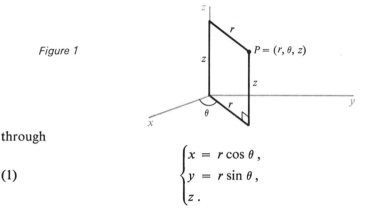

Figure 1

through

(1)
$$\begin{cases} x = r \cos \theta, \\ y = r \sin \theta, \\ z. \end{cases}$$

Precisely as for polar coordinates in the plane, the rectangular coordinates of P do not determine unique values of r and θ satisfying (1), and we enlarge the concept of cylindrical coordinates to include all number triples (r, θ, z) that satisfy (1).

The coordinate surfaces, $r = r_0$, $\theta = \theta_0$, and $z = z_0$ are a cylinder centered on the z-axis, a plane through the z-axis, and a horizontal plane, respectively; see Figure 2.

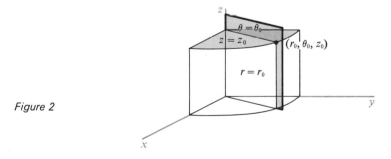

Figure 2

Example 1. In cylindrical coordinates, the right circular cone
$$x^2 + y^2 = c^2(z - a)^2,$$
which is axially symmetric to the z-axis, has the simple equation

$$r^2 = c^2(z - a)^2 .$$

Problems involving central symmetry with respect to the origin are often most conveniently expressed in terms of *spherical coordinates*. For a point P with rectangular coordinates $x, y,$ and $z,$ these coordinates are

ρ, the distance of P from the origin.

θ, the inclination with respect to the x-axis of the projection of P on the xy-plane.

ϕ, the angle between P and the positive z-axis.

(See Figure 3.) The cylindrical coordinates of P are given by

$$(2) \qquad \begin{cases} r = \rho \sin \phi , \\ \theta , \\ z = \rho \cos \phi , \end{cases}$$

and, thence, the rectangular coordinates by

$$(3) \qquad \begin{cases} x = \rho \cos \theta \sin \phi , \\ y = \rho \sin \theta \sin \phi , \\ z = \rho \cos \phi . \end{cases}$$

As for the other polar forms, we admit any triple (ρ, θ, ϕ) that satisfies (3) as a representation of P in spherical coordinates.

The coordinate surfaces $\rho = \rho_0 ,$ $\theta = \theta_0 ,$ and $\phi = \phi_0$ are a sphere centered at the origin, a plane through the z-axis, and a right circular cone with vertex at 0 and the z-axis as axis of symmetry; see Figure 4.

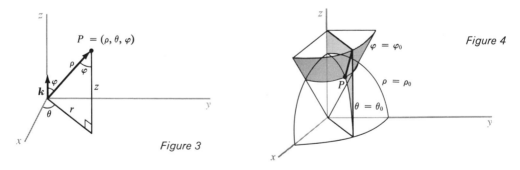

$P = (\rho, \theta, \varphi)$

Figure 3

Figure 4

Example 2. In spherical coordinates, the right circular cone

$$x^2 + y^2 = c^2 z^2$$

with vertex at the origin and z-axis as axis of symmetry has the equation

$$\rho^2 \sin^2 \phi = c^2 \rho^2 \cos^2 \phi ,$$

or, simply

$$\tan^2 \phi = c^2 .$$

Other coordinate systems. The general idea of a coordinate system should now be clear. If there are functions α, β, γ such that

$$x = \alpha(u, v, w), \quad y = \beta(u, v, w), \quad z = \gamma(u, v, w),$$

then (u, v, w) may be considered as a generalized coordinate representation of the point in E^3 with cartesian coordinates x, y, and z. Many coordinate systems have proved useful. Coordinate paper is commercially available for the more commonly used planar systems. We shall not attempt to describe any of these now. It is enough to know, for the time being, that we are free to invent a special coordinate system for any purpose we may desire.

A3.7b Exercises

1. Find the cartesian coordinates of the points given in cylindrical coordinates (r, θ, z) by
   a. $(1, \frac{1}{6}\pi, 2)$.
   b. $(-2, \frac{1}{4}\pi, 1)$.
   c. $(4, -\frac{3}{4}\pi, 2\sqrt{2})$.

2. Obtain the cartesian equations of the following curves whose equations are given in cylindrical coordinates.
   a. $r = c$.
   b. $r = az$.
   c. $z = \tan \theta$.

3. Find the cartesian coordinates of the points given in spherical coordinates (ρ, θ, ϕ) by
   a. $(4, \frac{1}{3}\pi, \frac{1}{4}\pi)$.
   b. $(2, \frac{3}{2}\pi, \frac{2}{3}\pi)$.
   c. (π, π, π).

4. Find both the cylindrical and spherical coordinates of the point given by the cartesian coordinates $x = \sqrt{2}$, $y = \sqrt{2}$, $z = 2$.

5. Given the following cartesian equations, obtain both their cylindrical and spherical forms.
   a. $z = x^2 + y^2$.
   b. $x^2 = y^2 - z^2$.
   c. $\dfrac{x^2}{a^2} + \dfrac{y^2}{a^2} - \dfrac{z^2}{b^2} = 1$.
   d. $x^3 + y^3 = axyz$.

6. Consider the generalized coordinates (α, β) defined by

$$\begin{cases} x = \dfrac{\tan \alpha + \tan \beta}{\tan \alpha - \tan \beta} \\[2mm] y = \dfrac{2 \tan \alpha \tan \beta}{\tan \alpha - \tan \beta} . \end{cases}$$

Interpret the coordinates geometrically and sketch the coordinate grid of curves $\alpha = \alpha_0$ and $\beta = \beta_0$.

Mathematical Induction

E A4.1 THE PRINCIPLE OF MATHEMATICAL INDUCTION

Induction, in common English, is the guessing of general propositions from a number of particular observations. The best way to show how to guess at a general principle from limited observations is to give examples.

Example 1. Consider the sums of consecutive odd integers:

$$1 = 1$$
$$1 + 3 = 4$$
$$1 + 3 + 5 = 9$$
$$1 + 3 + 5 + 7 = 16$$
$$1 + 3 + 5 + 7 + 9 = 25.$$

Notice that in each case the sum is the square of the number of terms.

Conjecture: The sum of the first n odd positive integers is n^2. (This is true. Can you prove it?)

Example 2. Consider the following inequalities:

$$1 < 100, \quad 2 < 100, \quad 3 < 100, \quad 4 < 100, \quad 5 < 100, \text{ etc.}$$

Conjecture: All positive integers are less than 100. (False, of course.)

Example 3. Consider the number of complex zeros, including repetitions, for polynomials of degree $0, 1, 2$, and so on.

Zero degree: a_0, no zeros $(a_0 \neq 0)$.

First degree: $a_1x + a_0$, one zero at $x = \dfrac{-a_0}{a_1}$.

Second degree: $a_2x^2 + a_1x + a_0$, two zeros at

$$x = \frac{-a_1 \pm \sqrt{a_1^2 - 4a_0a_2}}{2a_2}.$$

Conjecture: Every polynomial of degree n has exactly n complex zeros when repetitions are counted. (True.)

Example 4. Observe the operations necessary to compute the roots from the coefficients in Example 3.

Conjecture: The zeros of a polynomial of degree n can be given in terms of the coefficients by a formula which involves only addition, subtraction, multiplication, division, and the extraction of roots. (False.)

Example 5. Take any even number except 2 and express it as the sum of as few primes as possible:

$$4 = 2 + 2, \quad 6 = 3 + 3, \quad 8 = 3 + 5, \quad 10 = 5 + 5,$$
$$12 = 5 + 7, \quad 14 = 7 + 7, \text{ etc.}$$

Conjecture: Every even number but 2 can be expressed as the sum of two primes. (As yet, no one has been able to prove or disprove this.)

In all these examples, we are trying to assert something about all the members of a sequence of things: the sequence of odd integers, the sequence of positive integers, the sequence of polynomials, the sequence of even numbers greater than 2. The very character of the problems naturally suggests the idea of sequential proof. If we know something is true for the first few members of the sequence, can we use that result to prove its truth for the next member of the sequence? Having done that, can we now carry the proof on to one more member? Can we repeat the process indefinitely?

Let us try the idea of sequential proof on Example 1. Suppose we know for the first k odd integers $1, 3, 5, \ldots, 2k - 1$, that

(1) $$1 + 3 + 5 + \cdots + (2k - 1) = k^2.$$

Can we prove that upon adding the next higher odd number $2k + 1$ we obtain the next higher square? From (1), by adding $2k + 1$ on both sides, we have at once

$$[1 + 3 + 5 + \cdots + (2k - 1)] + (2k + 1) = k^2 + (2k + 1) = (k + 1)^2.$$

If the conjecture of Example 1 is true at any stage, it is clearly true at the next stage. Since the conjecture is true for the first stage, it must be true for the second, and, therefore, for the third, the fourth, the fifth, and so on, forever.

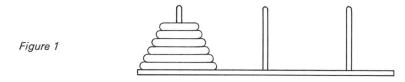

Figure 1

Example 6. In many good toy shops there is a puzzle which consists of three pegs and a set of graduated discs as depicted in Figure 1. The problem posed is to transfer the pile of discs from one peg to another under the following rules:

    a. Only one disc at a time may be transferred from one peg to another.
    b. No disc may cover a smaller disc.

Two questions arise naturally: Under the stated restrictions, can the task be done? If it is possible, how many moves does it take to complete the transfer of the discs? Were it not for the idea of sequential proof, one might have difficulty in attacking these questions.

Proceeding sequentially, we observe that there is no problem in transferring one disc.

If we have to transfer two discs, we transfer one, leaving a peg free for the second disc; we then transfer the second disc and cover it with the first.

If we have to transfer three discs, we transfer the top two, as above. This leaves a peg for the third disc to which it is moved, and the first two discs are then transferred to cover the third disc.

The pattern has now emerged. If we know how to transfer k discs, we can transfer $k + 1$ in the following way. First, we transfer k discs leaving the $(k + 1)$-th disc free to move to a new peg; we move the $(k + 1)$-th disc and then transfer the k discs again to cover it. We see that it is possible to move any number of graduated discs from one peg to another without violating the rules (a) and (b), since knowing how to move one disc, we have a rule that tells us how to transfer two, and then how to transfer three, and so on.

To determine the smallest number of moves it takes to transfer a pile of discs, we observe that a disc cannot be moved unless all the discs above it have been transferred to one peg so that a peg remains free to receive it. Let m_k be the minimum number of moves needed to transfer k discs from one peg to another. To move the $(k + 1)$-th disc, we need m_k moves beforehand to transfer the discs above it to another peg. After that, we can transfer the $(k + 1)$-th disc to the free peg. To move the $(k + 2)$-th disc, or to end the game if the $(k + 1)$-th disc is the last one, we must now cover the $(k + 1)$-th disc with the preceding k discs; this transfer of the k discs cannot be accomplished in less than m_k

moves. We see, then, that the minimum number of moves for $k + 1$ discs is

$$m_{k+1} = 2m_k + 1.$$

This is a recursive expression for the minimum number of moves, that is, if the minimum for a certain number of discs is known, the expression gives the minimum for one more. In this way, we have defined the minimum number of sequential moves: by adding one disc, we increase the number of necessary moves to twice the preceding number plus one. It takes one move to transfer one disc, therefore it takes three moves to transfer two discs, and so on. We tabulate the number of moves needed to transfer k discs, for $k = 1, 2, 3, \ldots, 7$.

k	1	2	3	4	5	6	7
m_k	1	3	7	15	31	63	127

Upon adding a disc, we roughly double the number of moves. This leads us to compare the number of moves with the powers of two: $1, 2, 4, 8, 16, 32, 64, 128, \ldots$; and we guess that $m_k = 2^k - 1$. If this is true for some value of k, we can easily see that it must be true for the succeeding value, for

$$\begin{aligned}
m_{k+1} &= 2m_k + 1 \\
&= 2(2^k - 1) + 1 \\
&= 2^{k+1} - 2 + 1 \\
&= 2^{k+1} - 1,
\end{aligned}$$

and this is the value of $2^n - 1$, for $n = k + 1$. We know that the formula $m_k = 2^k - 1$ is valid when $k = 1$, but now we can prove in sequence that it is true for $2, 3, 4$, and so on.

According to persistent rumor, there is a puzzle of this kind in a most holy monastery hidden deep in the Himalayas. The puzzle consists of 64 discs of pure beaten gold and the pegs are diamond needles. The story relates that the game of transferring the discs has been played night and day by the monks since the beginning of the world, and has yet to be concluded. It also has been said that when the 64 discs are completely transferred, the world will come to an end. The physicists say the earth is about four billion years old, give or take a billion or two. Assuming that the monks move one disc every second and play in the minimum number of moves, is there any cause for panic? (Cf. Ball, W. W., *Mathematical Recreations*. New York: Macmillan Co., 1947; p. 303 ff.)

The First Principle of Mathematical Induction

To make the principle of sequential proof explicit, let $A_1, A_2, A_3, \ldots$ be a sequence of assertions, and let H be the hypothesis that all of these are true. The hypothesis H is accepted as proved if

a. there is a general proof to show that the truth of any assertion A_k implies that the next assertion A_{k+1} is true;
b. there is a special proof to show that A_1 is true.

If there are only a finite number of assertions in the sequence, say ten, we need only carry out the chain of ten proofs explicitly to have a complete proof. If the assertions continue in sequence endlessly, as in Example 1, we cannot possibly verify directly every link in the chain of proof. It is just for this reason that the concept of sequential proof becomes so valuable. The ability to handle an infinite chain of proof without specifically examining every link is actually at the heart of the logical development of mathematics.

Through an unfortunate association of concepts, this method of sequential proof has been named *mathematical induction*. Induction, the guessing of general propositions from a number of observed facts, is the way one arrives at assertions that then require proof. Mathematical induction is actually a method of deduction or proof and not a procedure of guessing, although to use it, we ordinarily must have some guess to test. This usage has been in the language for a long time, and we would gain nothing by changing it now. Therefore, let us keep it, and remember that mathematical usage is special and often does not resemble in any respect the usage of common English.

In Example 1, the assertion A_n is

$$1 + 3 + 5 + \cdots + (2n - 1) = n^2.$$

First, we proved that if A_k is true (that is, if the sum of the first k odd numbers is k^2) then A_{k+1} is true, namely, that the sum of the first $k + 1$ odd numbers is $(k + 1)^2$. Second, we observed that A_1 is true: $1 = 1^2$. These two steps complete the proof.

Mathematical induction is a method of proving a hypothesis about a sequence of assertions. Unfortunately, it doesn't tell us how to discover the hypothesis. In the example just considered, it was easy to guess from a few specific instances that the sum of the first n odd numbers is n^2; but the next problem may not be so obvious.

Example 7. We seek a formula for the sum of the squares of the first n positive integers,

$$1^2 + 2^2 + 3^2 + \cdots + n^2.$$

We find that when $n = 1$, the sum is 1; when $n = 2$, the sum is 5; when $n = 3$, the sum is 14; and so on. Let us tabulate the first few values.

n	1	2	3	4	5	6	7	8
sum	1	5	14	30	55	91	140	204

Though some mathematicians might be immediately able to see a formula that will give the sum, most of us would have to admit that the situation is obscure. We must look around for some trick to help us discover the pattern which is surely there; what we do will, therefore, be a personal, individual matter. It is a mistake to think that only one approach is possible.

Sometimes experience is a useful guide. Do we know the solutions to any similar problems? Well, we have here the sum of a sequence. In Example 1 also, we had the sum of a sequence, the sum of the first n odd numbers. Consider the sum of the first n integers themselves (not their squares): what is

$$1 + 2 + 3 + \cdots + n?$$

This seems to be a related problem, and we can solve it with ease. The terms form an arithmetic progression in which the first term is 1 and the common difference is also 1; by the usual formula, the sum is

$$\tfrac{1}{2}n(n + 1) = \tfrac{1}{2}n^2 + \tfrac{1}{2}n.$$

So we have

$$1 + 3 + 5 + \cdots + (2n - 1) = n^2,$$
$$1 + 2 + 3 + \cdots + n = \tfrac{1}{2}n^2 + \tfrac{1}{2}n.$$

Is there any pattern here which might help with our present problem?

These two formulas have one common feature: both are quadratic polynomials in n. Might not the formula we want here also be a polynomial?

It seems unlikely that a quadratic polynomial could do the job in this more complicated problem, but how about one of higher degree? Let's try a cubic: assume there is a formula,

$$1^2 + 2^2 + \cdots + n^2 = an^3 + bn^2 + cn + d,$$

where a, b, c, and d are numbers yet to be determined. Substituting $n = 1, 2, 3$, and 4, successively, in this formula, we get

$$1^2 = a + b + c + d$$
$$1^2 + 2^2 = 8a + 4b + 2c + d$$
$$1^2 + 2^2 + 3^2 = 27a + 9b + 3c + d$$
$$1^2 + 2^2 + 3^2 + 4^2 = 64a + 16b + 4c + d.$$

Solving, we find

$$a = \tfrac{1}{3}, \quad b = \tfrac{1}{2}, \quad c = \tfrac{1}{6}, \quad d = 0.$$

We therefore conjecture that

$$1^2 + 2^2 + \cdots + n^2 = \tfrac{1}{3}n^3 + \tfrac{1}{2}n^2 + \tfrac{1}{6}n$$
$$= \tfrac{1}{6}n(n + 1)(2n + 1).$$

This then is our assertion A_n; now, let us prove it.

Assertion A_k states

$$1^2 + 2^2 + \cdots + k^2 = \tfrac{1}{6}k(k + 1)(2k + 1).$$

Add $(k + 1)^2$ to both sides, factor, and simplify:

$$1^2 + 2^2 + \cdots + k^2 + (k + 1)^2 = \tfrac{1}{6}k(k + 1)(2k + 1) + (k + 1)^2$$
$$= (k + 1)\left[\tfrac{1}{6}k(2k + 1) + (k + 1)\right]$$
$$= \tfrac{1}{6}(k + 1)(k + 2)(2k + 3),$$

and this last equation is simply A_{k+1}, which, therefore, follows from A_k. Moreover, since A_1, which states

$$1^2 = \tfrac{1}{6}(1)(2)(3),$$

is true, A_n is true for each positive integer n.

There is another formulation of the principle of mathematical induction which is extremely useful. This form involves a sequential step in which all the assertions up to a certain point are true, rather than just the one assertion immediately preceding.

The Second Principle of Mathematical Induction

Let $A_1, A_2, A_3, \ldots$ be a sequence of assertions and H the hypothesis that all of these are true. The hypothesis H is accepted as proved if:

a. there is a general proof to show that the truth of every assertion $A_1, A_2, \ldots, A_k$ implies the next assertion A_{k+1},
b. there is a special proof to show that A_1 is true.

This is the *second principle of mathematical induction*.

Either of the two principles of mathematical induction can easily be derived from the other; the demonstration is left to Exercise 11.

The value of the second principle of mathematical induction is that it solves many problems which would not yield to a direct application of the first principle.

Example 8. Every nonempty set S of natural numbers (whether finite or infinite) contains a least element.

Proof. Since S must contain some natural number, we may rephrase the proposition as a sequence of assertions A_k, where A_k states that if k is in S, then S contains a least element.

Initial Step: The assertion A_1 is that if S contains 1, it contains a least number. This is certainly true, since 1 is the smallest natural number and thus is smaller than any other member of S.

Sequential Step: We assume that A_n is true for all natural numbers up to and including k. Now, let S be a set containing $k + 1$. There are two possibilities:

1. That S contains a natural number p less than $k + 1$. In that case, p is less than or equal to k. It follows that S contains a least element.
2. That S contains no natural number less than $k + 1$. In that case, $k + 1$ is least. □

This example is valuable because it is a third principle of mathematical induction equivalent to the other two, although not an obvious one to be sure. An amusing example of a "proof" by this principle is given by Beckenbach in the *American Mathematical Monthly*, Vol. 52; 1945.

Theorem. Every natural number is interesting.

Argument. Consider the set S of all uninteresting natural numbers. This set contains a least element. What an interesting number, the smallest in the set of uninteresting numbers! So, S contains an interesting number after all. (Contradiction.)

The trouble with this "proof", of course, is that we have no definition of "interesting"; one man's interest is another man's boredom.

Definition by Recursion

One of the most important uses of mathematical induction is definition of a sequence by *recursion*: a definition is given for the initial object of the sequence, and a rule is supplied so that if any term is known, the rule provides a definition for the succeeding one. For example, we could have defined $a^n (a \neq 0)$ recursively in the following way:

Initial Step: $a^0 = 1$.
Sequential Step: $a^{k+1} = a \cdot a^k$ $\qquad\qquad (k = 0, 1, 2, 3, ...)$.

Similarly, n *factorial*, the product of the first n positive integers, written $n!$, is defined as follows:

Initial Step: $1! = 1$.
Sequential Step: $(k + 1)! = (k + 1)(k!)$ $\qquad (k = 1, 2, 3, ...)$.

Recursive definitions are convenient for proof by mathematical induction. The following example involves the two definitions just given.

Example 9. For n any natural number, $2^{n-1} \leq n!$. The proof by mathematical induction is direct.

Initial Step: $2^0 = 1 \leq 1! \leq 1$.
Sequential Step: Assuming that the assertion is true at the k-th step, we seek to prove it for the $(k + 1)$-th step. By definition,

$$(k + 1)! = (k + 1)(k!).$$

From the hypothesis, $k! \geq 2^{k-1}$, and, since $k \geq 1$ (k is a natural number),

$$(k + 1)! = (k + 1)(k!) \geq (k + 1)2^{k-1} \geq 2 \cdot 2^{k-1} \geq 2^k. \qquad \square$$

We frequently need to use expressions of the form

(2) $$f(1) + f(2) + f(3) + \cdots + f(n),$$

where f is any function on the domain $\mathfrak{N}$ of natural numbers. The three dots in (2) mean "and so on." Unfortunately, "and so on" is sometimes a vague prescription. Does $2 + 4 + \cdots + 16$ stand for the sum of the arithmetic progression $2, 4, 6, 8, 10, 12, 14, 16$ or the sum of the geometric progression $2, 4, 8, 16$? In this text, we avoid ambiguity by writing the initial terms of the sum in a form so that the varying element changes in arithmetic progression; thus, for the sum of the arithmetic progression we write

$$2 + 4 + \cdots + 16,$$

and for the sum of the geometric progression

$$2 + 2^2 + \cdots + 2^4.$$

It would be still clearer to specify the function f in (2). It would also be desirable to have a concise notation that avoids the redundant specification of f in every term of (2). We put

(3)
$$\sum_{k=1}^{n} f(k) = f(1) + f(2) + \cdots + f(n)$$

and call this new symbol, "the sum of $f(k)$ as k goes from 1 to n." The dots in (3) are actually a mask for an implied definition by recursion:

Initial Step: $\displaystyle\sum_{j=1}^{1} f(j) = f(1).$

Sequential Step: $\displaystyle\sum_{j=1}^{k+1} f(j) = f(k+1) + \sum_{j=1}^{k} f(j).$

In sum notation, (1) takes the form

$$\sum_{j=1}^{k} (2j - 1) = k^2.$$

The sequential step in the proof, that the sum of the first n odd numbers is n^2, then becomes

$$\sum_{j=1}^{k+1} (2j - 1) = [2(k+1) - 1] + \sum_{j=1}^{k} (2j - 1)$$
$$= k^2 + 2k + 1 = (k+1)^2.$$

In A4.2 we treat sum notation and summation (the evaluation of sums) in detail.

Before we conclude these remarks on mathematical induction, a word of caution. For a complete proof by mathematical induction it is important to show the truth of both the initial step and the sequential step of the induction principle being used. There are many examples of mathematical induction gone haywire because one of these steps fails. Here are two examples.

Example 10.

Assertion: All natural numbers are even.

Argument: For the proof, we utilize the Second Principle of Mathematical Induction and take for A_k the assertion that all natural numbers less than or equal to k are even. Now, consider the natural number $k + 1$. Let i be any natural number with $i \leq k$. The number j such that $i + j = k + 1$ can easily be shown to be a natural number with $j \leq k$. But if $i \leq k$ and $j \leq k$, both i and j are even; and hence

$$k + 1 = i + j,$$

the sum of two even numbers, and must itself be even!

Find the hole in this argument.

Example 11.

Assertion: All girls are the same.†

Argument: Given girls designated by a and b, let $a = b$ mean that a and b are the same. Consider any set S_1 containing just one girl. Clearly, if a and b denote girls in S_1, then $a = b$. Now, suppose it is true for any set of k girls that they are all the same. Let S_{k+1} be a set containing $k + 1$ girls $g_1, g_2, \ldots, g_k, g_{k+1}$. By hypothesis, the k girls, $g_1, g_2, \ldots, g_k$, are all the same, but by the same hypothesis, so are the k girls $g_2, g_3, \ldots, g_k, g_{k+1}$. It follows that $g_1 = g_2 = \cdots = g_k = g_{k+1}$. We conclude that all girls of a set containing any positive integral number of them are the same. Since there is only a positive integral number of girls in the whole world, the assertion is proved.

Find the hole in this argument.

A4.1 Exercises

1. Prove by mathematical induction that $1 + 2 + 3 + \cdots + n = \frac{1}{2}n(n + 1)$.

2. By mathematical induction prove the familiar result that gives

    a. the sum of an arithmetic progression to n terms:

$$a + (a + d) + (a + 2d) + \cdots + (a + [n - 1]d)$$
$$= \tfrac{1}{2}n[2a + [n - 1]d].$$

†We are not trying to express an overly blasé attitude about girls. The original of this example (attributed to the famous logician Tarski) had it that all positive integers are the same; but, isn't it more interesting to discuss girls?

b. the sum of a geometric progression to n terms:

$$a + ar + ar^2 + \cdots + ar^{n-1} = \frac{a(r^n - 1)}{r - 1} \qquad (R \neq 1).$$

3. Prove that

a. $1^2 + 3^2 + 5^2 + \cdots + (2n - 1)^2 = \frac{1}{3}(4n^3 - n)$.

b. $\displaystyle\sum_{j=1}^{n} j\,2^{j-1} = 1 + (n - 1)\,2^n$.

4. Prove the following statements by mathematical induction.

a. $2n \leq 2^n$.

b. If $p \geq -1$, then $(1 + p)^n \geq 1 + np$ (the Bernoulli Inequality), for all natural numbers n.

5. In the following problems, find a formula for the sum and prove by mathematical induction that it is correct.

a. $\dfrac{1}{1 \cdot 2} + \dfrac{1}{2 \cdot 3} + \dfrac{1}{3 \cdot 4} + \cdots + \dfrac{1}{n(n + 1)}$.

b. $1^3 + 2^3 + 3^3 + \cdots + n^3$. (Hint: Compare the successive sums with those of Exercise 1.)

c. $\displaystyle\sum_{j=1}^{n} j\,(j + 1)$. (Hint: Compare with Example 7 and Exercise 1.)

6. Prove for all natural numbers n,

$$\left(1 + \frac{3}{1}\right)\left(1 + \frac{5}{4}\right)\left(1 + \frac{7}{9}\right) \cdots \left(1 + \frac{2n + 1}{n^2}\right) = (n + 1)^2.$$

7. Prove that $(1 + x)(1 + x^2)(1 + x^4) \cdots (1 + x^{2^n}) = \dfrac{1 - x^{2^{n+1}}}{1 - x}$ for $x \neq 1$.

8. Prove that $n(n^2 + 5)$ is divisible by 6 for all integral n.

9. Prove the following statements by the second principle of mathematical induction.

a. For all natural numbers n, the number $n + 1$ either is a prime or can be factored into primes.

b. For each natural number n greater than one, let U_n be a real number with the property that for at least one pair of natural numbers p, q with $p + q = n$,

$$U_n = U_p + U_q.$$

When $n = 1$, we define $U_1 = a$ where a is some given real number. Prove that $U_n = na$ for all n.

10. Attempt to prove Exercises 9a, b from the first principle to see what difficulties arise.

11. Show that the first and second principles of mathematical induction are equivalent; that is, derive each as a consequence of the other.

12. Any straight line separates the plane into two parts; two intersecting straight lines separate the plane into four parts; and three nonconcurrent lines, of which no two are parallel, separate the plane into seven parts. Determine the number of parts into which the plane is separated by n straight lines of which no three meet in a single common point and no two are parallel; then prove your result. Can you obtain a more general result when parallelism is permitted? If concurrence is permitted? If both are permitted?

13. Let $f(n)$ be defined recursively as follows:

   Initial Step: $f(1) = 3$.
   Sequential Step: $f(n + 1) = 3^{f(n)}$.

   In particular, we have $f(3) = 3^{3^3} = 3^{27}$. Similarly, $g(n)$ is defined by

   Initial Step: $g(1) = 9$.
   Sequential Step: $g(n + 1) = 9^{g(n)}$.

   Find the minimum value m for each n such that $f(m) \geq g(n)$.

14. Consider the sequence of fractions

$$\frac{1}{1}, \frac{3}{2}, \frac{7}{5}, \frac{17}{12}, \dots, \frac{p_n}{q_n}, \dots$$

   where each fraction is obtained from the preceding by the rule

$$p_n = p_{n-1} + 2q_{n-1}$$
$$q_n = p_{n-1} + q_{n-1}.$$

   Show that for n sufficiently large, the difference between p_n/q_n and $\sqrt{2}$ can be made as small as desired. Show also that the approximation to $\sqrt{2}$ is improved at each successive stage of the sequence and that the error alternates in sign. Prove also that p_n and q_n are relatively prime, that is, the fraction p_n/q_n is in lowest terms.

15. Prove for all natural numbers n, that $\dfrac{(1 + \sqrt{5})^n - (1 - \sqrt{5})^n}{2^n\sqrt{5}}$ is an integer. (Hint: Try to express $x^n - y^n$ in terms of $x^{n-1} - y^{n-1}$, $x^{n-2} - y^{n-2}$, etc.)

16. Let p be any polynomial function of degree m. Let $q(n)$ denote the sum

   (i) $q(n) = p(1) + p(2) + p(3) + \cdots + p(n)$.

   Prove that there is a polynomial q of degree $m + 1$ satisfying (i).

17. The iterated radical

$$a_n = \sqrt{2 + \sqrt{2 + \sqrt{2 \dots + \sqrt{2}}}}$$

is defined recursively by $a_1 = \sqrt{2}$ and $a_{k+1} = \sqrt{2 + a_k}$. Prove that

$$a_n = 2 \cos \frac{\pi}{2^{k+1}}.$$

18. The *arithmetic mean* of n numbers $a_1, a_2, \ldots, a_n$ is

$$A_n = \frac{1}{n}(a_1 + a_2 + \cdots + a_n).$$

If the numbers a_i $(i = 1, 2, \ldots, n)$ are positive, their geometric mean is

$$G_n = \sqrt[n]{a_1 a_2 \cdots a_n}.$$

Derive the inequality between the two means,

$$G_n \leq A_n.$$

(Hint: Use the Bernoulli Inequality of Exercise 4b with $p = \dfrac{a_{k+1}}{A_k} - 1$.)

A4.2 SUMS AND SUM NOTATION

A4.2a Sum notation

In 1.2, as well as A4.1 and many other places, we use extended sums in which the terms exhibit a repetitive pattern. For example, in 1.2 the estimate of area for a standard region involves the sum

(1) $$1 \cdot 1 + 2 \cdot 3 + 3 \cdot 5 + \cdots + n(2n - 1).$$

In A4.1, we introduced a concise notation which indicates the repetition, instead of writing it all out. In this notation the sum (1) is written

$$\sum_{k=1}^{n} k(2k - 1).$$

This symbol means, "the sum of all terms of the form $k(2k - 1)$ where k takes on the integer values from 1 to n inclusive." The Greek capital "Σ" (sigma) corresponds to the Roman "S" and is intended to suggest the word "sum."

Example 1. If the area of a region is estimated as the sum of areas of rectangles R_k of height h_k and width w_k, the estimate may be written as

$$w_1 h_1 + w_2 h_2 + w_3 h_3 + \cdots + w_n h_n = \sum_{k=1}^{n} w_k h_k.$$

It is often convenient to take sums in which the index runs over a number of consecutive integers, not necessarily beginning with 1. We introduce the general notation

(2)
$$\sum_{k=m}^{n} f(k) = f(m) + f(m+1) + \cdots + f(n)$$

where $n \geq m$. Formally, we define this notation in terms of the symbol for which $m = 1$ by

$$\sum_{k=m}^{n} f(k) = \sum_{j=1}^{n-m+1} f(m+j-1)$$

Example 2.

a.
$$\sum_{k=0}^{3} \frac{k}{1+k^2} = \frac{0}{1+0} + \frac{1}{1+1} + \frac{2}{1+4} + \frac{3}{1+9} = \frac{6}{5}.$$

b.
$$\sum_{j=2}^{5} (j+3) = 5 + 6 + 7 + 8 = 26.$$

Sum notation concisely expresses some basic ideas: a linear combination

$$\sum_{j=1}^{n} a_j f_j(x) = a_1 f_1(x) + a_2 f_2(x) + \cdots + a_n f_n(x),$$

a polynomial of degree no greater than m

$$\sum_{i=0}^{m} c_i x^i = c_0 + c_1 x + c_2 x^2 + \cdots + c_m x^m.$$

A simple but important sum is $\sum_{k=m}^{n} c$, where c is a constant, that is, $f(k) = c$ in (2) for all values of the index k. The quantity $\sum_{k=m}^{n} c$ is the sum of $n - m + 1$ terms each of which is c; therefore,

$$\sum_{k=m}^{n} c = c(n - m + 1).$$

In any summation the values of the terms and the total are not affected by the choice of the index letter; thus

$$\sum_{k=m}^{n} \phi_k = \sum_{j=m}^{n} \phi_j.$$

We are free to choose the index letter and its initial value to suit our own convenience.

Example 3.

a. $\sum_{j=0}^{2} a_j = a_0 + a_1 + a_2 = \sum_{p=1}^{3} a_{p-1} = \sum_{n=0}^{2} a_{2-n}$.

b. $\sum_{i=0}^{n} a_i x^{n-i} = a_0 x^n + a_1 x^{n-1} + \cdots + a_n x^0 = \sum_{j=0}^{n} (a_{n-j}) x^j$.

Summation is a linear process; the proof is left to Exercise 1.

A4.2a Exercises

1. Prove

$$\sum_{k=1}^{n} (\alpha f_k + \beta g_k) = \alpha \sum_{k=1}^{n} f_k + \beta \sum_{k=1}^{n} g_k$$

(linearity of summation).

2. Write each of the following sums in expanded form and evaluate:

a. $\sum_{k=1}^{5} 2k$.

b. $\sum_{j=2}^{6} j^2$.

c. $\sum_{r=-1}^{3} (r^2 + r - 12)$.

d. $\sum_{m=2}^{5} m(m-1)(m-2)$.

e. $\sum_{i=0}^{10} 2^i$.

f. $\sum_{r=0}^{4} \frac{4!}{r!\,(4-r)!}$.

3. Which of the following statements are true and which are false? Justify your conclusions.

a. $\sum_{j=3}^{10} 4 = 7 \cdot 4 = 28$.

b. $\sum_{j=m}^{n} 4 = 4[(n-m)+1]$.

c. $\sum_{k=1}^{10} k^2 = 10 \sum_{k=1}^{9} k^2$.

d. $\sum_{k=1}^{1000} k^2 = 5 + \sum_{k=3}^{1000} k^2$.

e. $\sum_{k=1}^{n} k^3 = n^3 + \sum_{j=2}^{n} (j-1)^3$.

f. $\sum_{m=1}^{10} k^2 = \left(\sum_{m=1}^{10} k \right)^2$.

g. $\sum_{m=1}^{10} k^3 = \left(\sum_{m=1}^{10} k \right)^2$.

h. $\sum_{i=0}^{n} i(i-1)(n-i) = \sum_{i=2}^{n-1} i(i-1)(n-i)$.

i. $\displaystyle\sum_{k=0}^{m} f(a_{m-k}) = \sum_{k=0}^{m} f(a_k)$.

j. $\displaystyle n\sum_{k=0}^{n} A_k - \sum_{k=0}^{n} k\,A_k = \sum_{k=0}^{n} k\,A_{n-k}$.

k. $\displaystyle\sum_{k=0}^{m} k^2(A_k - A_{m-k}) = m^2 \sum_{k=0}^{m} A_{m-k} - 2m \sum_{k=0}^{m} k\,A_{m-k}$.

4. Evaluate $\displaystyle\sum_{k=1}^{n} f\left(\frac{k}{n}\right)\frac{(b-a)}{n}$ if $f(x) = x^2$, $a = 0$, $b = 1$, and

   a. $n = 2$,   b. $n = 4$,

   c. $n = 8$.

5. Subdivide the interval $[0,1]$ into n equal parts. In each subinterval obtain upper and lower bounds for x^2. Using sigma notation use these upper and lower bounds to obtain expressions for upper and lower estimates of the area under the curve $y = x^2$ on $[0,1]$. If you can evaluate these sums without reading elsewhere, do so.

6. a. In sigma notation, express the sum of the first 7 terms of an arithmetic progression with first term a and common difference d.

   b. In sigma notation, express the sum of the first n terms of a geometric progression with first term a and common ratio r.

7. a. Consider the function f defined by

$$f(n) = \sum_{r=1}^{n} \{(r-1)(r-2)(r-3)(r-4)(r-5) + r\} .$$

   Find $f(n)$ for $n = 1, 2, \dots, 5$.

   b. Give an example of a function g, similar to that in Part a, such that $g(n) = 1$, for $n = 1, 2, \dots, 10^6$, and $g(10^6 + 1) = 0$.

8. Write each of the following sums in expanded form and evaluate.

   a. $\displaystyle\sum_{n=1}^{4}\left\{\sum_{r=1}^{3} r\,(n-r)\right\}$.   b. $\displaystyle\sum_{n=1}^{N}\left\{\sum_{r=1}^{R} (rn-1)\right\}$.

9. The double sum $\displaystyle\sum_{i=0}^{m}\sum_{j=0}^{n} F(i,j)$ is a shorthand notation for

$$\sum_{i=0}^{m} \{F(i,0) + F((i,1) + \cdots + F(i,n)\}$$

   or

$$
\begin{aligned}
&F(0,0) + F(0,1) + \cdots + F(0,n)\\
&+ F(1,0) + F(1,1) + \cdots + F(1,n)\\
&+ \cdots\\
&+ F(m,0) + F(m,1) + \cdots + F(m,n) .
\end{aligned}
$$

   In particular,

$$\sum_{i=1}^{2}\sum_{j=1}^{3} i\cdot j = 1\cdot1 + 1\cdot2 + 1\cdot3 + 2\cdot1 + 2\cdot2 + 2\cdot3 = 18 .$$

Evaluate

a. $\displaystyle\sum_{i=1}^{m}\sum_{j=1}^{n} i \cdot j$,

b. $\displaystyle\sum_{i=1}^{m}\sum_{j=1}^{n} (i + j)$,

c. $\displaystyle\sum_{i=1}^{m}\sum_{j=1}^{n} \max\{i, j\}$,

d. $\displaystyle\sum_{i=1}^{m}\sum_{j=1}^{n} \min\{i, j\}$.

10. a. Evaluate $\displaystyle\sum_{k=2}^{1000} \frac{1}{k(k-1)}$.

b. Show that $\displaystyle\sum_{k=2}^{n} \frac{1}{k(k-1)} = 1 - \frac{1}{n}$.

11. If $S(n) = \displaystyle\sum_{i=1}^{n} f(i)$, determine $f(m)$ in terms of the sum function S.

12. Determine $f(m)$ in each of the following summation formulas (see Exercise 11).

a. $1 = \displaystyle\sum_{i=1}^{m} f(i)$.

b. $m = \displaystyle\sum_{i=1}^{m} f(i)$.

c. $m^2 = \displaystyle\sum_{i=1}^{m} f(i)$.

d. $am^2 + bm + c = \displaystyle\sum_{i=1}^{m} f(i)$.

e. $\cos mx = \displaystyle\sum_{i=1}^{m} f(i)$.

f. $\sin(am + b) = \displaystyle\sum_{i=1}^{m} f(i)$.

g. $m! = \displaystyle\sum_{i=1}^{m} f(i)$.

13. *Binomial Theorem:* We define $\dbinom{n}{r} = \dfrac{n!}{(n-r)!\, r!}$ where r, n are non-negative integers such that $0 \le r \le n$, and $0! = 1$.

If $r > n$, we set $\dbinom{n}{r} = 0$. Show that

a. $\dbinom{n}{0} = \dbinom{n}{n} = 1$, $\quad \dbinom{n}{1} = \dbinom{n}{n-1} = n$.

b. $\dbinom{n}{r} = \dbinom{n}{n-r}$.

c. $\dbinom{n}{r} + \dbinom{n}{r+1} = \dbinom{n+1}{r+1}$.

d. By mathematical induction, establish the Binomial Theorem

$$(x + y)^n = \sum_{r=0}^{n} \binom{n}{r} x^{n-r} y^r = x^n + nx^{n-1}y + \cdots + nxy^{n-1} + y^n,$$

for $n = 0, 1, 2, \ldots$.

14. Using the Binomial Theorem, expand the following.

a. $(x+y)^3$.   b. $(x-y)^3$.

c. $(2x-3y)^3$.   d. $(x-2y)^5$.

15. Evaluate the following sums.

a. $\displaystyle\sum_{r=0}^{n} \binom{n}{r}$.   b. $\displaystyle\sum_{r=0}^{n} (-1)^r \binom{n}{r}$.

16. Evaluate $\displaystyle\sum_{r=0}^{n} r \binom{n}{r}$ by   showing $\displaystyle\sum_{r=0}^{n} r \binom{n}{r} = \sum_{r=0}^{n} (n-r) \binom{n}{r}$ and

using Exercise 15a.

17. If $P_n(x)$ denotes a polynomial of degree n such that $P_n(x) = 2^x$ for
$x = 0, 1, 2, \ldots, n$ find $P_n(n+1)$.

A4.2b Summation

Exercise 10a of A4.2a illustrates a particularly useful summation technique, representation as a collapsible sum. To solve the problem, we write

$$\sum_{k=2}^{1000} \frac{1}{k(k-1)} = \frac{1}{2\cdot 1} + \frac{1}{3\cdot 2} + \frac{1}{4\cdot 3} + \cdots + \frac{1}{1000\cdot 999}$$

in the form

$$\sum_{k=2}^{1000} \left(\frac{1}{k-1} - \frac{1}{k}\right) = \left(1 - \frac{1}{2}\right) + \left(\frac{1}{2} - \frac{1}{3}\right)$$
$$+ \cdots + \left(\frac{1}{998} - \frac{1}{999}\right) + \left(\frac{1}{999} - \frac{1}{1000}\right).$$

Each quantity subtracted in one parenthesis is added back in the next, so
that the entire sum collapses into the difference of two numbers, the first
number in the first term and the second number in the last term. Symbolically, a collapsible sum has the form

(1) $$\sum_{k=m}^{n} \{f(k) - f(k-1)\} = f(n) - f(m-1).$$

In the given example, $m = 2$, $n = 1000$,   and $f(k) = -\dfrac{1}{k}$ so that

the sum collapses to

$$f(1000) - f(1) = -\frac{1}{1000} + 1 = \frac{999}{1000}.$$

We now use (1) with different functions $f(k)$ to construct a short
dictionary of summation formulas. Without loss of generality, we set
$m = 1$.

For $f(k) = k$,

(2) $$\sum_{k=1}^{n} \{k - (k-1)\} = \sum_{k=1}^{n} 1 = n,$$

not a new result, but part of a pattern we are developing.

Now, let $f(k) = k^2$, then

$$\sum_{k=1}^{n} \{k^2 - (k-1)^2\} = \sum_{k=1}^{n} (2k-1) = 2\sum_{k=1}^{n} k - \sum_{k=1}^{n} 1 = n^2$$

or, equivalently,

(3) $$\sum_{k=1}^{n} k = \tfrac{1}{2}n(n+1).$$

By linearly combining (2) and (3), we find the sum of a general arithmetic progression

$$\sum_{k=1}^{n} (ak + b) = a\left[\frac{n(n+1)}{2}\right] + bn.$$

To obtain the sum $\sum_{k=1}^{n} k^2$, we let $f(k) = k^3$. Then, by (1),

$$\sum_{k=1}^{n} \{k^3 - (k-1)^3\} = \sum_{k=1}^{n} (3k^2 - 3k + 1) = n^3,$$

that is,

$$3\sum_{k=1}^{n} k^2 - 3\sum_{k=1}^{n} k + \sum_{k=1}^{n} 1 = n^3.$$

Using (2) and (3), we get

(4) $$\sum_{k=1}^{n} k^2 = \frac{1}{3}\left[n^3 + \frac{3n(n+1)}{2} - n\right] = \frac{n(n+1)(2n+1)}{6}.$$

Thus, we have solved the problem of A4.1 Example 7 by a new method.

With this method we can find a formula for any sum $\sum_{k=1}^{n} P(k)$ where P is a polynomial function. Because a polynomial is a linear combination of powers, and summation is a linear process, it is sufficient to give a sequential method for $\sum_{k=1}^{n} k^r$, where r is a nonnegative integer. Choosing $f(k) = k^{r+1}$ in summation formula (1), we find

$$\sum_{k=1}^{n} [k^{r+1} - (k-1)^{r+1}] = n^{r+1}.$$

Using the Binomial Theorem (A4.2a Exercise 13), we obtain

$$k^{r+1} - (k-1)^{r+1} = (r+1)k^r + P(k),$$

where $P(k)$ is a polynomial of degree $r - 1$. Thus, the sum $\sum\limits_{k=1}^{n} k^r$ can be expressed in terms of sums of lower degree. Since we already have the sum for $r = 0, 1,$ and 2, we can repeat the method sequentially to obtain the sum for any r (compare with A4.1 Exercise 16).

We can enlarge our summation table by choosing other functional forms $f(k)$. For example, let $f(k) = \sin(ak + b)$. By (1),

(5) $\sum\limits_{k=1}^{n} \{\sin(ak + b) - \sin[a(k-1) + b]\} = \sin(an + b) - \sin b$.

We use the identity of A2.6 Exercise 6a,

$$\sin A - \sin B = 2 \sin \frac{A - B}{2} \cos \frac{A + B}{2},$$

in Equation (5), and simplify to obtain

(6) $\qquad \sum\limits_{k=1}^{n} \cos\left(ak + b - \frac{a}{2}\right) = \cos\left(b + \frac{an}{2}\right) \dfrac{\sin \frac{an}{2}}{\sin \frac{a}{2}}.$

If $b = \dfrac{a}{2}$, Equation (6) reduces to

(7) $\qquad \sum\limits_{k=1}^{n} \cos ak = \cos\left[\frac{a(n+1)}{2}\right] \dfrac{\sin \frac{an}{2}}{\sin \frac{a}{2}}.$

If $b = \dfrac{a}{2} + \dfrac{\pi}{2}$, (6) reduces to

(8) $\qquad \sum\limits_{k=1}^{n} \sin ak = \sin\left[\frac{a(n+1)}{2}\right] \dfrac{\sin \frac{an}{2}}{\sin \frac{a}{2}}.$

We leave to exercises the enlargement of our list of summation formulas by other choices of the function f in (1).

A4.2b Exercises

1. Write each of the following as a collapsible sum, that is, in the form

$$\sum\limits_{k=1}^{n} \{f(k) - f(k-1)\},$$

and evaluate.

a. $\displaystyle\sum_{k=1}^{n} k\,(k+1)$.

b. $\displaystyle\sum_{k=1}^{n} k\,(2k-1)$.

c. $\displaystyle\sum_{k=1}^{n} 2k\,(2k+1)$.

d. $\displaystyle\sum_{k=1}^{n} k\,(k+1)\,(k+2)$.

e. $\displaystyle\sum_{k=1}^{n} k^3$.

f. $\displaystyle\sum_{k=1}^{n} \frac{1}{k\,(k+1)\,(k+2)}$.

g. $\displaystyle\sum_{k=1}^{n} k\,(k!)$.

h. $\displaystyle\sum_{k=1}^{n} r^k$.

2. Using $\displaystyle\sum_{k=1}^{n} \{f(k) - f(k-1)\} = f(n) - f(0)$, establish a short dictionary of summation formulas by considering the following values of $f(k)$.

a. $(a+kd)(a+[k+1]d) \cdots (a+[k+p]d)$.
b. The reciprocal of the expression in Part a.

c. r^k .   d. $k\,r^k$.
e. $k^2 r^k$.   f. $k!$.
g. $(k!)^2$.   h. $\arctan k$.
i. $k \sin k$.

3. Simplify:

$$\frac{\sin x + \sin 3x + \cdots + \sin [(2n-1)x]}{\cos x + \cos 3x + \cdots + \cos [(2n-1)x]} .$$

4. Another method of summation for $\Sigma P(k)$, where P is a polynomial function, can be obtained by using a special case of Exercise 2a, that is,

$$\sum_{k=1}^{n} \{(k+1)\,k\,(k-1) \cdots (k-r+1) - k\,(k-1)\,(k-2) \cdots (k-r)\}$$
$$= (n+1)\,n\,(n-1) \cdots (n-r+1) ,$$

or

$$\sum_{k=1}^{n} k(k-1) \cdots (k-r+1) = \frac{(n+1)\,n\,(n-1) \cdots (n-r+1)}{r+1} .$$

First, observe that any polynomial $P(k)$ of degree r may be represented in the form

(i) $P(k) = a_0 + a_1 k + \dfrac{a_2 k(k-1)}{2!} + \cdots + \dfrac{a_r k(k-1) \cdots (k-r+1)}{r!}$.

If $k = 0$, then $a_0 = P(0)$; if $k = 1$, then $a_1 = P(1) - P(0)$; if $k = 2$, then $a_2 = P(2) - 2P(1) + P(0)$. In general, it can be shown that

(ii) $a_m = P(m) - \dbinom{m}{1} P(m-1) + \dbinom{m}{2} P(m-2) - \cdots + (-1)^m P(0)$,

$$m = 0, 1, \ldots, r .$$

Since both sides of (i) are polynomials of degree r and (i) is satisfied for

$m = 0, 1, \ldots, r$, it must be an identity. Now sum $\displaystyle\sum_{k=1}^{n} P(k)$.

5. Using Exercise 4, find the following sums.

a. $\displaystyle\sum_{k=1}^{n} k^2$.

b. $\displaystyle\sum_{k=1}^{n} k^3 - \left(\sum_{k=1}^{n} k\right)^2$.

c. $\displaystyle\sum_{k=1}^{n} k^4$.

6. a. Establish Equation (ii) of Exercise 4.
   b. Show that a_m is zero for $m > r$.

Index